WITHDRAWN

THYMIDINE METABOLISM AND CELL KINETICS

FRONTIERS OF BIOLOGY

VOLUME 6

Under the General Editorship of

A. NEUBERGER

London

and

E. L. TATUM

New York

NORTH-HOLLAND PUBLISHING COMPANY

AMSTERDAM

THYMIDINE METABOLISM
AND
CELL KINETICS

J. E. CLEAVER

Laboratory of Radiobiology
University of California
San Francisco (Calif.) U.S.A.

1967

This book is published and distributed
in the United States by
AMERICAN ELSEVIER PUBLISHING COMPANY, INC.
52 Vanderbilt Avenue, New York, N.Y. 10017

PUBLISHERS:
NORTH-HOLLAND PUBLISHING COMPANY – AMSTERDAM

SOLE DISTRIBUTORS FOR U.S.A. AND CANADA:
INTERSCIENCE PUBLISHERS, a division of
JOHN WILEY & SONS, INC. - NEW YORK

PRINTED IN THE NETHERLANDS

Editors' preface

The aim of the publication of this series of monographs, known under the collective title of '*Frontiers of Biology*', is to present coherent and up-to-date views of the fundamental concepts which dominate modern biology.

Biology in its widest sense has made very great advances during the past decade, and the rate of progress has been steadily accelerating. Undoubtedly important factors in this acceleration have been the effective use by biologists of new techniques, including electron microscopy, isotopic labels, and a great variety of physical and chemical techniques, especially those with varying degrees of automation. In addition, scientists with partly physical or chemical backgrounds have become interested in the great variety of problems presented by living organisms. Most significant, however, increasing interest in and understanding of the biology of the cell, especially in regard to the molecular events involved in genetic phenomena and in metabolism and its control, have led to the recognition of patterns common to all forms of life from bacteria to man. These factors and unifying concepts have led to a situation in which the sharp boundaries between the various classical biological disciplines are rapidly disappearing.

Thus, while scientists are becoming increasingly specialized in their techniques, to an increasing extent they need an intellectual and conceptual approach on a wide and non-specialized basis. It is with these considerations and needs in mind that this series of monographs, '*Frontiers of Biology*' has been conceived.

The advances in various areas of biology, including microbiology, biochemistry, genetics, cytology, and cell structure and function in general will be presented by authors who have themselves contributed significantly to these developments. They will have, in this series, the opportunity of bringing together, from diverse sources, theories and experimental data, and of integrating these into a more general conceptual framework. It is unavoidable, and probably even desirable, that the special bias of the individual authors will become evident in their contributions. Scope will also be given for presentation of new and challenging ideas and hypotheses for which complete evidence is at present lacking. However, the main emphasis will be on fairly complete and objective presentation of the more important and more rapidly advancing aspects of biology. The level will be advanced, directed primarily to the needs of the graduate student and research worker.

Most monographs in this series will be in the range of 200–300 pages, but on occasion a collective work of major importance may be included somewhat exceeding this figure. The intent of the publishers is to bring out these books promptly and in fairly quick succession.

It is on the basis of all these various considerations that we welcome the opportunity of supporting the publication of the series '*Frontiers of Biology*' by North-Holland Publishing Company.

E. L. TATUM
A. NEUBERGER, *Editors*

Preface

In this book I have attempted to deal with most of the principles of cell kinetics that have been studied with labelled thymidine, together with some aspects of the biochemistry of the incorporation of thymidine into DNA. It is impossible to review all of the relevant published work that deals with this subject. I have consequently selected work that I know best or work that I considered to be important in order to illustrate the various principles of cell biology that are described in this book. To a certain extent such a selection cannot avoid being preferential, and most of the examples discussed are drawn either from the work of my associates or myself. My experiences during the preparation of the manuscripts were rather like shovelling water uphill. The rate of publication of relevant papers during 1966, alone, almost exceeds one's ability to comprehend them, let alone the thought of reproducing them in book form. I hope, however, that my description of cell kinetics, and the methods by which they may be studied, will be of use to those who read this book and that they will excuse me if I neglect to include a 'stop press' of the very latest, and perhaps undigested, discoveries. By avoiding the temptation to be absolutely up to date then, perhaps this book may not fall out of date too rapidly. Some people who are involved in full time research in any of the topics of my chapters may find that I have dealt with their speciality in a superficial way. It is to be hoped that they will excuse me since every detail cannot be mentioned for every case. I have tried to set each aspect of thymidine studies in the context of this compound's contribution to modern biology. A few things I have neglected completely. One of these is the problem of cytoplasmic DNA. There was little that I could say about this, apart from the mere but undeniable fact of the existence of DNA in mitochondria and plastids. I have presupposed that the reader is familiar with base pairing and the Watson–Crick model of

DNA. I have also neglected to mention many details of radiobiology which would be relevant to the contents of chapter 7. I preferred to concentrate on the study of the kinetics of normal healthy tissues in order to clarify the definitions employed in such studies. The kinetics of disturbed tissues may then be considered in terms of those known of the normal tissues.

Things have changed rapidly since the introduction of labelled thymidine. The initial cost of H³Tdr was about $ 1,000 per millicurie and one of the earliest experiments cost $ 8,000 for H³Tdr alone. Fortunately for us all, this compound's remarkable usefulness has made it one of the few things that has not inflated in price over the last 10 years. With the manufacture of ever cheaper H³Tdr, together with C¹⁴Tdr and the Tdr analogues BUdr and IUdr, the future uses of these compounds may well be more fruitful than their past.

It will be clear from the contents of this book, that although our knowledge of cell kinetics in some tissues is already quite detailed, our knowledge of cell kinetics in human tissues is very limited. It is a platitude to remark that cancer is a disturbance of cell kinetics, but we need to know the details of both normal and malignant kinetics before we can understand or adequately treat this disease. Having said this, I must admit that few of the methods described in this book are suitable for determining cell kinetics in man, although they are suitable for such determinations in animals. The long-term effects of H³Tdr or C¹⁴Tdr incorporated into DNA are too dangerous for these compounds to be used in humans, except in the case of terminal patients. The use of such labelled compounds in patients with a view to possible benefit to patients in general, and not with reference to the patients' own immediate treatment cannot be justified if there is any risk, whatsoever, in their use.

'...science is not the highest value to which all other orders of values should be subordinated.' ... Pope Pius XII.

I am convinced that a detailed understanding of the human kinetic aspects of malignancy will be achieved sooner and more precisely by extensive research in animals than by the use of patients as experimental subjects under the restricted conditions of clinical research. A thorough investigation of normal and malignant tissues in animals on a quantitative basis through the methods described in some of the chapters of this book would then provide a sure basis from which to extrapolate to human tissues. Methods that could be used to determine the parameters of cell kinetics on biopsied material, without the necessity of injecting labelled Tdr into a patient, would be extremely valuable.

I am grateful to all of those who have helped, either directly or indirectly, in the preparation of this book. Many helpful suggestions on style and content were offered, and often though not always taken, by S. Bullivant, N. L. R. Bucher, J. A. Heddle, R. Hogan, R. M. Holford, P. K. Lala, M. A. Maloney, R. B. Painter, and E. D. Whittle. The opinions (and prejudices) expressed in this book are my own responsibility, as are also any errors that may be expressed. One disadvantage of producing a book of this sort is that it exposes, irrevocably, what its author does and does not understand. But this is a risk that was worth taking, if only for what the past six months of reading and thinking has taught me personally. The photographic work was done by J. J. Fields and G. Thomas, and the latter also did a valuable job in checking and correcting the bibliography. In some cases I have redrawn original diagrams in order to standardise all the illustrations, and I hope that I have not inadvertently distorted anyone's work in so doing. I am also grateful to Mrs. C. James for preparing the final typescript. My wife deserves especial mention for her patience with me over the last six months; without her support this book would never have been finished. I began writing during my tenure of a research fellowship at Massachusetts General Hospital, Boston, and completed the manuscripts at the University of California Medical Center, San Francisco, and I am grateful to both for allowing me a considerable amount of time.

My own work that is reproduced in this book was done over the past 5 years and supported by three different bodies during this interval. These were, in chronological order, the Medical Research Council of Great Britain, for work in the University of Cambridge Department of Radiotherapeutics; the National Institutes of Health, U. S. Public Health Service grants no. GM 11427–02 & 11427–03, & CA 07368–02, for work in the Department of Neurosurgery, Massachusetts General Hospital, Boston; and the U. S. Atomic Energy Commission for work in the Laboratory of Radiobiology, University of California Medical Center, San Francisco. A final word of gratitude to the editors and publishers of this series is also appropriate, because without their support I would never have even considered writing this book.

J. E. CLEAVER

Contents

Chapter 4.   *Interphase replication of DNA and the cell cycle*

Chapter 5.   *The replication of DNA during interphase*

Chapter 6.   *Replication and segregation of DNA in chromosomes of higher organisms*

Chapter 7. *Population kinetics in animal tissues*

Chapter 8. *Appendix*

CHAPTER 1

Preparation, stability, and detection of labelled thymidine

1.1 Introduction

Once the chemical composition of DNA and RNA was established it became clear that only three of the four component bases were common to both nucleic acids. Each nucleic acid contains adenine, guanine and cytosine, but only DNA contains thymine and RNA contains uracil. Only a few exceptions have been found to this generalisation. A uracil-containing DNA has been identified in the bacteriophage PBS2 (LANGRIDGE and MARMUR 1965) and a small amount of thymine is found in some RNAs, but in such cases the amount is only 1 to 2% of the uracil content (POTTER 1959; PRICE et al. 1963; HOLLEY et al. 1965). On account of this specificity of thymine and of the nucleoside thymidine, these compounds constitute almost ideal tracers for use in studies of DNA metabolism.

1.2 Introduction of labelled thymidine (Tdr) into biological studies

Some of the earliest experiments performed with labelled Tdr used the stable isotope N^{15} as the labelling atom. Tdr labelled in this way was obtained by chemical extraction from cultures of *E. coli* grown on N^{15}-labelled medium (REICHARD and ESTBORN 1951). A few years later C^{14}-labelled Tdr became available and this was immediately used in a number of experiments in various organisms (FRIEDKIN et al. 1956; FRIEDKIN and WOOD 1956). However, it was the successful synthesis of tritium (H^3) labelled Tdr which was first reported in 1957, and the introduction of autoradiography for the detection of the subcellular location of labelled molecules, that has made Tdr so invaluable in experimental work.

1.3 Preparation of labelled Tdr

The first successful attempts to introduce H^3 atoms into the Tdr molecule
occurred almost simultaneously in Belgium (VERLEY and HUNEBELLE 1957;
FIRKET and VERLEY 1958) and in the United States at Brookhaven, L. I.
(TAYLOR et al. 1957). Tritiation was achieved by means of catalytic
exchange between Tdr and tritiated water by the former group in Belgium,
and Tdr and tritiated acetic acid by the latter. The exchange with tritiated
water was achieved by heating Tdr at 100 °C for 24 hr in the presence of
Adam's catalyst and water. This was followed by heating in alkaline
solution to remove labile H^3 atoms and purified H^3Tdr then obtained by
recrystallisation from butanol. These methods resulted in general labelling of the molecule with H^3 atoms located mainly in the base portion.
Although it was claimed that this method resulted in labelling of the base
only, to the exclusion of the deoxyribose portion of the molecule, subsequent experiments have not substantiated this claim (EVANS and STAN-
FORD 1963). Catalytic exchange does not introduce H^3 atoms into every
possible non labile site with equal probability and the procedure is consequently referred to as 'general labelling'. When each position contains
radioactive atoms with equal probability the labelling is referred to as
'uniform', and this type of labelling is most commonly obtained with C^{14}.
Contemporary commercial methods use similar catalytic exchange processes with H^3 gas or tritiated liquids. But to ensure that no label is in the
deoxyribose portion the exchange is performed with thymine which is then
converted enzymatically to Tdr (FRIEDKIN and ROBERTS 1954).

The thymine molecule has four sites at which H^3 atoms can be substituted for hydrogen, these are positions 1, 3, 6, and the methyl group,
but not all of these are equally stable. Hydrogen atoms at positions 1 and
3 are labile and H^3 may be lost from these sites by exchange with hydrogen
atoms in aqueous solution. Proton transfer may also occur between
positions 1 and 2, or between 3 and 4, which results in a keto-enol transition (from HN—CO to N=COH, see PULLMAN 1964). This mechanism
will involve movement of the H^3 nucleus within the thymine molecule, but
it is extremely rare and loss of H^3 label by this mechanism is unimportant
compared to loss by exchange in aqueous solution. After catalytic
exchange, treatment with weak alkali (e.g. O· 2 N NaOH, VERLEY and
HUNEBELLE 1957) removes the H^3 from the labile positions and the only

remaining H^3 atoms are those in the methyl group and at position 6, which are firmly bound. The locations of H^3 in H^3Tdr are consequently only in the methyl group and 6, no H^3 being bound at position 3 (fig. 1.1).

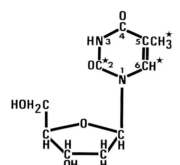

Fig. 1.1. Thymidine molecule showing locations (*) of labelling positions in specifically labelled Tdr (2-C^{14}, 5-methyl-H^3, 6-H^3).

Originally it was thought that the first commercial methods for manufacturing H^3Tdr produced a molecule with H^3 in both the methyl group and at position 6. Later work discovered that this was a misconception and the H^3 atom was located exclusively in the methyl group (PASTORE and FRIEDKIN 1962; FRIEDKIN personal communication). Specifically labelled H^3Tdr of high specific activity can also be obtained with H^3 located either in the methyl group or in position 6 by an appropriate choice of the starting compound for catalytic exchange. To obtain methyl-H^3Tdr, 5-hydroxymethyluracil or a 5-substituted halogen derivative of thymine is used. For 6-H^3Tdr, uracil or uridine can be used as a starting compound and subsequent methylation removes all of the H^3 from position 5.

Uniformly labelled $C^{14}Tdr$ is obtained by degradation of DNA from the alga *Chlorella* that has been grown on $C^{14}O_2$ as the carbon source. Specifically labelled $C^{14}Tdr$ is usually obtained with the C^{14} atom in the 2-position, but Tdr-methyl-C^{14} is also obtainable. Specifically labelled $C^{14}Tdr$ is obtained from the correspondingly labelled thymine molecules that have been synthesised chemically by reaction sequences which specify the precise location of the C^{14} atom in the pyrimidine ring.

The specific activities of H^3Tdr which are currently available lie in the range from 0.36 Ci/mmole to above 10 Ci/mmole. For $C^{14}Tdr$ the range is from about 1 to 350 mc/mmole.

1.4 Chemical stability of labelled Tdr

Chemically, Tdr is a relatively stable compound and can be heated in neutral or alkaline solution for an hour at 120 °C without significant decomposition or loss of the H^3 or C^{14} atoms from the molecule. Solutions of labelled Tdr can consequently be sterilised by autoclaving without any decomposition (CROWTER et al. 1960). In aqueous solution at room temperature hydrolytic cleavage of the N-glycosidic bond occurs at a very slow rate of about 1 to 2% of the original Tdr per year (EVANS and STANFORD 1963). This rate increases with rise in temperature and is also higher in acid solution, particularly in the presence of mineral acids. The C^{14} atom in the 2-position can only be lost by complete disruption of the pyrimidine ring and the labels in the 6-position and the methyl group are chemically stable, except in the presence of a catalyst at high temperatures (EVANS and STANFORD 1963). However, if solutions of Tdr are stored in a non-sterile condition then infection by microorganisms may result in enzymatic degradation and this will result in loss of the labelled Tdr and accumulation of breakdown products (see ch. 2 § 6).

1.5 Self decomposition of labelled thymidine

The breakdown of Tdr by irradiation with the β-particles emitted by H^3 or C^{14} is similar to the breakdown caused by irradiation with external sources. Four main radiation processes which contribute to self decomposition can be distinguished (BAYLEY and WEIGEL 1960):

(1) Primary (internal) radiation effect – arising from the transmutation of the radioactive atoms; e.g. H^3 to He^3 and C^{14} to N^{14}.

(2) Primary (external) radiation effect – arising from the passage of the ionizing radiation directly through the molecules.

(3) Secondary radiation effect – arising from the interaction of ionised molecules and free radicals.

(4) Chemical effects – arising from chemical reactions in solution following the interactions of free radicals and ionised molecules.

In the case of C^{14} the primary (internal) effect is negligible, on account of the long half life of the isotope (table 1.1) and the low specific activities commonly employed, and is unlikely to account for more than 0.01%

TABLE 1.1

Characteristics of radioactive decay and β-particle ranges for H^3 and C^{14}. (The values for β-particle ranges have been estimated from the range energy curve for electrons published by EVANS (1955), p. 624, and may differ slightly from the values quoted by other authors in discussions on autoradiography.)

	H^3	C^{14}
Half life	12.26 yr	5680 yr
Disintegration rate	0.016 %/day	0.000034 %/day
Maximum energy E_m	0.018 MeV	0.155 MeV
Maximum recoil energy of product nucleus	3.2 eV($_2$He^3)	6.9 eV($_7$N^{14})
Initial rate of energy loss from electrons with energy E_m*	2.5 keV/μ	0.7 keV/μ
Range of β-particle with maximum energy	0.54 mg/cm^2	29 mg/cm^2
Range in tissue (density 1)	5.4 μ	290 μ
Range in emulsion (density 3–4)	1.5 μ	83 μ
Mean energy (approx. $E_m/3.2$) **	5.7 keV	50 keV
Range of β-particle with mean energy	0.045 mg/cm^2	3.7 mg/cm^2
Range in tissue (density 1)	0.45 μ	37 μ
Range in emulsion (density 3–4)	0.13 μ	10 μ

* Estimates based on the energy loss of electrons in photographic emulsion with density 3.5, from tables of energy loss in silver bromide (NELMS 1956, 1958).

** The spectrum of β-particle energies is weighted in favour of particles with energies much lower than E_m and the mean energy is not a constant fraction of E_m. For low E_m spectra from H^3 and C^{14} the mean energy is about 1/3.2 of E_m, but for higher energies this fraction is slightly smaller. Full details on this point may be found in EVANS (1955), p. 619.

self decomposition per year. This effect may be important in biological studies, however, and the biological consequences of transmutation are discussed in ch. 3 § 14. The self decomposition of H^3Tdr can occur through any of the effects listed, since the half life of H^3 is relatively short and high specific activities are commonly employed. The primary (internal) effect may again be negligible, because in this case the recoil energy of the He nucleus is too low to cause any damage (maximum is 3.2 eV) and there are sufficient H atoms in solution to replace the decayed H^3 immediately (STRAUSS 1958).

The exact nature of the products formed during self decomposition depends on the location of the labelling atom, but in the case of C^{14} the amounts are so small that they have not been determined. Generally, labelled H^3Tdr gives two major products, thymine and 2-deoxyribose, both of which are generally labelled (EVANS and STANFORD 1963). Specifically labelled H^3Tdr, both methyl-H^3 and 6-H^3, produces much less

TABLE 1.2

Self decomposition of labelled thymidine in aqueous solution (EVANS and STANFORD 1963; EVANS 1966).

Location of label	Specific activity (Ci/mmol)	Concentration (μCi/ml)	Storage temp. (°C)	Age (months)	% decomposition
Tdr-2-C^{14}	0.0183	–	+2 to −40	–	0.9 per yr
Tdr-2-C^{14}	0.0183	–	+20	–	1–2 per yr
Tdr-2-C^{14}	0.0183	–	+20 (occ. sunlight)	5	8
Tdr-H^3(G)	0.26	–	−40	39	55
Tdr-methyl-H^3	1.06	0.7	0	2	0
Tdr-methyl-H^3	1.52	0.5	0	3	5.0
Tdr-methyl-H^3	3.2	3.8	−40	14	15
Tdr-methyl-H^3	4.2	4.0	−40	8	8
Tdr-methyl-H^3	4.2	0.4	+2	22	40
Tdr-methyl-H^3	4.2	1.3	−196	7	2
Tdr-6-H^3	2.5	6.9	−40	12	28
Tdr-6-H^3	2.5	6.9	−40	7	10
Tdr-6-H^3	2.5	6.9	0	8	10
Tdr-6-H^3	1.14	2.0	20	10	0
Tdr-6-H^3	14.1	4	−40	1.5	10
Tdr-6-H^3	14.1	4	−40	12	45
Tdr-6-H^3	14.1	4	20	3.5	0
Tdr-6-H^3	14.1	2	20	5	3
Tdr-6-H^3	3.6	1	−40	10	20
Tdr-6-H^3	1.4	2	−40	10	10
Tdr-6-H^3	12.1	1	0	10	35
Tdr-6-H^3	4.8	0.4	0	10	30

G = generally labelled in both base and deoxyribose portions of molecule.

thymine than the generally labelled nucleoside and produces other compounds including peroxides and glycols of Tdr (APELGOT and EKART 1963). These arise through an attack by the ionisation products of water at the 5–6 double bond of the pyrimidine ring, and similar mechanisms have been postulated to explain the decomposition of Tdr by irradiation with external sources (BROWN et al. 1965). Most of these products which have been detected are labelled molecules, but other unlabelled molecules may also be formed although these would be much more difficult to detect due to the small quantities involved.

The overall rate of decomposition is approximately proportional to the dose rate which results from the passage of β-particles through the medium, and is consequently dependent on the concentration of labelled molecules, i.e. on both the specific activity and the concentration of Tdr in solutions which are not carrier-free. A series of investigations into the rate of decomposition of labelled Tdr have been described by EVANS and STANFORD (1963) and EVANS (1966), and some of their results for aqueous solutions are summarized in table 1.2. When allowance is made for the difference in the energy of the β-particles from C^{14} and H^3, C^{14}Tdr appears to be much more stable than H^3Tdr. The results of table 1.2 indicate that the average rate of self decomposition in aqueous solution between $+2$ °C and -40 °C is about 1% per year for Tdr-2-C^{14}, about 0.5 to 1% per month for methyl-H^3Tdr, and about 1 to 2% per month for 6-H^3Tdr. The rate of self decomposition can be reduced by adding scavengers to remove the free radicals formed by the radiation induced breakdown of water. Suitable compounds include benzyl or ethyl alcohol, sodium formate (EVANS 1966) or cysteamine (APELGOT et al. 1964). Although these additives may be effective protecting agents, they may interfere with experimental investigations and their value must be weighed against possible disadvantages for any particular experiment. The rate of self decomposition is higher at -20 °C than at either 0 °C or -70 °C and is much reduced by storage at -196 °C. The enhanced rate of self decomposition at -20 °C is not fully explained at present (APELGOT et al. 1964) but some enhancement may result from the formation of a eutectic mixture containing pockets of labelled Tdr at high concentrations. There is consequently little advantage to be gained by storing solutions of labelled Tdr in the frozen state, rather than at 0 °C or $+4$ °C, unless it is possible to store them at temperatures as low as -196 °C (EVANS 1966).

1.6 Detection and assay of labelled Tdr in biological material

Both C^{14} and H^3Tdr may be detected and assayed in similar ways to those used for any radioactive isotope, by means of liquid scintillation counting, gas flow counting, etc. The extremely low energy of the H^3 β-particles presents certain technical problems since detection of these requires sensitive instruments, but these are now standard in most laboratories. A description of some of the detection methods for H^3 is to be found in: Tritium in the biological sciences, Volume I (1962). By far the most important method that has been introduced for detection of H^3 and C^{14}-labelled compounds is that of autoradiography. This method is an extension of those which have been used in physics for registering the passage of charged particles by the tracks they leave in photographic emulsions. One of the first emulsions suitable for registering the tracks of electrons was introduced by DEMERS (1947) and other emulsions were soon developed for registering the tracks of low energy β-particles (< 1 MeV) with very short ranges in emulsion (table 1.1). By application of these emulsions in intimate contact with the specimens it became possible to locate the precise source of radiations emitted from radioactive atoms in biological structures. The techniques of autoradiography have advanced extremely rapidly since the introduction of the method and it is now employed in large numbers of investigations with the light microscope and the electron microscope. Experimental and theoretical aspects of the technique are to be found in numerous books and reviews and some of the most useful have been listed in the bibliography at the end of this chapter. Rather than repeat the contents of these works in detail here, discussion will be restricted to those aspects of autoradiography which are directly relevant to experimental studies with labelled Tdr and H^3Tdr in particular. These aspects include problems of resolution, sensitivity, and efficiency of the commercially available emulsions, the accuracy that can be expected in experiments involving grain counts, and the stability of incorporated Tdr to various histological procedures.

1.7 Autoradiograph resolution

In an autoradiograph a particular distribution of radioactive atoms within a biological structure is detected by means of the pattern of developed silver grains that the emitted radiation produces in the overlaying nuclear emulsion. The problem of resolution is the problem of deriving the most probable distribution of radioactive atoms from the observed pattern of silver grains. The resolution of an autoradiograph depends on a wide range of experimental factors and also on the particular definition of resolution that is adopted for any particular experiment. If the density of developed silver grains above a point source of radiation is considered, then the resolution may be defined as twice the distance in the plane of emulsion, at which the grain density falls to half the maximum density (CARO 1962). Two similar point sources of radiation could then be resolved if they were at least this distance apart, and this definition is analogous to the definition of resolution used in classical optics. In practice, it is more common to deal with a small finite number of silver grains in autoradiographs, rather than a grain density. For this situation resolution may be defined as the radius of a circle, centered on the developed silver grain, within which there is a high probability (say 90%) of finding the source of the radiation (MOSES 1964). Of the many experimental factors which affect the resolution, the following three are among the most important when H^3- or C^{14}-labelled molecules are used (CARO 1962):

(1) The distance between the source of β-particles and the silver halide crystals struck by the particles.

(2) The relationship between the passage of an electron through a silver halide crystal in the emulsion and the position of the latent image formed.

(3) The relationship between the developed silver grain, of variable size and shape, and the latent image from which it originated.

The first of these factors can be controlled by the choice of isotope and by the geometry of the preparation and is important in both light and electron microscope autoradiography. The second and third factors are only important in electron microscope autoradiography because the structures of the silver halide crystal and the developed grains cannot usually be resolved in the light microscope. It is clear that the shorter the range of the emitted β-particle the better is the resolution that can be obtained. Both H^3 and C^{14} emit short range β-particles (table 1.1), and illustrations of autoradiographs obtained with both of these isotopes are shown in fig. 1.2 and 1.3. The short range particles from H^3 can afford better resolution than those from C^{14}, but the developed grains from both are clearly localised over, or very near to, the nucleus of each labelled cell.

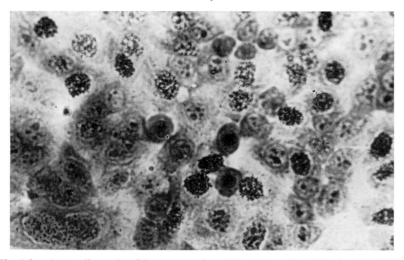

Fig. 1.2. Autoradiograph of human amnion, FL strain, cells labelled with H³Tdr, NTB3 emulsion (× 300).

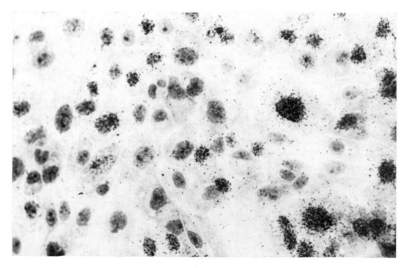

Fig. 1.3. Autoradiograph of marsupial kidney, strain PtKl, cells labelled with C¹⁴Tdr, NTB3 emulsion (× 300).

But for biological structures smaller than the nucleus, e.g., individual chromosomes, it is clear that only H^3 can give suitable resolution.

In light microscope autoradiographs, sections or monolayers of whole cells are employed that are commonly about 2 to 5 μ thick and the layer of overlaying emulsion has a similar thickness. Only those β-particles which are emitted from within the biological material towards the emulsion will be able to strike a silver halide grain and give rise to a latent image. The spread in developed grains above any one radioactive source is caused by those particles which are emitted at an angle to the emulsion rather than normal to plane of the emulsion. This spread can be reduced and the resolution improved by using thin sections and ensuring close contact between the emulsion and biological material (DONIACH and PELC 1950). The high density of nuclear emulsions results in a sharp reduction in the range of β-particles as compared to the range in tissue (table 1.1) and for a

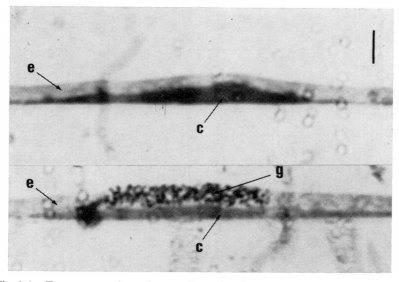

Fig. 1.4. Transverse sections of autoradiographs of mouse L strain cells labelled with H^3Tdr. These sections were obtained by growing cultures on the surface of polymerised Epon and then embedding the developed autoradiograph in Epon and sections cut at 1 μ. Due to the embedding procedures the dimensions of emulsion thickness etc., may have been altered by shrinkage. Top – unlabelled cell; bottom – labelled cell; e – emulsion (NTB 3); g – grains; c–cell (line equals 10 μ).

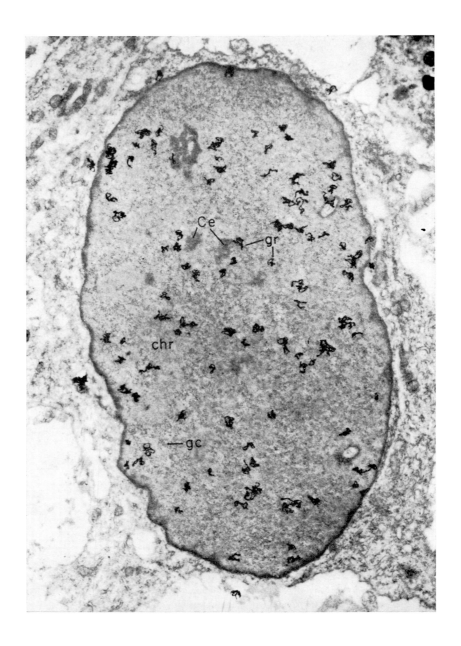

H³ β-particle an emulsion more than 1 to 2 μ thick is effectively infinite. Most of the developed grains will be clustered at, or just above, the interface between the biological material and the emulsion and the emulsion thickness will have little effect on the resolution (DONIACH and PELC 1950). The relative locations of emulsion, grains and cell are illustrated in fig. 1.4 which shows a transverse section of a H³Tdr autoradiograph.

It is possible to make use of the different ranges of H³ and C¹⁴ β-particles to distinguish between cells labelled with C¹⁴Tdr and H³Tdr in the same culture, as a result of double labelling experiments. This can be achieved by using one film of nuclear emulsion and distinguishing between the two classes of labelled cells on the basis of the different appearance of C¹⁴ and H³ autoradiographs (PILGRIM and MAURER 1962; WIMBER and QUASTLER 1963). An alternative method which has been used consists of applying two successive films of nuclear emulsion to the labelled cells so that the lower film, which is in contact with the cells, will register both C¹⁴ and H³ β-particles while the upper film will only register the longer-ranged C¹⁴ particles (BASERGA 1962 a, b; DAWSON et al. 1962; see also TRELSTAD 1965). The resolution that is obtained with the second film of emulsion and the C¹⁴ β-particles is quite low because of the distance between the labelled cell and the emulsion but this can be tolerated in the types of experiment for which double labelling is used. All that is usually required in these experiments is the identification of labelled nuclei and their classification into C¹⁴Tdr and H³Tdr labelled classes.

The highest resolution in autoradiographs is obtained using very thin electron microscope sections and a very thin layer of silver halide grains for the emulsion (CARO and VAN TUBERGEN 1962). An illustration of an electron microscope autoradiograph is shown in fig. 1.5 and in addition to the detailed fine structure that can be studied in the biological material by this method, it can be seen that the silver grains have considerable

Fig. 1.5. Electron microscope autoradiograph of a cell in the regenerating limb of salamander, *Amblystoma*, larva labelled with H³Tdr, 5 μCi/ml 1.9 Ci/mmole, 1 hour before fixation in osmium tetroxide. Ilford L4 emulsion, diluted 1:8, and developed in Dektol for 2 min. Section stained after development with Karnovsky's lead stain. Ce: central dense regions of chromatin which are rarely labelled; chr: chromatin regions; gc: granular component of the nucleus; gr: autoradiograph grains. (× 9,000, reproduced from HAY and REVEL 1963).

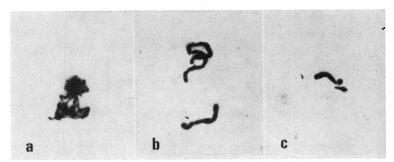

Fig. 1.6. Grains of Ilford L4 emulsion exposed by H³ decay. Tritiated leucine was mixed with an emulsion which was applied as a monolayer of crystals. Exposure was calculated to give a low grain count (× 3000).

(a) Developed in D9 at 20 °C for 2 min. The grain appears as a large, complex filamentous structure.

(b) Developed in Microdol-X for 5 min. The grains have a simple structure usually consisting of a single filament. The position of the grain may be defined as the midpoint of a straight line joining its two extremities, since it is impossible to know which is the starting point.

(c) Developed in physical developer for 1 min at 20 °C. Three distinct grains have been produced from a single hit by a β-particle in one crystal. The common point of all three grains, indicating the position of the original crystal, seems to be their pointed end. (Reproduced from CARO and VAN TUBERGEN 1962.)

fine structure themselves. The fine structure in the silver grains is produced by photographic development and has little relationship to the actual track of the β-particle. The structures produced by a number of different developers is illustrated in fig. 1.6. In electron microscope autoradiography it is consequently important to consider the effect of the size of both the silver halide grain and the developed grain (points 2 and 3 above). A detailed treatment of resolution which takes these factors into account has been given by CARO (1962) for electron microscope autoradiography (see also PELC 1962). The silver halide grain size is characteristic of the nuclear emulsion and cannot be controlled experimentally. The effect of this grain size on resolution is to make it difficult to resolve two labelled structures which are less than a grain diameter apart (i.e. less than 1000 Å in the case of L4 emulsion). The size and shape of the developed silver grain is also a limiting factor to the resolution because there is no way of telling which portion of the grain corresponds to the point of impact of the β-particle. For the highest resolution it is necessary to use a special fine-grain developer or a 'physical' developer which produces small simple grains (CARO and VAN TUBERGEN 1962; MOSES 1964).

Numerical estimates of resolution have been quoted by various workers and these are similar in magnitude, despite the different criteria and experimental situations which have been employed. For light microscope autoradiography with H³Tdr the resolution usually obtained is 0.2 to 0.3 μ (ROBERTSON et al. 1959; HILL 1962) and with C¹⁴Tdr is about 2 μ (ROBERTSON et al. 1959). In electron microscopy a resolution of 0.1 μ has been suggested theoretically and confirmed experimentally by CARO (1962) and a resolution of 0.3 μ, or less, has been estimated by MOSES (1964).

1.8 Sensitivity of nuclear emulsions

Sensitivity is a term used in autoradiography to describe the response of nuclear emulsions to impinging β-particles, and can be expressed numerically as the number of developed silver grains produced per β-particle. A developed silver grain is derived from the latent image produced in a grain of silver halide in the emulsion by the passage of the β-particle, and the probability that a particle will produce a latent image will depend on the energy deposited within the grain. The total number of latent images produced by a particular β-particle will consequently be a function of the total energy of the particle and its rate of energy loss in the emulsion. The isotopes commonly employed in biology emit β-particles with maximum energies in the range from 18 keV (H³) to 1.72 MeV (P³²). The rate of energy loss decreases with increase in the energy of the β-particle and reaches a minimum at about 1 MeV, after which the rate of energy loss increases (NELMS 1956). The study undertaken by CARO and SCHNÖS (1965) clearly illustrates the effect of differences in the rate of energy loss on emulsion sensitivity. These workers used H³- and P³²-labelled *E. coli* in electron microscope autoradiographs and used a monolayer of silver halide grains (L4 emulsion) as the nuclear emulsion. Since the specimen and emulsion were in intimate contact the energy deposited by the β-particles in the silver halide grains depended mainly on the initial rate of energy loss at the point of origin of the particles. This rate of energy loss is 3.5 keV/μ for electrons with maximum energy from H³ and 0.53 keV/μ for P³² (CARO and SCHNÖS 1965) and the number of developed grains that were produced per incident β-particle was 0.4 and 0.025 respectively. The

TABLE 1.3

Sensitivity and grain size of commercial nuclear emulsions. The exact numerical value of the emulsion sensitivity varies according to the experimenter and depends to some extent on the exact conditions of storage and preparation of the autoradiographs. Also the differences in emulsion sensitivities depend on the grain size since an emulsion with large silver halide grains will have fewer per unit volume and an inherently lower sensitivity (CARO and VAN TUBERGEN 1962).

Emulsion	Development time (min) (D19 at 20 °C)	Grain size (μ)	Grains/100 β-particles	Reference
Eastman Kodak NTE	2	0.05	130	CARO (1966)
Gevaert NUC 307	2	0.07	150	CARO (1966)
Ilford L4	4	0.12	132	CARO (1966)
Ilford L4	–	–	29	ADA et al. (1966)
Ilford L4 (monolayer)	4	–	40	CARO (1966)
Demers (unsensitised)	2	0.12	61	CARO and VAN TUBERGEN (1962)
Demers (sensitised)	2	0.12	130 (approx.)	CARO and VAN TUBERGEN (1962)
Gevaert NUC 715	2	0.15	180	CARO (1966)
Ilford K5	2	0.18	100	CARO (1966)
Kodak AR10	2	0.2–0.4	57	CARO (1966)
Kodak AR10	4	–	70	CARO (1966)
Kodak AR10	–	–	70–80	BLEECKER (1964)
Kodak AR10	–	–	42	MAURER and PRIMBSCH (1964)
Kodak AR10	–	–	15	ADA et al. (1966)
Kodak V1055	2	0.17	51	CARO (1966)
Eastman Kodak NTB3	2	0.23	48	CARO (1966)
Eastman Kodak NTB2	2	0.27	94	CARO (1966)
Eastman Kodak NTB2	2	–	15	ADA et al. (1966)

values obtained for emulsion sensitivity are consequently unique for each particular isotope. In addition, the sensitivity is likely to be affected by a number of experimental factors such as the conditions of exposure, storage, photographic development etc. Values consequently vary to a certain extent between different workers, and a number of estimates for thick emulsions using H^3 are given in table 1.3. Extensive determinations for other isotopes have not been made.

The relative sensitivity of nuclear emulsions can be easily determined from the grain counts obtained over standard labelled material such as bacteria. The absolute sensitivity is less easy to determine, and requires a source of known activity so that the actual number of β-particles striking the emulsion is known. The source used by CARO and SCHNÖS (1965), for example, consisted of phage lambda fully labelled with H^3Tdr. The molecular weight and thymine content of this phage is known and the number of H^3 disintegrations per unit time could then be estimated. The grain count distribution in L4 emulsion over *E. coli* C infected with these labelled phage was found to fit a Poisson distribution and the mean grain count was a linear function of the exposure time. After correcting for the self absorption of β-particles within the bacteria and assuming that 50 % of the particles are emitted in a direction away from the emulsion, CARO and SCHNÖS (1965) estimated that each β-particle gave rise to 1.3 grains. The other values of sensitivity from CARO (1965) and CARO and VAN TUBERGEN (1962) included in table 1.3 are based on this value of absolute sensitivity. The values obtained by the other workers cited in table 1.3 were based on other similar methods of ascertaining the number of β-particles striking the emulsions.

The estimate of the sensitivity of L4 emulsion obtained by CARO and SCHNÖS (1965) is greater than one grain per β-particle, and this indicates that some of the particles are able to produce more than one grain. On the basis of the grain distribution around weakly labelled bacteria these workers estimate that 78 % of the particles produced one grain, 16.5 % two grains, 5 % three grains and 0.5 % four grains. Consequently, it is probable that for layers of L4 emulsion every β-particle which strikes the emulsion produces at least one grain, though this is not true for every emulsion as may be seen from the values of table 1.3.

The situation in electron microscope autoradiography is slightly different from that discussed above because very thin emulsion layers are used.

In this case a β-particle which strikes a silver halide grain will be either absorbed or scattered out of the plane of the emulsion completely. The silver halide grains immediately above the source of β-particles will consequently shield those further away and a β-particle passing through a grain already exposed by a previous particle will not respond by the production of further latent images. Consequently the shielding effect in thin emulsions will reduce the sensitivity in comparison to the sensitivity of thick layers of emulsion. The sensitivity of L4, for example, is only 0.4 grains per β-particle in monolayers of silver halide as compared to 1.3 grains per β-particle for thick layers (CARO and SCHNÖS 1965).

1.9 Efficiency of autoradiography in detection of radioactive decays

Autoradiograph efficiency has a distinct meaning from the sensitivity of the nuclear emulsions and refers to the number of developed silver grains produced in the emulsion by the radioactive disintegrations within the biological material. The term is used here in the same sense as it is used with reference to other detectors of radioactive decays. The efficiency is rarely 100% because some of the particles are absorbed within the biological material and never reach the detector. The numerical values of efficiency and of sensitivity will only be identical if every β-particle emitted is recorded as a developed silver grain. Since in autoradiographs half of the β-particles are emitted in a direction away from the emulsion the maximum attainable efficiency will be half of the emulsion sensitivity. In practice, self absorption of β-particles within biological material is extremely important and a large fraction of them, particularly in the case of H^3, do not reach the emulsion.

In table 1.1 the ranges of H^3 β-particles in tissue and emulsion have been included and it can be seen that particles emitted from regions of tissue which are further than about 1 μ from the emulsion will rarely be able to produce latent images in the emulsion. A thorough investigation into the influence of self absorption on the grain counts over H^3-labelled material in AR10 emulsion has been made by MAURER and PRIMBSCH (1964). These workers determined the grain counts over the nuclei, nucleoli and cytoplasm of rat and mouse liver cells labelled with H^3-

labelled tyrosine, DL-proline, or cytidine, as a function of section thickness over a range from 0.3 to 6 μ. The dry mass of each of three compartments of the cell was also determined by interference microscopy so that it was possible to relate the self absorption to measured amounts of absorbing material. Their results showed that the grain counts obtained from a very thin section would be halved by interposing a layer of unlabelled absorbing material between the section and emulsion which had a dry mass of about 0.015 mg/cm². This corresponds to section thicknesses of about 1 μ for the nucleus, 0.5 μ for the cytoplasm, or 0.2 μ for the nucleolus. The grain counts would be reduced to 10% by 0.05 mg/cm² of absorbing material. On the basis of these observations it followed that 90% of the grains produced in autoradiographs of H³-labelled material comes from disintegrations in the upper 0.05 mg/cm² of the section, which corresponds to a wet thickness of 1.8 μ of cytoplasm, 2.8 μ of nucleus, and 0.5 μ of nucleolus. In tissue culture cells there is usually a thin layer of cytoplasm between the nucleus and the emulsion and this layer consequently absorbs a significant number of the β-particles emitted by H³Tdr in the nucleus.

Several estimates have been made of the number of H³ disintegrations which are necessary for the production of a single silver grain in an

TABLE 1.4

Number of H³ disintegrations in biological material for each grain observed in light microscope autoradiographs with AR10 emulsion. (With the exception of the first value the remainder were previously listed in table II of CLEAVER and HOLFORD 1965.)

Material	H³ disintegrations/grain	Per cent efficiency	Reference
Phage (within bacteria)	2.6 (L4 emulsion)	38	CARO and SCHNÖS (1965)
Bacteria	5	20	HUGHES et al. (1958)
Cell smear	20	5	HUGHES et al. (1958)
Cell squash (3 μ)	10.9	9.2	WIMBER et al. (1960)
Tissue culture	19	5.3	CLEAVER and HOLFORD (1965)
Section (3 μ)	16	6.3	MAURER and PRIMBSCH (1964)
Section (3 μ)	100–200	0.5–1.0	KISIELSKI et al. (1961)

autoradiograph, but it is clear that this number will depend on the self absorption of the particular biological material employed. The number of disintegrations per unit time can be obtained from the total H^3 content of the material and this has been determined in a number of cases either by chemical extraction (HUGHES et al. 1958; WIMBER et al. 1960; KISIELSKI et al. 1961; CARO and SCHNÖS 1965) or by more indirect means (MAURER and PRIMBSCH 1964; CLEAVER and HOLFORD 1965). These values have been summarised in table 1.4. In mammalian tissues the average efficiency is about 5%. Since the efficiency in different tissues or in different regions of the same tissue is very sensitive to variations in the self absorption, autoradiography is a poor method for accurate estimation of the quantities of H^3-labelled material in any particular region.

1.10 Distribution and reliability of grain count

Although the influence of self absorption precludes the use of autoradiography as a method for determination of absolute amounts of H^3 in biological material, it can still be used as an approximate relative method. It is important in this respect because it is one of the only methods by which a cell population in culture or in a tissue can be analysed on a single cell basis. So long as significant systematic changes in the self absorption of the cells do not occur under the particular experimental conditions employed, it is possible to use the grain count over a single cell as a relative measure of the amount of H^3Tdr incorporated into that cell. The mean or median grain count over the labelled cells in a population can also be used as a relative measure of the mean amount of H^3Tdr incorporated into that fraction of the population. The implicit assumption in using grain counts in this way is that the region of the cells which is within range of the nuclear emulsion, i.e. the upper 3μ of the nucleus, is typical of the whole of the labelled nucleus. This assumes an approximately uniform distribution of H^3 within each labelled nucleus and although this is not strictly true (see ch. 5 §§ 4,5) it is sufficiently accurate for most purposes. An experiment which demonstrates that the mean grain count can be used as a valid estimate of the rate of DNA synthesis in that culture is described in ch. 8 § 1.

In any one autoradiograph the grain count over each labelled cell is not the same, and several factors contribute to the variation between individual grain counts. These factors include the natural randomness of radioactive decay, variations in self absorption and variations between the amounts of H^3Tdr incorporated into each cell. If the only cause of the variation between individual grain counts were the randomness of radioactive decay then the grain counts should fit a Poisson distribution. If other factors were also relevant then a wider distribution would result. A Poisson distribution of grain counts has been obtained for the cases of H^3Tdr-labelled bacteria (PAINTER et al. 1960) and labelled phage within bacteria (CARO and SCHNÖS 1965). In the case of H^3Tdr-labelled mammalian cells the distribution is normally very much wider than a Poisson distribution (LAJTHA et al. 1960; PAINTER et al. 1960) and a typical distribution is illustrated in fig. 1.7.

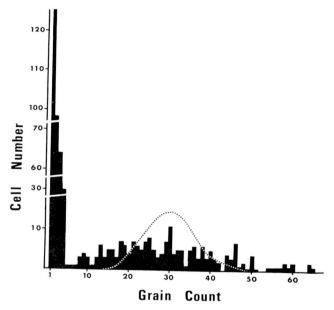

Fig. 1.7. Distribution of grain counts over mouse L strain cells in an autoradiograph (NTB3 emulsion) of a culture labelled for 10 min with H^3Tdr, 2.5 μCi/ml 0.36 Ci/ mmole. From a total of 800 cells scored, 300 had no grains and the remaining 500 with one grain or more are recorded in the distribution. A Poisson distribution with a mean of 30 has been included for comparison. The ratio of variance to mean for the grain count distribution, excluding cells with 5 grains or less, $S^2/M = 6.2$. For the Poisson distribution, $S^2/M = 1.0$

The analysis of a histogram such as that of fig. 1.7 presents many problems from a statistical point of view and it is difficult to fully characterise the distribution in terms of merely a mean and variance. The cells that are distinctly labelled form a group which are distributed about a mean of approximately 30 grains per labelled cell, in the case illustrated in fig. 1.7. The population of lightly labelled cells that have grain counts below five per cell are commonly considered to be unlabelled and the grains probably originate from background in the emulsion or other artefacts (STEWART et al. 1965). If these lightly labelled cells are ignored the distribution of labelled cells may be analysed in terms of a mean and variance. The median grain count is sometimes used instead of the mean because the former parameter is less sensitive to the exact choice of the level of background (STEWART et al. 1965). In the absence of a thorough and valid statistical theory on which to base the analysis of such autoradiograph data, the mean (or median) and variance remain the best parameters to use.

In the histogram for mammalian tissue culture cells illustrated in fig. 1.7, the distribution of labelled cells is clearly wider than the Poisson distribution with the same mean that is drawn for comparison. Such a tissue culture population contains cells at all stages of the life cycle and variation in the rate of H^3Tdr incorporation at different stages may contribute to this variation in grain counts (LAJTHA et al. 1960; DENDY and CLEAVER 1965). Experiments which demonstrate variations in the rate of H^3Tdr incorporation at different stages of the life cycle are discussed in ch. 5 §§ 5–7. An analysis of the effect of these variations on the grain count distributions is also included in ch. 8 § 2.

In some experiments in which low grain counts are obtained (i.e. mean below 10 or 15 grains/labelled cell) the contributions of labelled cells and background grains to the grain count distribution cannot be clearly distinguished. The distribution then simply falls steadily from the left. The mean grain count in such a case is a rather unreliable measure of the H^3Tdr incorporation, and should only be used with caution. If possible it would be preferable to repeat such experiments and use a longer exposure time or a higher specific activity H^3Tdr in order to detect labelled cells clearly and to discriminate against the background.

The mean grain counts in autoradiographs are generally a linear function of the exposure time up to about a year, as would be expected since the decay rate of H³ does not alter significantly over these periods (BASERGA and NEMEROFF 1962, KOPRIWA and LEBLOND 1962; CLEAVER and HOLFORD 1965; CARO and SCHNÖS 1965). Some slight deviation from this linear relationship may occur with long exposure times due to fading of the latent image (BASERGA and NEMEROFF 1962), but this can be prevented by storage in a dry inert atmosphere of carbon dioxide or nitrogen (RAY and STEPHENS 1953). If a series of autoradiographs are made of identical labelled material the mean grain counts obtained are distributed with a standard error that is usually about 10%, if the exposure and development are done together. If the exposures are for different periods of time and the development done separately then the mean grain counts per day exposure have a slightly larger standard error of about 15% (CLEAVER and HOLFORD 1965). The precise value of the standard errors obtained in autoradiograph experiments may differ between different workers but this range of 10 to 15% is normally attainable in routine work and must be borne in mind when interpreting small differences in mean grain counts after experimental treatments.

1.11 Stability of incorporated H³Tdr to histological procedures

After fixation with methanol, formalin, acetic acid-ethanol or other fixatives H³Tdr that has been incorporated into DNA is quite stable to a variety of histological procedures. The fixatives may, however, remove any small molecular weight compounds such as the phosphorylated derivatives of H³Tdr that are present within the cell (see ch. 3 § 5). The label in DNA is also quite resistant to extraction with dilute perchloric acid (2–10% between 4 to 20 °C) which is a procedure that can remove most of the RNA from the cell (BASERGA 1963). Treatment with RNase also has no effect on the label from H³Tdr but treatment with DNase can remove almost all of the label. The removal of H³Tdr label from the cell by DNase was one of the early tests that was employed in demonstration of the specificity of Tdr as a precursor for DNA synthesis (AMANO et al. 1959). This test is still necessary when label appears to be in an unusual location, such as the cytoplasm, and may have been incorporated into some other molecule than DNA.

One histological procedure which has caused some concern on account of the possibility of extraction of H³Tdr is that for the Feulgen stain. This stain involves a reaction between DNA that has been hydrolysed in hydrochloric acid and a decolourised fuchsin dye. The stain intensity in the nucleus which is produced by the Feulgen reaction can be used as a quantitative measure of the amount of DNA present, and the chemical reactions involved in the procedure have been reviewed in detail by SWIFT (1955) and KASTEN (1960). This technique is very valuable for quantitative cytological work and is particularly informative when it is combined with autoradiography and other techniques for studying single cells (SEED 1962, 1966; DENDY and CLEAVER 1964; COOPER and HALE 1962). A typical staining procedure involves passing tissue sections etc., through the following successive steps:

(1) Acid hydrolysis; treatment with N/1 HCl at 60 °C for 12 min (or alternative period of time as required).
(2) Staining; treatment with the Schiff reagent for 20 to 40 min at room temperature.
(3) Sulphurous acid; treatment with a fresh solution of sulphurous acid (100 ml water, 5 ml of 10% potassium metabisulphite, 5 ml N/1 HCl) for three successive periods of 10 min each.
(4) Water rinse; stained preparations are finally washed in distilled water and then air-dried or dehydrated in alcohol and mounted.

It is generally agreed that the initial acid hydrolysis removes purine bases from DNA leaving reactive aldehyde groups in the polynucleotide chains (SWIFT 1955; KASTEN 1960). These aldehyde groups link to the Schiff reagent producing a pink stain which is stabilised by the subsequent treatment with sulphurous acid. The stain intensity depends on the duration and temperature of acid hydrolysis and the particular fixation that was used for the tissue, but 12 min hydrolysis at 60 °C usually gives an intensity which is near to maximum. If longer times are used the stain intensity is less than maximum on account of extensive disruption of the DNA molecules, and it is only at these longer hydrolysis times that significant amounts of pyrimidine bases are lost from DNA.

An experiment which illustrates the effect of varying the duration of acid hydrolysis on the loss of purine and pyrimidine bases from the DNA of tissue culture cells is shown in fig. 1.8. In these experiments cultures were labelled with a H³-labelled purine or pyrimidine deoxyribonucleoside, treated with RNase to remove any label that had been incorporated into RNA (significant labelling of RNA only occurred with the purine deoxyribonucleosides) and then stained with the Feulgen reaction. The duration of acid hydrolysis was varied from 1 min to 25 min, and the label remaining in DNA after staining was measured in terms of the mean grain counts in autoradiographs. The results of fig. 1.8 are shown for intact

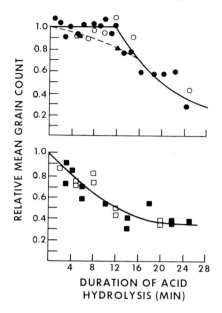

Fig. 1.8. Relative mean grain counts over mouse L strain cells as a function of the duration of acid hydrolysis, 1/N HCl at 60 °C, during the Feulgen reaction. Top: ● H³Tdr, 5 μCi/ml 2 Ci/mmole labelled for 10 min (monolayer cultures); ○ H³Cdr, 125 μCi/ml 0.88 Ci/mmole labelled for 10 min (monolayer cultures); ▲ H³Tdr, 2.5 μCi/ml 0.36 Ci/mmole labelled for 45 min (paraffin sections). Bottom: □ H³Adr, 2.5 μCi/ml 0.8 Ci/mmole labelled for 45 min (monolayer cultures); ■ H³Gdr, 2.5 μCi/ml, 0.5 Ci/mmole labelled for 45 min (monolayer cultures).

cells in monolayer cultures and for 5 μ sections of the same cells. It can be seen that no loss of label occurred from the monolayer cultures labelled with H³Cdr or H³Tdr until hydrolysis exceeded the optimum of 12 min, but loss of purine label increased steadily from the shortest hydrolysis times studied. In the case of sections, which were only studied with H³Tdr labelling, a small but significant amount of label was lost at earlier times than from monolayer cultures. After 6 min hydrolysis the mean grain counts fell to 93% of control, and after 12 min fell to 80% of control. This may be due to mechanical damage caused by paraffin embedding and sectioning which had made the cells more sensitive to acid hydrolysis. A similar loss of H³Tdr label from sections has been detected by WOODS (1957) and by LANG and MAURER (1965). However, Feulgen staining also causes a loss of nuclear protein with a consequent reduction in the self absorption of the cell to H³ β-particles and a slight loss of H³Tdr label from monolayer cultures could be masked by a simultaneous reduction in the self absorption. This is unlikely to be of major importance, however, because the strong acid used for fixation removes a considerable amount of nuclear protein from all of the cultures, including the controls, before Feulgen staining.

In conclusion, the Feulgen stain is a reliable stain to use in conjunction with autoradiography of H³Tdr (or H³Cdr) so long as intact and not sectioned cells are used. Since loss of the pyrimidine bases from DNA begins as soon as hydrolysis exceeds that required for maximum staining (12 min at 60 °C) it may be advisable to use a slightly shorter time to ensure against any loss of label.

References

ADA, G. L., J. H. HUMPHREY, B. A. ASKONAS H. O. MCDEVITT, and J. V. NOSSAL, 1966, Exp. Cell Res. *41*, 551

AMANO, M., B. MESSIER, and C. P. LEBLOND, 1959, J. Histochem. Cytochem. 7, 153

APELGOT, S., and B. EKART, 1963, J. Chim. Phys. *60*, 505

APELGOT, S., B. EKART, and M. R. TISNE, 1964, in Conference on methods of preparing and storing marked molecules, Euratom, p. 939

BASERGA, R., 1962a, J. Cell Biol. *12*, 632

BASERGA, R., 1962b, Biochim. Acta *31*, 445

BASERGA, R., 1963, Lab. Invest. *12*, 648

BASERGA, R., and K. NEMEROFF, 1962, Stain Technol. *37*, 21

BAYLEY, R. J., and H. WEIGEL, 1960, Nature *188*, 384

BLEECKEN, S., 1964, Atompraxis *8*, 1

BROWN, P. E., M. CALVIN, and J. F. NEWMARK, 1965, Science, *151*, 68

CARO, L. G., 1962, J. Cell Biol. *15*, 189

CARO, L. G., and R. P. VAN TUBERGEN, 1962, J. Cell Biol. 15, *172*

CARO, L. G., 1966, Progr. Biophys. Molec. Biol. *16*, *171*

CARO, L. G., and M. SCHNÖS, 1965, Science *149*, 60

CLEAVER, J. E., and R. M. HOLFORD, 1965, Biochim. Biophys. Acta *103*, 654

COOPER, E. H., and A. J. HALE, 1962, Biochem. J. *85*, 28P

CROWTER, D. G., E. A. EVANS, and R. W. LAMBERT, 1960, Chem. Ind. 899

DAWSON, K. B., E. O. FIELD, and G. W. W. STEVENS, 1962, Nature *195*, 510

DEMERS, P., 1947, Can. J. Res. *25A*, 223

DENDY, P. P., and J. E. CLEAVER, 1964, Intern. J. Radiation Biol. *8*, 301

DONIACH, I., and S. R. PELC, 1950, Brit. J. Radiol. *23*, 104

EVANS, R. D., 1955, The atomic nucleus, McGraw-Hill, New York, Toronto, London

EVANS, E. A., 1966, Nature *209*, 169

EVANS, E. A., and F. G. STANFORD, 1963, Nature *199*, 762

FIRKET, H., and W. G. VERLEY, 1958, Nature *181*, 274

FRIEDKIN, M., and D. ROBERTS, 1954, J. Biol. Chem. *207*, 245

FRIEDKIN, M., and H. WOOD, 1956, J. Biol. Chem. *220*, 639

FRIEDKIN, M., D. TILSON, and D. ROBERTS, 1956, J. Biol. Chem. *220*, 627

HILL, D. K., 1962, Nature *194*, 831

HOLLEY, R. W., J. APGAN, G. A. EVERETT, J. T. MADISON, M. MARQUISEE, S. H. MERRILL, R. PENSWICK, and A. ZAMIN, 1965, Science *147*, 1462

HUGHES, W. L., V BOND, G. BRECHER, E. P. CRONKITE, R. B. PAINTER, H. QUASTLER, and F. G. SHERMAN, 1958, Proc. Natl. Acad. Sci. *44*, 476

KASTEN, F. H., 1960, Intern. Rev. Cytol. *10*, 1

KISIELSKI, W. E., R. BASERGA, and J. VAUPOTIC, 1961, Radiation Res. *15*, 341

KOPRIWA, B. M., and C. P. LEBLOND, 1962, J. Histochem. Cytochem. *10*, 269

LAJTHA, L. G., R. OLIVER, R. J. BERRY, and E. HELL, 1960, Nature *187*, 919

LANG, W., and W. MAURER, 1965, Exp. Cell Res. *39*, 1

LANGRIDGE, L., and J. MARMUR, 1965, Science *143*, 1450

MAURER, W., and E. PRIMBSCH, 1964, Exp. Cell Res. *33*, 8

MOSES, M. J., 1964, J. Histochem. Cytochem. *12*, 115

NELMS, A. T., 1956, Natl. Bur. Std. U.S. Circ. 577

NELMS, A. T., 1958, Natl. Bur. Std. U.S. Circ. 577 (suppl.)

PAINTER, R. B., R. M. DREW, and B. G. GIAUQUE, 1960, Exp. Cell Res. *21*, 98

PASTORE, E. J., and M. FRIEDKIN, 1962, J. Biol. Chem. *237*, 3802

PELC, S. R., 1962, J. Roy. Microscop. Soc. *81*, 131

PILGRIM, C. H., and W. MAURER, 1962, Naturwiss. *49*, 544

POTTER, V. R., 1959, in Kinetics of cellular proliferation, F. Stohlman, ed., Grune and Stratton, New York, p. 104

PRICE, T. D., H. A. HUNDS, and R. J. BROWN, 1963, J. Biol. Chem. *238*, 311

PULLMAN, B., 1964, Biopolymers *1*, 141

RAY, R. C., and G. W. W. STEPHENS, 1953, Brit. J. Radiol. *26*, 362

REICHARD, P., and B. ESTBORN, 1951, J. Biol. Chem. *188*, 839

ROBERTSON, J. S., V. P. BOND, and E. P. CRONKITE, 1959, Intern. J. Appl. Radiation Isotopes *7*, 33

SEED, J., 1962, Proc. Roy. Soc. *B 156*, 41

SEED, J., 1966, J. Cell Biol. *28*, 233, 249, 257, 263

STEWART, P. A., H. QUASTLER, M. R. SKOUGAARD, D. R. WIMBER, M. F. WOLFSBERG, C. A. PERROTTA, B. FERBEL, and M. CARLOUGH, 1965, Radiation Res. *24*, 521

STRAUSS, B. S., 1958, Radiation Res. *8*, 234

SWIFT, H., 1955, in The nucleic acids, Vol. 2, E. Chargaff, J. N. Davidson, eds., Academic Press, New York, p. 51

TAYLOR, J. H., P. S. WOODS, and W. L. HUGHES, 1957, Proc. Natl. Acad. Sci. *43*, 122

TRELSTAD, R. L., 1965, Exp. Cell Res. *39*, 318

VERLEY, W. G., and G. HUNEBELLE, 1957, Bull. Soc. Chim. Belges *66*, 640

WIMBER, E. E., H. QUASTLER, O. STEIN, and D. R. WIMBER, 1960, J. Biophys. Biochem. Cytol. *8*, 327

WIMBER, D. E., and H. QUASTLER, 1963, Exp. Cell Res. *30*, 22

WOODS, P. S., 1957, J. Biophys. Biochem. Cytol. *3*, 71

Selected references on autoradiograph theory and experiment

ADAMIK, E. R., 1959, Laboratory procedures for tritium autoradiography, distributed by Schwartz BioResearch Inc., Orangeburg, New York

BOYD, G. A., 1955, Autoradiography in biology and medicine, Academic Press, New York and London

CARO, L. G., and R. P. VAN TUBERGEN, 1962, High resolution autoradiography, I. Methods. J. Cell Biol. *15*, 173

CARO, L. G., 1962, High resolution autoradiography, II. The problem of resolution. J. Cell Biol. *15*, 189

CARO, L. G., 1964, High resolution autoradiography, in Methods in cell physiology, Vol. I, D. M. Prescott, ed., Academic Press, New York and London, p. 327

CARO, L. G., 1966, Progress in high resolution autoradiography, in Progr. Biophys. Molec. Biol. *16*, 171

Conference in autoradiography, 1959, Lab. Invest. *8*, 59

FICQ, A., 1959, Autoradiography, in The cell, Vol. I, J. Brachet and A. E. Mirsky, eds., Academic Press, New York and London, p. 67

FITZGERALD, P. J, E. SIMMEL, J. WEINSTEIN, and C. MARTIN, 1953, Radioautography theory and technique and applications, Lab. Invest. *2*, 181

LEBLOND, C. P., and K. B. WARREN, eds., 1965, The use of radioautography in investigating protein synthesis, Academic Press, New York and London

MILLER, O. L., Jr., G. E. STONE, and D. M. PRESCOTT, 1964, Autoradiography of water-soluble materials, in Methods in cell physiology, Vol. I, D. M. Prescott, ed., Academic Press, New York and London, p. 371

PELC, S. F., 1962, Theory of electron autoradiography, J. Roy. Microscop. Soc. *81*, 131

PERRY, R. P., 1964, Quantitative autoradiography, in Methods in cell physiology, Vol. I, D. M. Prescott ed., Academic Press, New York and London, p. 305

PRESCOTT, D. M., 1964, Autoradiography with liquid emulsion, in Methods in cell physiology, Vol. I, D. M. Presscott ed., Academic Press, New York and London, p. 365

see also:

Tritium in the physical and biological sciences, Vols. I and II, 1962, International Atomic Energy Agency, Vienna

CHAPTER 2

Thymidine metabolism: pathways of incorporation and degradation

2.1 Introduction

Thymidine itself does not occur naturally on the main intracellular pathways that lead to DNA synthesis but is introduced into them by a single phosphorylation step to thymidine monophosphate, TMP (see fig. 2.1). Although Tdr is not essential for DNA synthesis except in organisms which cannot make their own TMP, it is incorporated rapidly into DNA in most organisms. Thymine, in contrast, is incorporated much less efficiently than Tdr, and its rate of incorporation into DNA in most mammalian tissues is less than 4% of the rate of Tdr incorporation (FRIEDKIN and WOOD 1956; FRIEDKIN et al. 1956).

Organisms which are dependent on Tdr for DNA synthesis include, for example, mutants of *E. coli* which lack TMP synthetase (SIMON and TESSMAN 1963) and tissue culture cells in which TMP synthesis is blocked by amethopterin (HAKALA and TAYLOR 1959; GENTRY et al. 1965a,b). These are exceptional cases, however, and in this chapter the metabolic pathways of Tdr are described, together with an examination of possible reasons why such pathways exist for an apparently superfluous compound.

2.2 Incorporation pathway

The incorporation of Tdr into DNA proceeds by a sequence of phosphorylation steps through TMP, TDP, and TTP followed by the assembly of TTP, together with the other nucleoside triphosphates, into DNA (see figs. 2.1 and 2.2). The enzymes involved in the phosphorylation steps are known

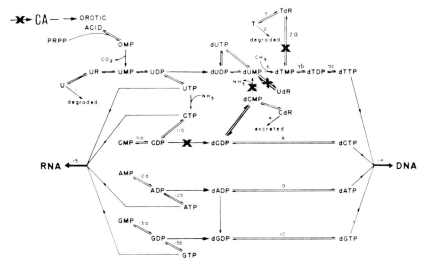

Fig. 2.1. The general pathways leading to DNA and RNA synthesis. Double arrows indicate that one compound can be reversibly transformed into another but not necessarily by the same reaction, since in most cases different enzymes are involved in anabolic and catabolic steps. It is not certain at what levels of phosphorylation some of these reactions occur. The sites of inhibition by TTP (X) are also shown. CA represents carbamyl aspartic acid which leads to orotic acid by a number of steps. The numbers locate the following steps:

(1) degradative pathway for uracil
(2) degradative pathway for thymine
(3) thymidine phosphorylase
(4) elimination of deoxycytidine by excretion rather than degradation
(5) deoxycytidylate deaminase
(6) thymidylate synthetase
(7a) thymidine kinase
(7b) thymidine monophosphate kinase

(7c) thymidine diphosphate kinase
(8) deoxycytidylate kinase
(9) deoxyadenylate kinase
(10) deoxyguanylate kinase
(11a and b) cytidylate kinase
(12a and b) adenylate kinase
(13a and b) guanylate kinase
(14) DNA polymerase
(15) RNA polymerase

(reproduced from BUCHER 1963, with the addition of the steps from CA to orotic acid, Udr to dUMP, and the sites of feedback inhibition by TTP which act on the anabolic steps.)

as thymidine kinase, thymidine monophosphate kinase and thymidine diphosphate kinase, respectively, though the latter two are commonly discussed under the combined term of thymidylate kinase (see for example GRAV and SMELLIE 1963, 1964). Although these terms are sufficiently precise to be used without ambiguity, they are not the only ones in use and the full names in the nomenclature and numerals of the Report of the Commission on Enzymes (1961) are as follows,

Tdr kinase ... ATP:thymidine 5'-phosphotransferase
EC 2.7.1.21 (for the bacterial enzyme)

TMP kinase ... ATP:thymidinemonophosphate phosphotransferase
EC 2.7.4.9

TDP kinase ... ATP:thymidinediphosphate phosphotransferase

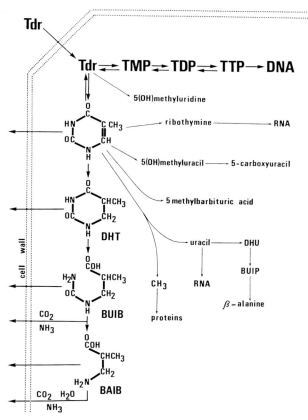

Fig. 2.2. Pathways of incorporation and degradation of thymidine. Major degradation pathway is via reduction to dihydrothymine (DHT), β-ureidoisobutyric acid (BUIB), β-aminoisobutyric acid (BAIB), and CO_2, NH_3 and H_2O. Minor pathways are included on the basis of at least one publication but may not be equally prevalent in all organisms.

When Tdr is added to a biological system the time course of phosphorylation depends in detail on the precise nature of that system. Two examples
are shown in figs. 2.3 and 2.4. The former shows results obtained when
Tdr is added to a cell-free extract of ascites cells, and the end product of
the phosphorylation sequence in this case is TTP. The latter shows results
obtained when a single injection of H³Tdr is given to rats and radioactivity
in both the acid soluble pool and in DNA of the regenerating liver is
determined. Several factors make it difficult to derive the exact reaction
sequence from such kinetic experiments alone. These include, the rapid-
ity of some of the steps, the instability of the enzymes in cell free extracts,
and the possibility of reverse reactions due to phosphatases in the incubation media. It was suggested at one time on the basis of kinetic experiments that TMP was converted directly to TTP by the enzymatic addition of
pyrophosphate (BIANCHI et al. 1961). This suggestion was based on the
observation that when Tdr was incubated with enzyme extracts from
mammalian cells, TDP was formed in detectable quantities slightly earlier
than TTP. It was then assumed that TDP was only formed by degradation

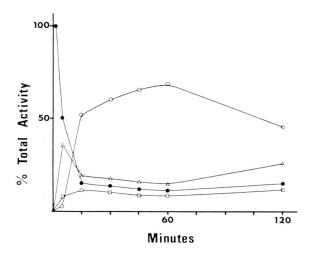

Fig. 2.3. Time course of phosphorylation of H³Tdr by extracts of Landschutz ascites
cells, expressed as a percentage of total radioactivity recovered from columns of
ECTEOLA-cellulose. ● Tdr, △ TMP, □ TDP, ○ TTP (redrawn from GRAV and SMELLIE 1963).

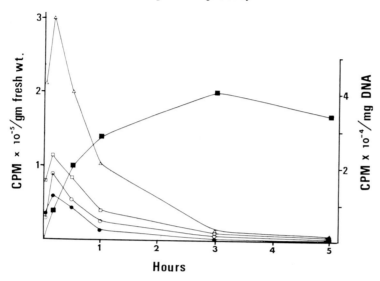

Fig. 2.4. Tritium activity in labelled precursors (expressed as cpm × 10⁻⁵ per g fresh weight) and in DNA (expressed as cpm × 10⁻⁴ per mg DNA) in cells of the regenerating rat liver. ● Tdr, △ TMP, □ TDP, ○ TTP, ■ DNA (redrawn from CHANG and LOONEY 1965).

of TTP. Subsequent experiments, however, by GRAV and SMELLIE (1963) and IVES (1965) have made it clear that TDP is definitely on the phosphorylation pathway and not the degradation pathway alone.

In the experiments of IVES (1965), for example, the transfer of the phosphate groups from ATP during the phosphorylation of Tdr was investigated by using ATP, labelled with P³² in the β- or γ-position, and enzyme preparation from Novikoff hepatoma cells. TMP was incubated with ATP labelled with P³² and the distribution of label in the TDP and TTP products was determined. If TDP is an intermediate on the pathway to TTP, then using (γ P³²) ATP the product TDP would be singly labelled with P³² and the product TTP doubly labelled. If TTP was formed by the addition of pyrophosphate, and TDP by degradation from TTP, then with (γ P³²) ATP, the product TDP would be unlabelled and the product TTP singly labelled in the terminal phosphate group. By means of experiments of this type the position and role of TDP in the phosphorylation pathway has been unambiguously determined.

The reaction steps involving Tdr kinase and TDP kinase are relatively rapid whereas that involving TMP kinase is relatively slow (GRAV and SMELLIE 1963; IVES 1965). Consequently the TDP that is formed is rapidly converted to TTP and precise data on the pool size of TDP and changes in the pool with time are more difficult to obtain than for the other Tdr derivatives. This difficulty contributed to some of the uncertainty of the role played by TDP in the incorporation of Tdr into DNA. However, there is little doubt that the reaction sequence shown in figs. 2.1. and 2.2 is essentially correct.

In addition to the main phosphorylation pathway to Tdr-5′-triphosphate there have been a number of reports which describe the phosphorylation of Tdr to Tdr-3′-triphosphate in mammalian tissue (COUTSO-GEORGOPOULOS et al. 1966) and microorganisms (CANELLAKIS et al. 1965). Although these triphosphates may play a role in DNA synthesis it is premature to speculate on their significance until it is known how common they are.

Tdr is also converted to TDP-sugar compounds in a number of organisms. TDP-glucose has been identified in *Pseudomonas aeruginosa* (KORNFELD and GLASER 1960), TDP-rhamnose in *Lactobacillus acidophilus* and *Escherichia coli* 15T⁻ (OKAZAKI 1959), and a similar TDP-sugar in *Lactobacillus leichmannii* (GOULIAN and BECK 1966). In mouse liver, COUNTS and FLAMM (1966) have identified a compound that contains both glycogen and a phosphorylated derivative of Tdr. In microorganisms these TDP sugar compounds may function as intermediates in cell wall synthesis, and they are probably synthesised from TDP or TTP as the immediate precursors.

2.3 *Properties of thymidine kinase*

Of the three phosphorylating enzymes involved in the incorporation of Tdr into DNA, only Tdr kinase has been studied in detail up to the present time. Some progress has been made in isolation and characterisation of TMP and TDP kinases but these are more unstable than Tdr kinase when extracted from the cell (GRAV and SMELLIE 1964). Tdr kinase itself is unstable in solution and decays with a half life of about 30 min at 38°C, but each of the enzymes can be stabilised by the addition of its respective substrate.

Tdr kinase has the same substrate specificity irrespective of the tissue of origin; deoxyuridine and 5-substituted derivatives including Tdr and the halogenated derivatives are all substrates for the enzyme, but other deoxynucleosides or ribonucleosides are not phosphorylated to any significant extent. The relative efficiency of these nucleosides as substrates are shown in table 2.1. These nucleosides are all phosphorylated by the

TABLE 2.1

Substrate specificity of thymidine kinase. (Tdr kinase from Walker tumor, 10 mg of protein, was incubated with $MgCl_2$, 2.5 mM; ATP-^{14}C, 0.4 mM, 0.1 μCi; compounds tested as acceptors at 0.4 mM; Tris buffer 0.05 M, pH 8, to total volume 0.25 ml. Incubation at 37°C for 15 min. The ADP-^{14}C was separated by electrophoresis in 0.1 M citrate buffer, pH 5.2, at 900 V for 2 hr.) Reproduced from BRESNICK and THOMPSON (1965).

Acceptor	ADP formed (mμmole)	Tdr activity (%)
Deoxyuridine	0.10	67
Thymidine	0.15	100
Bromodeoxyuridine	0.14	93
Iododeoxyuridine	0.14	93
Fluorodeoxyuridine	0.11	73
Chlorodeoxyuridine	0.15	100
Azadeoxyuridine	0.04	27
Deoxycytidine	0.00	0
Uridine	0.00	0

same active site in Tdr kinase, since they inhibit the phosphorylation of each other competitively. The relative efficiency of each nucleoside as a substrate is probably determined to some extent by the size of the 5-substituted group.

In addition to the substrate, the Tdr kinase reaction has an absolute requirement for ATP and Mg^{2+} ions in mmolar concentrations. Other divalent ions such as Ca^{2+}, Co^{2+}, or Mn^{2+} are much less effective in supporting enzymatic activity. The role of ATP in the reaction may be not only as a phosphate donor but also an activator, so that two molecules of ATP are required for each molecule of Tdr and Tdr kinase (OKAZAKI and KORNBERG 1964b).

Some of the main properties of Tdr kinases from a number of different

TABLE 2.2

Some properties of thymidine kinases isolated from various sources.

Source	Michaelis const. (M)	Velocity$_{max}$ (M)	E_a (kcal/mole)	pH opt.	Half life (min)	Ref.
Mouse fibroblasts	3.5×10^{-5}	2.5×10^{-5}	9.2	8	30 (38 °C)	1
Green monkey kidney	2.9×10^{-5}	–	–	–	–	2
Mouse embryo	1.8×10^{-5}	–	–	–	–	2
Novikoff hepatoma	2.7×10^{-6}	0.07×10^{-6}	11.1	8	–	3
McCoy hepatoma	3.2×10^{-6}	0.07×10^{-6}	–	8	–	3
Walker carcino sarcoma	3.7×10^{-6}	0.5×10^{-6}	–	8	3 (60 °C)	3
Landschutz ascites	–	–	–	7.8–8.1	30–60 (38 °C)	4 5
Vaccinia virus	7.2×10^{-5}	2.6×10^{-5}	11.2	8	300 (38 °C)	1
SV40	8.1×10^{-5}	–	–	–	–	2
Polyoma virus	2×10^{-5}	–	–	–	–	2

References:
1) KIT and DUBBS (1965)
2) KIT et al. (1965)
3) BRESNICK and THOMPSON (1965)
4) GRAV and SMELLIE (1964)
5) CRATHORN and SHOOTER (1964)

sources are summarised in table 2.2. The Michaelis constants and other properties are not identical for every enzyme and this may be due to small differences between the structures of the enzymes. After viral infection, for example, it is possible to detect the synthesis of a Tdr kinase characteristic of the virus and different from the kinase of the host cell (KIT and DUBBS 1965; KIT et al. 1965, 1966a, b).

The molecular weight of Tdr kinase is greater than 10^5 (BRESNICK and THOMPSON 1965; KIT and DUBBS 1965) and the enzyme exists in a number of different states of aggregation. The enzyme from mammalian cells,

for example, occurs in an aggregated form in dilute solution and disso-
ciates into six subunits of molecular weight 1.1×10^5 when the ionic
strength of the solution is increased (BRESNICK and THOMPSON 1966).
The enzyme isolated from plants is different from the mammalian enzyme
and has two main components. One of the components is found in most
plant tissues, but the other is only found in tissues engaged in DNA
synthesis (HOTTA and STERN 1963, 1965; WANKA et al. 1964). Whereas Tdr
kinase from mammalian cells is active in both the aggregated and the
disaggregated forms, the plant enzyme is only active when the two components are combined. The activity of enzymes like Tdr kinase, with
several subunits, can be regulated by alteration of the relative arrangement
or the degree of aggregation of the subunits. This can be caused by the
attachment of small molecules to specific sites on the enzyme and these
molecules need not be structurally related to the substrate or product of
the enzyme (the allosteric effect, see MONOD et al. 1963). The inhibition of
Tdr kinase by TTP, a typical end product inhibition (see ch. 2 § 4), may be
an example of this type of enzyme regulation. In general the structure of
Tdr kinase consists of several subunits with three or four sites for attachment of the substrate (Tdr), inhibitor (TTP), phosphate donor (ATP) and
the activator (ATP) molecules, respectively. The sites for substrate and
inhibitor molecules may not be completely distinct in the case of the *E.
coli* enzyme for which competitive inhibition was observed (OKAZAKI and
KORNBERG 1964b).

2.4 End-product inhibition by TTP

The end product of a sequence of enzymatic reactions is often found to
regulate its own synthesis by means of end product inhibition (i.e. negative
feedback). By this mechanism, the end product of a synthetic pathway
inhibits the activity of the initial enzyme, or enzymes, in the sequence of
synthetic steps (MONOD et al. 1963). A particular example of this is the end
product inhibition exerted by TTP on a number of enzymes. The first
distinct step in the main biochemical pathway that leads to the synthesis
of pyrimidine nucleotides is the reaction between carbamyl phosphate and
aspartic acid which yields carbamyl aspartic acid (see, for example,
SCHULMAN 1961). The enzyme that mediates this step, aspartate trans-

carbamylase, is inhibited by TTP, one of the final products of the nucleotide pathways (GERHART and SCHACHMAN 1965). Other enzymes which
contribute to the synthesis of TTP by pathways alternative to the one that
starts with carbamyl aspartic acid, are also inhibited by TTP. These
enzymes include Tdr kinase, deoxyuridine kinase, deoxycytidine monophosphate deaminase, and cytidine diphosphate reductase (REICHARD
1962; BREITMAN 1963; IVES et al. 1963; MORRIS and FISCHER 1963; SIMON
and TESSMAN 1963; OKAZAKI and KORNBERG 1964b; MALEY and MALEY
1965). BRESNICK (1962) has also demonstrated that Tdr will inhibit aspartate transcarbamylase. WHITTLE (1966) has demonstrated that high
concentrations of Tdr in the incubation medium of rat thymus cells
inhibit either the incorporation of cytidine into the cells or the phosphorylation of cytidine to CTP. The concentration of Tdr required to
demonstrate this particular inhibition is about 10 times the concentration
that is required to inhibit cytidine diphosphate reductase, and this may
represent the inhibition of cytidine kinase by TTP, although the details of
the inhibition have not been established. The sites of TTP inhibition have
been marked in fig. 2.1, and it is clear in this illustration that the end product inhibition exerts a control at some step in each of the independent
pathways which contribute to TTP synthesis.

The kinetics of inhibition of Tdr kinase by TTP have been extensively
studied, and may differ in different organisms. OKAZAKI and KORNBERG
(1964b) concluded that the inhibition was competitive with the substrate
Tdr for the *E. coli* enzyme system; BRESNICK and THOMPSON (1965) on the
other hand, concluded that the kinetics were complex but non-competi-
tive with Tdr for the enzyme system isolated from animal tumours. The
inhibition of cytidine diphosphate reductase, when the level of TTP is
excessively high, can result in the inhibition of DNA synthesis due to a
deficiency of deCTP. This occurs in tissue culture, for example, when
cultures are grown in medium that contains Tdr at concentrations above
approximately 10^{-5} to 10^{-4} molar (e.g. CLEAVER and HOLFORD (1965),
see ch. 3 § 12).

In many of the studies which elucidated parts of the network of end
product inhibition, and were quoted above, the inhibition was detected by
the addition of Tdr to the incubation medium of whole cell systems. The
precise nature of the phosphorylated derivative which gave rise to the
inhibitions was not always determined. In those studies in which the

derivative was identified it was found to be TTP, and the scheme presented here is probably essentially correct.

2.5 Occurrence of Tdr kinase

Although Tdr itself is not on the main pathways of intracellular DNA synthesis, Tdr kinase is absent only from selected mutants of cells and viruses and from very few other organisms. Mutant strains of mouse L cells (KIT et al. 1963; LITTLEFIELD 1965) and of HeLa S3 cells (KIT et al. 1966c) have been isolated by selecting cells which were capable of unlimited growth in the presence of BUdr. Using similar methods it has been possible to isolate a number of mutant viruses lacking Tdr kinase activity, including *vaccinia* and *herpes simplex* (KIT and DUBBS 1963).

The microorganism *Euglena* lacks Tdr kinase naturally (SAGAN 1965; COOK 1966) and the enzyme may also be missing from a number of rodents (ADELSTEIN et al. 1964). The rodents *Citellus* (ground squirrel) and *Marmota* (woodchuck) appear to be severely limited in their ability to incorporate H³Tdr into DNA, and the rodents *Tamais* (chipmunk) and *Tamasciurus* (red squirrel) are limited to a lesser extent. These limitations are not uniform for every tissue of the animals in question and may be due either to a lack of Tdr kinase, a large intracellular pool of TTP or a very active degrative pathway for Tdr. Amphibian embryos in water are impermeable to many substances, including Tdr, but this is not due to a lack of enzymes because they will incorporate H³Tdr when the surrounding medium is a saline at 10 to 100% of the isosmotic concentration of the amphibian cells (LOEFFLER and JOHNSTON 1964). Strains of *E. coli* also incorporate very little Tdr into DNA, except for thymine requiring mutants which incorporate it readily (SIMONOVITCH and GRAHAM 1955; BOYCE and SETLOW 1962). The limitation in the wild type bacteria is due mainly to the induction of Tdr phosphorylase and consequent degradation of Tdr, rather than an absence of Tdr kinase (RACHMELER et al. 1961), and Tdr incorporation can be increased by adding other deoxynucleosides to the growth medium (BOYCE and SETLOW 1962).

Although other organisms may exist which do not incorporate Tdr into DNA, this property is exceptional and Tdr kinase is a widespread and common enzyme.

2.6 *Degradation pathways of thymidine*

The main known pathways for degradation of Tdr have been summarised in fig. 2.2. The first step in degradation consists of the cleavage of the glycosidic bond in Tdr to form thymine and deoxyribose-1-P by Tdr phosphorylase. This step has been known since the 1930s (DEUTSCH and LASAR 1930; KLEIN 1935). The phosphorylase is extremely widespread and is found in many mammalian tissues, plants and microorganisms. In mammalian tissues the phosphorylase is found, in the order of decreasing activity, in the intestinal mucosa, liver, bone marrow, kidney, spleen, lung, and heart, and much less activity is found in the brain and muscle (FRIEDKIN and ROBERTS 1954). In the regenerating rat liver catabolism is diminished and the activity of Tdr phosphorylase is lower than in the normal liver (CANELLAKIS et al. 1959). Normal leucocytes have a higher phosphorylase activity than leukemic leucocytes or normal bone marrow cells, and relatively low catabolism may be one feature associated with the immaturity of the leukemic cells (MARSH and PERRY 1964). Leucocytes are able to degrade Tdr to β-ureidoisobutyric acid and they release this into surrounding medium (MARSH and PERRY 1964b). In cases of severe malnutrition in man, greater breakdown of Tdr occurs than in normal individuals (RUBINI et al. 1960). The phosphorylase appears to be missing in the case of the Novikoff hepatoma (POTTER 1963; MORSE and POTTER 1965).

The major pathway for degradation is through thymine, dihydrothymine, β-ureidoisobutyric acid (BUIB), β-aminoisobutyric acid (BAIB), to carbon dioxide and water (FINK et al. 1956a,b; POTTER 1959; ARMSTRONG et al. 1963). The final degradation steps to BAIB, CO_2, etc. may only occur in the liver, spleen and kidneys, whereas the earlier steps, particularly the one involving the phosphorylase, occur in many tissues (FRIEDKIN and ROBERTS 1954; RUBINI et al. 1960; MARSH and PERRY 1946b). In microorganisms thymine is also degraded by an oxidative pathway with the formation of 5-methylbarbituric acid but this pathway may be less common in higher organisms (SCHULMAN 1961). Some systems such as ascites cells (ZAJICEK et al. 1963) and plant tissues (TAKATS and SMELLIE 1963) release thymine from the cells as a breakdown product of Tdr, though the latter also degrade Tdr further. Leucocytes, in vitro, also release Tdr phosphorylase into the incubation medium which degrades some of the

Tdr to thymine without incorporation into the cells (MARSH and PERRY 1964a). In mammals, including man, the main excretory products of Tdr are BAIB, CO_2 and H_2O, of which the latter two predominate.

In man, about 17 % of the injected C^{14}Tdr is retained in DNA, 3 % is excreted as C^{14}-labelled BAIB and 80 % as $C^{14}O_2$ (KRISS et al. 1965). About 22 % of the label in $C^{14}O_2$ appears within 30 min of injection and acid-soluble derivatives of Tdr are cleared rapidly from the body. When H^3Tdr is used in man there appears to be a greater retention of label in the body than was observed by KRISS et al. (1965) with C^{14}Tdr, and only about 1/3 of the injected H^3Tdr is degraded to water and BAIB (RUBINI et al. 1960). The difference in the amounts of C^{14} and H^3 retained in the body may be due to a difference in the excretion of breakdown products that are derived from various portions of the pyrimidine ring. The use of different isotopes is unlikely to actually cause a difference in the retention, and similar total amounts of Tdr of 1 to 10 μmoles were used per injection in both series of experiments. Although a considerable amount of injected H^3Tdr is retained in the body, the amount retained in any particular tissue is a small fraction of the amount supplied. In the rat, for example, only about 1 % of the injected H^3Tdr is incorporated into DNA in the regenerating liver and breakdown products are detectable in the acid soluble fraction of the liver within 2 min of the injection (CHANG and LOONEY 1965).

When high specific activity H^3Tdr is used, some of the breakdown pathways which are relatively unimportant in terms of the actual quantities of Tdr degraded may become more important from an experimental point of view. This is particularly true when the labelled breakdown product is incorporated into some acid insoluble macromolecule such as protein. The methyl group, for example, may be lost either by demethylation of Tdr itself (FINK and FINK 1962; TAKATS and SMELLIE 1963; BRYANT 1966), or by demethylation of BAIB. This methyl group can then be used for the synthesis of some amino acids and eventually be incorporated into proteins (BRYANT 1966). This may be the reason why only 40 % of the injected C^{14}Tdr is degraded to $C^{14}O_2$ when the C^{14} label is in the methyl position whereas 60 % is degraded to $C^{14}O_2$ when the label is in the 2-position (POTTER 1959). The amount of label incorporated into proteins is very small compared to the amount incorporated into DNA and is usually only detectable in autoradiographs when long exposure times are used,

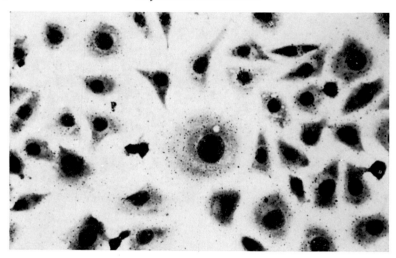

Fig. 2.5. Autoradiograph of mouse L strain cells labelled with H³Tdr for 10 min. The H³Tdr was originally labelled in the methyl group and was stored at 2.5 μCi/ml, 3 Ci/mmole, for 3 months at 4 °C in a non-sterile condition. Breakdown products resulting from bacterial degradation have given rise to cytoplasmic labelling that was never observed in these cells with fresh H³Tdr solutions (× 500).

but this does give rise to cytoplasmic labelling (fig. 2.5) which may be confused with incorporation into cytoplasmic DNA. If labelled Tdr is used, with the C14 or H3 atoms elsewhere than the methyl group, demethylation and phosphorolysis can give rise to labelled uracil which is incorporated into RNA (FINK and FINK 1962; ROYCHOUDHURY and PEN 1964). Since thymine is found to a small extent in RNA, labelled RNA can also result from conversion of Tdr to ribothymine (POTTER 1959; PRICE et al. 1963; HOLLEY et al. 1965). In general, however, most of the breakdown products are acid soluble, easily washed out of tissues by normal fixation procedures, and not incorporated into cell structures to any significant extent. Consideration of the role played by breakdown products is usually only necessary when the level of incorporation into DNA itself is very low such as after high doses of radiation, or when high resolution studies are undertaken.

2.7 Availability time of Tdr in various systems

The time for which Tdr is available as a precursor of DNA after it has been supplied depends on the particular experimental system employed. In tissue cultures grown as monolayers where there is usually a large volume of fluid, Tdr in the medium may not be significantly depleted for several days.* In animals, however, breakdown and excretion of injected Tdr results in a short availability time of only a few hours. In ch. 3 § 9 an estimate is given for the rate at which thymine bases are assembled into DNA, and if it is assumed that these are all derived from the external medium, Tdr will be used up at a rate of about 1.7×10^{-17} moles/cell/min. In monolayer cultures roughly 10 ml of medium is sufficient for a culture bottle containing about 10^6 cells, so the medium will be depleted at about 3×10^{-10} moles/hr (assuming about 30% of the cells are in DNA synthesis at any one time). At a concentration of about 10^{-6} M Tdr would then be completely used up in about 1 to 2 days. In suspension cultures a cell density of about 10^6 cells/ml is commonly employed, and 10^{-6} molar Tdr would then be used up in about 3 hr. These are, of course, just rough estimates and take no account of the decrease in the rate of incorporation that occurs with a reduction in Tdr concentration (CLEAVER and HOLFORD 1965, ch. 3 § 3), but they serve to show the approximate periods of time for which Tdr can be available when supplied to tissue cultures.

A similar long availability time is obtained when root tips or other plant material is labelled by immersing the material in a Tdr solution. In one experiment a concentration of 6×10^{-6} M H^{3}Tdr, for example, was completely depleted in about 8 hours by root tips of *Vicia* and by that time the composition of the medium was predominantly H^3 thymine (TAKATS and SMELLIE 1963).

In a number of biological systems such as the fertile hen's egg or the insect pupa there is negligible excretion of waste products, and injected Tdr is available for DNA synthesis for long periods of time. In the chick embryo, for example, FRIEDKIN et al. (1956) observed a constant rate of incorporation of C^{14}Tdr for at least 42 hr after injection, and in the insect

---

* If cultures degrade Tdr in addition to using it as a precursor for DNA replication, the availability time will be much shorter than estimated above (LANG et al. 1966).

pupa H³Tdr was still available for DNA synthesis at least one week after injection (BOWERS and WILLIAMS 1964).

In animals, however, Tdr is only available for a short period of time after intravenous or intraperitoneal injection and most of the incorporation into DNA occurs during the first 30 to 60 min (see fig. 2.4, HUGHES et al. 1958; RUBINI et al. 1960; STAROSCIK et al. 1964; CHANG and LOONEY 1965). Tdr is available to most tissues after injection, and diffuses rapidly from the blood vessels at approximately 2 μ/sec (PELC and APPLETON 1965). The concentration of Tdr that is available for DNA synthesis may not be identical for every tissue, and the availability will depend on the distribution of blood vessels, permeability of cell membranes, etc. The decline in the concentration of labelled Tdr in the blood stream usually follows a curve that can be described as the sum of two exponential components with different half lives. In man the two components have half lives of 1 and 2 min (RUBINI et al. 1960), in the C3H mouse the half lives are about 1 to 2 min and 25 min (STAROSCIK et al. 1964) and in the rat during liver regeneration about 8 and 30 min (CHANG and LOONEY 1965). In these studies clearance from the blood stream and intracellular pools seem to follow almost identical time courses. The rate of clearance of H³Tdr from the body is slightly faster following intravenous injection than intraperitoneal injection (HUGHES et al. 1958). A clearance rate similar to that following intravenous and intraperitoneal injection is observed when H³Tdr is injected into the anterior chamber of the eye (MAENZA and HARDING 1962; REDDAN and ROTHSTEIN 1966). Following a single injection into the eye the concentration of H³Tdr falls very rapidly, and the amount left at 60 min is only about 10% of the original inoculum. A single injection into an animal is consequently similar to a pulse label in tissue culture of about 30 to 60 min in duration, although the pulse shape is different in the two systems. In tissue culture, a pulse label may be administered with Tdr at a constant concentration during the pulse, but in the animal the concentration declines steadily after the initial injection.

When Tdr is supplied by feeding it remains available for DNA synthesis during a longer period than after injection, and incorporation may continue for at least two hours. This is on account of the time required for assimilation from the gastrointestinal tract. The labelled Tdr may be incorporated preferentially into DNA by cells in the epithelium of the gastrointestinal tract (RUBINI et al. 1961) although this has not always been observed (FIELD et al. 1961). This method of labelling may consequently be less satisfactory than injection, if it is necessary to ensure that the label is uniformly available to all tissues of the body.

In the case of hair bulbs, phosphorylated derivatives of Tdr can remain available for DNA synthesis for much longer than the usual availability time of a few hours (MOFFAT and PELC 1966). In one experiment hairs were plucked at the time of injection of H^3Tdr in mice, and a H^3-labelled pool remained in about 10% of the cells of the hair bulb that was used for DNA synthesis 16 to 32 hr after the injection.

Some incorporation of label into DNA can be detected from several days to a week after a single injection of H^3Tdr (BRYANT 1962; DIDERHOLM et al. 1962; STEEL 1966). This is due to the degradation of labelled DNA from cells which die during this period. The incorporation of this material into newly synthesised DNA through a salvage process is discussed in the following section.

2.8 *The role of thymidine kinase in salvage (reutilisation) mechanisms*

Since Tdr itself is not normally found on the pathways that lead to DNA synthesis inside the cell, the existence of Tdr kinase has been an enigma, although a very useful one from an investigator's point of view. It has been difficult to find a reason for the existence of such an apparently superfluous enzyme. The problem, however, should not be viewed solely with reference to this one kinase. Although none of the deoxynucleosides occur naturally within the cell on the pathways of DNA synthesis, each are readily incorporated into the cell and phosphorylated by the appropriate kinase. These kinases are probably all salvage enzymes which are important for making use of the breakdown products from dead cells in the whole animal. Since most cells also contain 5'-nucleotidases and phosphorylases there is probably competition for the available Tdr, or other nucleosides, between the synthetic and degradative pathways; the former pathway will then predominate when cells require TTP for DNA synthesis. Parasitic organisms such as *E. coli* also possess nucleoside kinases and these organisms make similar use of breakdown products for their own synthetic pathways. Four main types of salvage process have been suggested by STEEL and LAMERTON (1965) and these may have different relative importance in different tissues. These four types of salvage are:

(1) DNA from dead cells is incorporated by cells within the same tissue.

(2) DNA from dead cells, having been broken down into relatively small molecules, is incorporated by cells throughout the whole organism.

(3) The special case of the gastrointestinal tract in which DNA of cells which are sloughed off into the lumen may be absorbed lower down the tract and incorporated into epithelial cells. If the absorbed material is not used for local synthesis but is then distributed elsewhere in the body, this is equivalent to the previous salvage process (2).

(4) The special case of the bone marrow, in which the nucleus is discarded at the orthochromatic stage in erythropoiesis and in which there may be overproduction of cells and consequent cell death during myelopoiesis.

Under normal conditions the concentration of deoxynucleosides in the blood stream is very low, except for deoxycytidine which is found at concentrations up to about 10 μg/ml in rodents (SCHNEIDER 1955; ROTHERHAM and SCHNEIDER 1958) and similar concentrations in other animals. Although a considerable fraction of the deoxynucleosides in the blood stream is eventually degraded and excreted, salvage of these breakdown products occurs to a significant extent and may be an important factor in the interpretation of long term experiments with H³Tdr in vivo. For example, about 10% of the TTP required for DNA synthesis during the regeneration of the rat liver is derived from the salvage of breakdown products (BRYANT 1962). In the bone marrow, about 35% of the thymine bases in the DNA of erythroid precursors are used for local DNA synthesis after the nuclei are extruded at the orthochromatic stage (FEINENDEGEN et al. 1966a).

Salvage mechanisms have been detected in a number of experiments in which DNA synthesis in a tissue has occurred several days after the injection of H³Tdr. BRYANT (1962) labelled animals with injections of H³Tdr prior to partial hepatectomy, and was able to detect labelled cells in the regenerating liver up to 30 hr after the final injection. Since there was very little detectable H³Tdr in the blood in an acid-soluble form, the probable source of the labelled precursors was the death and breakdown of labelled leucocytes in the liver. This hypothesis implies that some of the leucocytes which become labelled in the marrow die and are broken down after only a short lifetime in the blood stream.

Similar observations were made by DIDERHOLM et al. (1962) in studies in the host–graft reaction. Animals were labelled with H³Tdr, by means of three daily injections, and two days after the final injection skin grafts were made onto the labelled animal. Cells in the epidermis of the grafted skin were found to be labelled when the tissue was fixed 7 days after grafting. The most probable source of the label were the leucocytes which accumulate around the graft and it was also suggested that the epidermis may be a normal disposal area for leucocytes.

In other experiments the incorporation of labelled breakdown products has been detected in bone marrow cells of an irradiated animal after the injection of labelled leucocytes (HILL 1962), and in ascites cells which had been injected into a labelled animal (RIEKE 1962). The latter was probably due to degradation of labelled host lymphocytes in the peritoneal cavity.

A particularly clear example of the incorporation of labelled breakdown products from cells originally labelled with H³Tdr has been found by STEEL (1966). In this example, STEEL (1966) determined the total H³ activity in a rapidly growing mammary tumour of the rat (doubling time 30 hr) as a function of time after a single injection of 50 μCi of H³Tdr. For the first 3 days the total H³ activity remained approximately constant, since there was no loss of cells by necrosis or metastasis; during the subsequent 5 days the total H³ increased until it reached a value about 4 times the original value. The specific activity of the tumour decreased over this period because the tumour increased in size and reached a final weight, at the end of the experiment, that was about 25 times the original weight. The only source for the H³ that was incorporated into the tumour during the period between the 4th and the 8th days of the experiment must have been the DNA of labelled cells which died during this interval. An increase in tumour H³ by the salvage of breakdown products was detectable in this system because the tumour was growing rapidly, and it was not possible to detect any similar increase in slowly growing tumours which had doubling times of 7.8 days and 14 days. The period over which labelled breakdown products are available for DNA synthesis in significant quantities is generally found to be between 2 to 7 days following an injection of H³Tdr (STEEL and LAMERTON 1965; STEEL 1966).

Similar salvage mechanisms may operate for each of the deoxyribonucleosides in DNA synthesis. With the exception of Tdr, these deoxyribonucleosides may be used as precursors for RNA synthesis, since the precursor pools for DNA and RNA synthesis are interrelated (FEINENDEGEN et al. 1961a,b; BUCHER 1963, see fig. 2.1). The first step in using the deoxy-ribonucleosides for RNA synthesis would involve cleavage of the glycosidic bond by the phosphorylase to leave a free base which is then readily converted to the corresponding ribonucleoside (JACQUEZ 1962; WARREN 1961). Thymine, however, is only found very rarely in RNA and Tdr kinase is then of no use in tissues where there is RNA synthesis but no DNA synthesis. In such tissues Tdr may be incorporated into the cells and then degraded. In consequence, it is not surprising that the activity of Tdr and thymidylate kinases is low in non growing tissues, in contrast to the high activity of the kinases for the other deoxynucleosides in most tissues (BELTZ 1963; BUCHER 1963; WEISSMAN et al. 1960). It has also been suggested that the same kinase is able to use either the ribonucleoside or the corresponding deoxynucleoside as substrates (KIELLEY 1961) so that the same kinase may be responsible for salvage of both RNA and DNA precursors.

In some experiments, in vivo, such as those described in ch. 7 §§ 9, 10 for the determination of turnover times, the effect of salvage processes is to extend to period over which H^3Tdr is incorporated into DNA, and render accurate estimation of cellular turnover times difficult. This can be almost completely avoided by using the thymidine analogue, 5-iododeoxyuridine (IUdr), as the labelling molecule. This analogue is incorporated into DNA in a similar manner to Tdr, but at a much lower efficiency, and is salvaged to a negligible extent when compared to Tdr (FEINENDEGEN et al. 1966a,b). A number of radioactive atoms may be used in the iododeoxyuridine molecule and two which have been used in bone marrow studies are I^{131} (FEINENDEGEN et al. 1966a) and I^{125} (FEINENDEGEN et al. 1966b). The former, I^{131}, emits a high energy γ-radiation and the retention of I^{131} Udr in vivo can be measured by the emission of this radiation from the living animal. The half life of I^{131} is short, 8 days, and consequently large amounts of I^{131} Udr are required for accurate experiments. This may be a technical hazard because large amounts of IUdr are toxic. I^{125} has a longer half life of 56 days and emits a soft γ-radiation, and I^{125} Udr has been used successfully in autoradiographic experiments by FEINENDEGEN et al. (1966b). The technical problems set by the relatively short half life of these iodine derivatives can be avoided by using IUdr labelled with H^3 (HOFFMAN and POST 1966). IUdr labelled in this manner would then be closely analagous to H³Tdr or C¹⁴Tdr, respectively, apart from the absence of significant salvage of IUdr-labelled DNA.*

If Tdr kinase, and the other kinases, are important solely for salvage purposes then the DNA from dead cells must be degraded to nucleosides before being used as a source of precursors for DNA synthesis. There is also the possibility that larger pieces of DNA may be used in a manner analogous to transformation in microorganisms but this has not been unambiguously demonstrated (KAY 1961, 1966; BENSCH and KING 1961; SZYBALSKA and SZYBALSKI 1962; BENSCH et al. 1966).

The role of Tdr kinase is consequently not that of an enzyme essential for DNA synthesis, but rather of an enzyme which enables the cells in the body to synthesise DNA more economically by salvaging material from dead cells that would otherwise have been discarded from the body.

2.9 *Variations in the activity of thymidine kinase and thymidylate kinase and the control of DNA synthesis*

In most cell types, both microorganisms and higher organisms, variations in the activity of Tdr kinase and thymidylate kinase occur which are closely linked with events in the life cycle of the organism. In most cases the activity of the enzymes in non growing cells is low, but increases just before the onset of DNA synthesis. This increase in activity is observed when DNA synthesis is induced by a stimulus to a nondividing tissue or when DNA synthesis occurs normally at a particular phase in the life cycle, and is usually due to de novo synthesis of the enzymes. Examples of stimuli include partial hepatectomy (BUCHER 1963), injury to skin epidermis (BULLOUGH 1965), hormones (BRESCIANI 1964; BOWERS and WILLIAMS 1964), phytohemagglutinin (NOWELL 1960) and serum proteins (TODARO et al. 1965). The main features of the initial response to these stimuli include an early rise in RNA synthesis which is followed by an increase in protein synthesis and then by DNA synthesis. The initial increase in RNA and protein synthesis results in an increase in the enzymes that are required

---

* Incorporation of IUdr into DNA of mammalian cells, however, results in abnormal breakdown and turnover of the DNA which will limit the usefulness of this compound in tracer studies (MATHIAS et al. 1959; CHEONG et al. 1960; MORRIS and CRAMER 1966; CRAMER and MORRIS 1966).

for synthesis of DNA, nuclear protein and other cell structures which are necessary for cell division. These enzymes include Tdr kinase, thymidylate kinase and DNA polymerase, but these enzymes alone do not account for all of the protein synthesis (TAYLOR 1965). Viral infection similarly causes de novo synthesis of Tdr kinase (KIT and DUBBS 1965; KIT et al. 1966a,b; SHEININ 1966) and DNA polymerase (KEIR et al. 1966) and these new enzymes are characteristic of the infecting virus.

In microorganisms, variations in the activity of enzymes leading to the synthesis of TTP have been observed in *Tetrahymena*, *Chlorella* and *Physarum*. In *Tetrahymena*, synthesis of Tdr kinase and thymidylate kinase begins with onset of DNA synthesis and ceases with the completion of DNA synthesis (STONE and PRESCOTT 1964, 1965). In *Chlorella* both Tdr kinase and deoxycytidine monophosphate kinase increase in activity about 1 hour before the onset of DNA synthesis (JOHNSON and SCHMIDT 1966) and in *Physarum* the activity of Tdr kinase similarly increases just before the onset of DNA synthesis (SACHSENMAIER and IVES 1965).

In tissue cultures the activity of Tdr kinase and thymidylate kinase is low during the initial lag phase of growth and increases to a high level with the onset of rapid growth (BUKOVSKY and ROTH 1965). During the first cycle of growth in primary cultures (LIEBERMAN et al. 1963) or in synchronous cultures (LITTLEFIELD 1966; STUBBLEFIELD and MUELLER 1965) the activity of Tdr kinase increases with the onset of DNA synthesis. At the end of DNA synthesis the synthesis of Tdr kinase ceases and the activity of the enzyme declines (LITTLEFIELD 1966; STUBBLEFIELD and MUELLER 1965), although activity is maintained by the addition of Tdr to the culture medium to stabilise the enzyme (see ch. 2 § 3, table 2.2). In the case of the regenerating liver, Tdr kinase and thymidylate activity remains at a high level for a long period after DNA synthesis has ended (BUCHER 1963). In a number of transplantable hepatomas the activity of Tdr kinase is correlated with the growth rate of the tumours, the highest activity being found in the tumours with the fastest growth rate (BUKOVSKY and ROTH 1965). In the microspores of *Lilium* and in wheat embryos both synthesis and removal of Tdr kinase is tightly controlled and occurs during a brief period just before the onset of DNA synthesis (HOTTA and STERN 1963, 1965). A high Tdr kinase activity and rapid growth are not always associated however, because in the developing chick embryo the activity of Tdr kinase is low and of thymidylate kinase high (ROTH and ASKEW 1965).

This may be because there is little cell death in the embryo and the salvage pathway involving Tdr kinase is inactive.

On the basis of these observations it is clear that there is a close temporal relationship between the synthesis of Tdr kinase, thymidylate kinase, and DNA, and without thymidylate kinase DNA synthesis could not occur. The close relationship between these enzymes and DNA synthesis has led to the idea that the former are involved in the control of the initiation of DNA synthesis. The mere fact that the kinases and DNA are synthesised at closely related times, however, does not prove that one exercises control on the other. The presence of Tdr kinase and thymidylate kinase in the absence of DNA synthesis and the absence of Tdr kinase in some cells during DNA synthesis (see ch. 2 § 5) make it apparent that control of DNA synthesis involves many other factors in addition to the activity of these kinases. In the diapausing pupa of the silkworm, for example, both Tdr kinase and thymidylate kinase are active but the cells do not incorporate H^3Tdr into DNA (BROOKES and WILLIAMS 1965). Only at the end of diapause when insect development resumes is H^3Tdr incorporated into DNA in the tissues of the pupa. After injury to the diapausing pupa the activity of both Tdr and thymidylate kinase increases by a factor of 3 to 5, in the same manner as in injured mammalian or adult insect tissues, but DNA synthesis and H^3Tdr incorporation do not occur (BROOKES and WILLIAMS 1965).

In conclusion, it is likely that DNA synthesis is controlled by other factors than merely the activity of the enzymes which lead to the synthesis of TTP. To quote STONE and PRESCOTT (1965), 'The appearance of these enzymes required for the synthesis of DNA precursors only at the beginning of S serves as an example of the type of controlled derepression in the genome which must be operating in continuous sequence to maintain the orderly progress of biosynthetic events which make up the cell life cycle.' The pathway involving Tdr kinase and thymidylate kinase may consequently be considered as an important example of a controlled pathway for the synthesis of one of the precursors of DNA rather than a control mechanism for DNA synthesis itself.

References

ADELSTEIN, J., C. P. LYMAN, and R. C. O'BRIEN, 1964, Comp. Biochem. Physiol. *12*, 223

ARMSTRONG, M. D., K. YATES, Y. KAKIMOTO, K. TANIGUCHI, and T. KAPPE, 1963, J. Biol. Chem. *238*, 1447

BELTZ, R. E., 1963, Arch. Biochem. Biophys. *99*, 304

BENSCH, K. G., G. GORDON, and L. MILLER, 1966, Trans. N. Y. Acad. Sci. Ser. II, *28*, 715

BENSCH, K. G., and D. W. KING, 1961, Science, *133*, 381

BIANCHI, P. A., J. A. V. BUTLER, A. R. CRATHORN, and K. V. SHOOTER, 1961, Biochim. Biophys. Acta *48*, 213

BOWERS, B., and C. M. WILLIAMS, 1964, Biol. Bull. *126*, 205

BOYCE, R. P., and R. B. SETLOW, 1962, Biochim. Biophys. Acta *61*, 618

BREITMAN, T. R., 1963, Biochim. Biophys. Acta *67*, 153

BRESCIANI, F., 1964, Science *146*, 653

BRESNICK, E., 1962, Biochim. Biophys. Acta *61*, 598

BRESNICK, E., and U. B. THOMPSON, 1965, J. Biol. Chem. *240*, 3967

BRESNICK, E., and U. B. THOMPSON, 1966, Arch. Biochem. Biophys. (in press)

BROOKES, V. J., and C. M. WILLIAMS, 1965, Proc. Natl. Acad. Sci. *53*, 770

BRYANT, B. J., 1962, Exp. Cell Res. *27*, 70

BRYANT, B. J., 1966, J. Cell Biol. *29*, 29

BUCHER, N. L. R., 1963, Intern. Rev. Cytol. *15*, 245

BUKOVSKY, J., and J. S. ROTH, 1965, Cancer Res. *25*, 358

BULLOUGH, W. S., 1965, Cancer Res. *25*, 1683

CANELLAKIS, E. S., J. J. JAFFE, R. MANTSAVINOS, and J. S. KRAKOW, 1959, J. Biol. Chem. *234*, 2096

CANELLAKIS, E. S., H. O. KAMMEN, and D. R. MORALES, 1965, Proc. Natl. Acad. Sci. *53*, 184

CHANG, L. O., and W. B. LOONEY, 1965, Cancer Res. *25*, 1815

CHEONG, L., M. A. RICH, and M. L. EIDENOFF, 1960, J. Biol. Chem. *235*, 1441

CLEAVER, J. E., and R. M. HOLFORD, 1965, Biochim. Biophys Acta *103*, 654

COOK, J. R., 1966, J. Cell Biol. *29*, 369

COUNTS, W. B., and W. G. FLAMM, 1966, Biochim. Biophys. Acta *114*, 628

COUTSOGEORGOPOULOS, C., B. HACKER, and R. MANTSAVINOS, 1966, Biochim. Biophys. Acta *119*, 439

CRAMER, J., and N. MORRIS, 1966, Mol. Pharmacol. *2*, 363

CRATHORN, A. R., and K. V. SHOOTER, 1964, Intern. J. Radiation Biol. *7*, 575

DEUTSCH, W., and R. LASAR, 1930, Z. Physiol. Chem. *186*, 1

DIDERHOLM, H., K. E. FICHTELIUS, and O. LINDEN, 1962, Exp. Cell Res. *27*, 431

FEINENDEGEN, L. E., V. P. BOND, and W. L. HUGHES, 1961a, Exp. Cell Res. *25*, 627

FEINENDEGEN, L. E., V. P. BOND, and R. B. PAINTER, 1961b, Exp. Cell Res. *22*, 381

FEINENDEGEN, L. E., V. P. BOND, and W. L. HUGHES, 1966a, Proc. Soc. Exp. Biol. Med. *122*, 448

FEINENDEGEN, L. E., V. P. BOND, and W. L. HUGHES, 1966b, Exp. Cell Res. *43*, 107

FIELD, E. O., J. P. KRISS and L. A. TUNG, 1961, Cancer Res. *21*, 2

FINK, K., R. E. CLINE, R. B. HENDERSON, and R. M. FINK, 1956a, J. Biol. Chem. *221*, 425

FINK, R. M., and K. FINK, 1962, J. Biol. Chem. *237*, 2889

FINK, R. M., C. McGAUGHEY, R. E. CLINE and K. FINK, 1956b, J. Biol. Chem. *218*, 1

FRIEDKIN, M., and D. ROBERTS, 1954, J. Biol. Chem. *207*, 245

FRIEDKIN, M., D. TILSON, and D. ROBERTS, 1956, J. Biol. Chem. *220*, 627

FRIEDKIN, M., and H. WOOD, 1956, J. Biol. Chem. *220*, 639

GENTRY, G. A., P. A. MORSE, Jr., and D. H. IVES, 1965a, Cancer Res. *25*, 509

GENTRY, G. A., P. A. MORSE, and V. R. POTTER, 1965b, Cancer Res. *25*, 517

GERHART, J. C., and H. K SCHACHMAN, 1965, Biochem. *4*, 1054

GOULIAN, M., and W. S. BECK, 1966, Biochim. Biophys. Acta *129*, 336

GRAV, H. J., and R. M. S. SMELLIE, 1963, Biochem. J. *89*, 486

GRAV, H. J., and R. M. S. SMELLIE, 1964, Biochem. J. *94*, 518

HAKALA, M. I., and E. TAYLOR, 1959, J. Biol. Chem. *234*, 126

HILL, M., 1962, Exp. Cell Res. *28*, 21

HOFFMAN, J., and J. POST, 1966, Cancer Res. *26*, 1313

HOLLEY, R. W., J. APGAR, G. A. EVERETT, J. T. MADISON, M. MARQUISEE, S. H. MERRILL, J. R. PENSWICK, and A. ZAMIR, 1965, Science *147*, 1462

HOTTA, Y., and H. STERN, 1963, Proc. Natl. Acad. Sci. *49*, 648, 861

HOTTA, Y., and H. STERN, 1965, J. Cell Biol. *25*, 99

HUGHES, W. L., V. P. BOND, G. BRECHER, E. P. CRONKITE, R. B. PAINTER, H. QUASTLER, and F. G. SHERMAN, 1958, Proc. Natl. Acad. Sci. *44*, 476

IVES, D. H., 1965, J. Biol. Chem. *240*, 819

IVES, D. H., P. A. MORSE, Jr., and V. R. POTTER, 1963, J. Biol. Chem. *238*, 1467

JACQUEZ, J. A., 1962, Biochim. Biophys. Acta *61*, 265

JOHNSON, R. A., and R. R. SCHMIDT, 1966, Biochim. Biophys. Acta (in press)

KAY, E. R. M., 1961, Nature *191*, 387

KAY, E. R. M., 1966, Trans. N. Y. Acad. Sci., Ser. II, *28*, 726

KEIR, H. M., J. HAY, J. M. MORRISON, and H. SUBAK-SHARPE, 1966, Nature *210*, 150

KIELLEY, R. K., 1961, Biochim. Biophys. Acta *53*, 150

KIT, S., and D. R. DUBBS, 1963, Biochem. Biophys. Res. Commun. *13*, 500

KIT, S., and D. R. DUBBS, 1965, Virology *26*, 16

KIT, S., D. R. DUBBS, M. ANKEN, and J. C. MELNICK, 1965, J. Cell Biol. *27*, 52A

KIT, S., D. R. DUBBS, and P. M. FREARSON, 1966a, Cancer Res. *26*, 638

KIT, S., D. R. DUBBS, P. M. FREARSON, and J. L. MELNICK, 1966b, Virology *69*, 69

KIT, S., D. R. DUBBS, and P. M. FREARSON, 1966c, Intern. J. Cancer. *1*, 19

KIT, S., D. R. DUBBS, L. J. PIEKARSKI, and T. C. HSU, 1963, Exp. Cell Res. *31*, 297

KLEIN, W., 1935, Z. Physiol. Chem. *231*, 125

KORNFELD, S., and L. GLASER, 1960, Biochim. Biophys. Acta *42*, 548

KRISS, J. P., R. K. SHAW, and N. A. EDMUNDS, 1965, Ninth Symp. in Tracer Methodology in Atomlight no. 47, New England Nuclear Corporation. Boston, Mass.

LANG, W., D. MULLER, and W. MAURER, 1966, Exper. Cell Res. *44*, 645

LIEBERMAN, I., R. ABRAMS, N. HUNT, and P. OVE, 1963, J. Biol. Chem. *238*, 3955

LITTLEFIELD, J. W., 1965, Biochim. Biophys. Acta *95*, 14

LITTLEFIELD, J. W., 1966, Biochim. Biophys. Acta *114*, 398

LOEFFLER, C. A., and M. C. JOHNSTON, 1964, J. Embryol. Exp. Morphol. *12*, 407

MAENZA, R. M., and C. V. HARDING, 1962, Nature *196*, 786

MALEY, F., and G. F. MALEY, 1965, J. Biol. Chem. *240*, 3226

MARSH, J. C., and S. PERRY, 1964a, J. Clin. Invest. *43*, 267

MARSH, J. C., and S. PERRY, 1964b, Arch. Biochem. Biophys. *104*, 116

MATHIAS, A. P., G. A. FISCHER, and W. H. PRUSOFF, 1959, Biochim. Biophys. Acta *36*, 560

MOFFAT, G. H., and S. R. PELC, 1966, Exp. Cell Res. *42*, 460

MONOD, J., J. P. CHANGEAUX, and F. JACOB, 1963, J. Mol. Biol. *6*, 306

MORRIS, N. R., and G. A. FISCHER, 1963, Biochim. Biophys. Acta *68*, 84

MORRIS, N. R., and J. W. CRAMER, 1966, Mol. Pharmacol. *2*, 1

MORSE, P. A., Jr., and V. R. POTTER, 1965, Cancer Res. *25*, 499

NOWELL, P. C, 1960, Cancer Res. *20*, 462

OKAZAKI, R., 1959, Biochem. Biophys. Res. Commun. *1*, 34

OKAZAKI, R., and A. KORNBERG, 1964a, J. Biol. Chem. *239*, 269

OKAZAKI, R., and A. KORNBERG, 1964b, J. Biol. Chem. *239*, 275

PELC, S. R., and T. C. APPLETON, 1965, Nature *205*, 1287

POTTER, V. R., 1959, in Kinetics of cellular proliferation, F. Stohlman ed., Grune and Stratton, New York, p. 104

POTTER, V. R., 1963, Exp. Cell Res. (suppl.) *9*, 259

PRICE, T. D., H. A. HUNDS, and R. J. BROWN, 1963, J. Biol. Chem. *238*, 311

RACHMELER, M., J. GERHART, and J. ROSNER, 1961, Biochim. Biophys. Acta *49*, 222

REDDAN, J. R., and H. ROTHSTEIN, 1966, J. Cell Physiol. *67*, 307

REICHARD, P., 1962, J. Biol. Chem. *237*, 3513

Report of the commission on enzymes of the international union of biochemistry, 1961, Pergamon Press, Macmillan Co., New York

RIECKE, W. O., 1962, J. Cell Biol. *13*, 205

ROTH, J. S., and J. ASKEW, 1965, J. Cell Biol. *27*, 91A

ROTHERHAM, J., and W. C. SCHNEIDER, 1958, J. Biol. Chem. *232*, 853

ROYCHOUDHURY, R., and S. P. PEN, 1964, Biochem. Biophys. Res. Commun. *14*, 7

RUBINI, J. R., E. P. CRONKITE, V. P. BOND, and T. M. FLEIDNER, 1960, J. Clin. Invest. *39*, 909

RUBINI, J. R., S. KELLER, L. WOOD, and E. P. CRONKITE, 1961, Proc. Soc. Exp. Biol. Med. *106*, 49

SACHSENMAIER, W., and D. H. IVES, 1965, Biochem. Z. *343*, 399

SAGAN, L., 1965, J. Protozool. *12*, 105

SCHNEIDER, W. C., 1955, J. Biol. Chem. *216*, 287

SCHULMAN, M. P., 1961, in Metabolic pathways, Vol. II, D. M. Greenberg, ed., Academic Press, New York and London, p. 389

SHEININ, R., 1966, Virology *28*, 47

SIMONOVITCH, L., and A. F. GRAHAM, 1955, Can. J. Microbiol. *1*, 721

SIMON, E. H., and I. TESSMAN, 1963, Proc. Natl. Acad. Sci. *50*, 526

STAROSCIK, R. N., W. H. JENKINS, and M. L. MENDELSOHN, 1964, Nature *202*, 456

STEEL, G. G., 1966, Nature *210*, 806

STEEL, G. G., and L. F. LAMERTON, 1965, Exp. Cell Res. *37*, 117

STONE, G. E., and D. M. PRESCOTT, 1964, J. Cell Biol. *21*, 275

STONE, G. E., and D. M. PRESCOTT, 1965, in The use of radioautography in investigating protein synthesis, L. Leblond and K. B. Warren, eds., Academic Press, New York and London

STUBBLEFIELD, E., and G. C. MUELLER, 1965, Biochem. Biophys. Res. Commun. *20*, 535

SZYBALSKA, E. H., and W. SZYBALSKI, 1962, Proc. Natl. Acad. Sci. *48*, 2026

TAKATS, S. T., and R. M. S. SMELLIE, 1963, J. Cell Biol. *17*, 59

TAYLOR, E. W., 1965, Exp. Cell Res. *40*, 316

TODARO, G. J., G. K. LAZAR, and H. GREEN, 1965, J. Cell Comp. Physiol. *66*, 325

WANKA, F., I. K. VASIL, and H. STERN, 1964, Biochim. Biophys. Acta *85*, 50

WARREN, L., 1961, in Metabolic pathways, Vol. II, D. M. Greenberg, ed., Academic Press, New York and London, p. 459

WEISSMAN, S. W., R. M. S. SMELLIE, and J. PAUL, 1960, Biochim. Biophys. Acta *45*, 101

WHITTLE, E., 1966, Biochim. Biophys. Acta *114*, 44

ZAJICEK, G., N. BERNSTEIN, A. ROSIN, and J. GROSS, 1963, Exp. Cell Res. *31*, 390

CHAPTER 3

Thymidine metabolism: the four factor model, pool sizes and growth inhibition

3.1 Introduction

The metabolic pathways for the incorporation and degradation of thymidine can be represented by a simple model which can be used for the interpretation of the kinetics of H^3Tdr incorporation into DNA under various experimental conditions. This model was introduced by QUASTLER (1963) as the 'four factor model' and is illustrated in fig. 3.1. The model is based on the assumption that the pathways of Tdr metabolism meet in a freely mixing pool of acid soluble derivatives (TMP, TDP, TTP, and Tdr itself). This pool has two inputs, one consisting of the internal synthetic pathways of the cell and the other the incorporation pathway for externally supplied Tdr. The two outputs from the pool consist of one leading to DNA and the other to the degradation products of Tdr.

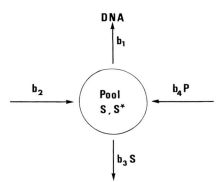

Fig. 3.1.   The four factor model for the metabolic pathways of Tdr (redrawn from QUASTLER 1963).

On the basis of this model a number of equations can be set up which may be used to interpret the results of labelling experiments either in tissue cultures (CLEAVER and HOLFORD 1965; HOLFORD 1965) or in vivo (STEWART et al. 1965).

3.2 Analysis of the four factor model

The four main pathways, the pool size and the external Tdr concentration will be defined for the four factor model as follows:

(1) *External Tdr*, the total concentration of Tdr, both radioactive and non-radioactive, will be P molecules/litre. The concentration of radioactive Tdr alone will be P^* molecules of H^3Tdr/litre and the specific activity of the labelling solution will be $P^*/P = Z$. (If there is one labelling atom per labelled molecule, then Z H^3 atoms/molecule $= 30.1 \times Z$ Ci/mmole, and Z C^{14} atoms/molecule $= 0.641 \times Z$ Ci/mmole.)

(2) *DNA replication (DNA polymerase or nucleotidyl transferase)*, b_1 molecules/min are incorporated into DNA from the pool, and this rate is assumed to be constant and uninfluenced by pool size. This seems reasonable if it is assumed that DNA synthesis depends on the balanced supply of all four nucleotides and an excess of one does not cause unbalanced synthesis. In the extreme case where the pool is totally depleted on account of starvation or metabolic inhibitors then the rate of DNA synthesis will of course drop to zero, but for most purposes it is satisfactory to assume that b_1 is constant. In ch. 5 §§ 5–7 a number of cases are discussed in which the rate of DNA replication varies systematically during the cell cycle. To accommodate these cases b_1 may be defined as a mean rate or as a time-dependent function but this refinement will not be used here.

(3) *Endogenous synthetic pathway (TMP synthetase etc.)*. b_2 molecules/min enter the pool from the internal synthetic pathways of the cell, and this rate is assumed to remain constant under conditions of varying external Tdr concentration and pool size. This may not be true under all experimental conditions because one of the pool components, TTP, is known to inhibit some of the enzymes on pathways leading to deUMP, the substrate for TMP synthetase (IVES et al. 1963). In some situations when the pool size is abnormally high b_2 may be reduced by end-product inhibition and the incorporation rate could be represented by $b_2'/$(pool size).*

(4) *Degradation pathway (Tdr phosphorylase)*. This is assumed to exert a regulating

---

* The exact form of expression used to represent the effect of feedback inhibition will depend on the type of inhibition that is assumed to occur. However, all forms of inhibition produce the following simple approximation for high inhibitor concentration and low substrate concentration:

$$\text{rate} = \text{constant} \; x \; \frac{\text{substrate concentration}}{\text{inhibitor concentration}} \quad \text{(DIXON and WEBB 1964)}.$$

function on the size of the internal pool of the cell and the rate of degradation is given by b_3 (pool size) molecules/min.

(5) *Incorporation pathway (Tdr kinase)*. The incorporation rate is given by $b_4' P$ molecules/min. Since Tdr kinase is inhibited by TTP, the incorporation rate may be modified to take this into account and is then given by $b_4' P$/(pool size) (see footnote on previous page).

(6) *Pool size*. In the absence of any external Tdr there is a small pool of Tdr derivatives, S_0 molecules/cell. When Tdr is supplied to the cell externally, it is assumed that this will result in an increase in the pool size to a value of S molecules/cell. When the Tdr supplied is radioactive then the pool will contain S^* molecules of H^3/cell. The pool specific activity will be equal to S^*/S. This pool is made up of a number of components but it will be considered as a single pool consisting predominantly of TTP for the purposes of the calculations.

Several comments need to be made about these definitions of the four factor model before using it to interpret the results of a number of experiments. The four rate constants are not all of the same dimension, and the introduction of inhibition factors also affects the magnitude and dimensions of these constants, but in any one experimental situation they are independent of the values of S, S^*, P, and P^*. Although the rate constants have been defined in terms of molecules they can equally well be defined in molarities, since 1 mole equals 6×10^{23} molecules.

Since the pool size may affect the value of the incorporation rate directly by inhibition of Tdr kinase, but only affects the endogenous pathway indirectly by inhibition of enzymes earlier in the synthetic pathway than TMP synthetase, the former will probably be more important. In all of the following calculations the endogenous pathway will be considered as independent of the pool size. Different terminology will be found in the calculations of QUASTLER (1963), STEWART et al. (1965) and CLEAVER and HOLFORD (1965) but the principles employed are identical in each case.

When whole animal experiments are considered in terms of this model the Tdr concentration available to individual cells will vary with time after the initial Tdr injection. In these cases the incorporation rate may be modified to allow for this, and is then given by $b_4'' Pf(t)$ where $\int_0^\infty (t) \, dt = 1$, and $P = $ total Tdr injected per g, per cell, or per animal. In the case of intraperitoneal injection in mice $f(t) = 0.24 \exp(-t/4.15)$ (STEWART et al. 1965).

In the presence of external Tdr and H^3Tdr the incorporation rate, pool

size and external concentration are related by the following set of differential equations:

(1) The rate of change of the total pool size is equal to the difference
between the inputs and outputs of the pool.

$$dS/dt = b_4 P - b_3 S + b_2 - b_1 \qquad (3.1)$$

or $\quad dS/dt = b_4' \, P/S - b_3 S + b_2 - b_1. \qquad (3.2)$

(2) The rate at which the total pool contents are used in DNA replication
is simply equal to b_1, by definition.

$$dL/dt = b_1, \qquad (3.3)$$

where L represents the number of thymine bases in DNA

(3) The rate of change of labelled material in the pool is equal to the
difference between the inputs and outputs of labelled material.

$$dS^*/dt = b_4 P^* - b_3 S^* - b_1 S^*/S \qquad (3.4)$$

or $\quad dS^*/dt = b_4' \, P^*/S - b_3 S^* - b_1 S^*/S \qquad (3.5)$

(4) The rate at which labelled material is incorporated into DNA from the
pool is simply equal to $b_1 \times$ (pool specific activity)

$$dL^*/dt = b_1 \, S^*/S \qquad (3.6)$$

The alternative eqs. (3.1) and (3.2), and (3.4) and (3.5), are given for the
four factor model without or with end-product inhibition, respectively.
Consequently, the four factor model can be described in terms of eqs.
(3.1), (3.3), (3.4), and (3.6) if end-product inhibition is omitted; and in
terms of eqs. (3.2), (3.3), (3.5), and (3.6) if end-product inhibition is
included. These equations cannot be solved completely in any simple
manner, but some useful information and results can be obtained by
solving them for restricted, steady-state conditions. This will be attempted
in the following sections.

3.3 *The incorporation rates of H^3Tdr into DNA*

The quantities that are normally interesting in labelling experiments with
H^3Tdr are the concentrations and specific activities of the H^3Tdr supplied

and the amount of label that is incorporated into DNA. Relationships between these quantities may be derived from the equations derived in the preceding section. One important point which is occasionally neglected when labelling experiments are described is that there are three related parameters associated with a solution of H^3Tdr, the total concentration of Tdr plus H^3Tdr, the specific activity, and the activity per unit volume. These are related as follows.

$$\text{total concentration (molar)} = \frac{\text{activity per unit volume } (\mu Ci/ml \times 10^{-6})}{\text{specific activity (Ci/mmole)}}.$$

To specify the experimental labelling conditions completely at least two of these parameters must be stated. The concentration determines the rate of incorporation into the pool ($b'_4 P$ or $b'_4 P/S$), and the specific activity determines the fraction of the incorporated nucleoside that is actually labelled and the rate of incorporation of labelled Tdr into the pool is determined by the activity per unit volume.

If H^3Tdr plus carrier Tdr is supplied to tissue cultures in excess, so that a steady state is reached in which the pool size and the external concentration are constant and there is a steady flow of label through the pool into DNA, the equations for this equilibrium may be derived from those stated in the previous section (ch. 3 § 2). The four factor model with end-product inhibition will be used, since the model without end-product inhibition is simpler and can be analysed in a similar manner.

(1) Initial conditions, P and $P^* = 0$, no exogenous nucleoside.

If it is assumed that the natural pool size is small then the value of $b_3 S_0$ may be neglected in comparison with b_1 and b_2. This would seem to be a reasonable assumption because there is unlikely to be a great deal of catabolism of any substrate from DNA synthesis (POTTER 1960).

Hence, on these assumptions,

$$b_1 = b_2. \tag{3.7}$$

(2) Equilibrium conditions of labelling, P and $P^* \neq 0$.

In the steady state both the pool size and the pool specific activity will be constant with time and eqs. (3.2) and (3.5) will equal zero. Although the pool size is not now zero, and the conditions of (1) above do not apply, the result of eq. (3.7), $b_1 = b_2$, is still valid because these two rate parameters are, by definition, independent of labelling conditions. Hence, from eq. (3.2), with S_e representing the equilibrium pool size.

$$b_4' P/S_e = b_3 S_e. \tag{3.8}$$

Under these conditions the rate of incorporation of H^3 label into DNA, dL^*/dt, can be derived from the pool specific activity and eq. (3.6). The pool-specific activity is different from the specific activity of the external nucleoside because of dilution by the internal synthetic pathway, b_2, and is given by

$$\text{pool-specific activity} = \frac{b_4' P^*/S_e}{b_2 + b_4' P/S_e} \tag{3.9}$$

$$\text{and,} \quad dL^*/dt = b_1 \frac{b_4' P^*/S_e}{b_2 + b_4' P/S_e'} \text{molecules/min.} \tag{3.10}$$

This expression for the rate at which label is incorporated into DNA has two limiting forms. At one limit the external Tdr supplies all of the TTP that is required for DNA replication and the contribution of b_2 is negligible. At the other limit the external Tdr forms a trace addition to the normal pathways of synthesis of precursors for DNA and $b_4' P/S_e$ is negligible compared to b_2. These two labelling conditions, flooding and trace respectively, give the following relationship between the incorporation rate and the Tdr concentration from eq. (3.10).

Flooding, $dL^*/dt = b_1 \cdot P^*/P = b_1 \cdot z$
Trace, $\quad dL/dt = b_1 \cdot b_2^{-1} \cdot b_4' P^*/S_e$
$\qquad\qquad = B' \cdot P^*/P^{\frac{1}{2}}$ from eq. (3.8), $B' = b_1 (b_4' \cdot b_3)^{\frac{1}{2}} \cdot b_2^{-1}$
$\qquad\qquad = B' \cdot P^{\frac{1}{2}} \cdot z.$

The four factor model with end-product inhibition consequently predicts that under flooding conditions the rate of incorporation of label into DNA is independent of the external Tdr concentration and proportional to the specific activity. Under trace conditions the incorporation rate is proportional to the product of specific activity and the square root of the concentration. Similar trace and flooding conditions can be derived for the simpler case with no end-product inhibition and the results for both modifications of the four factor model are shown in table 3.1.

Examples of the determination of the incorporation rate as a function

TABLE 3.1

Incorporation rates of H³Tdr according to the four factor model.

Labelling condition	Incorporation rate	
	No end-product inhibition	End-product inhibition
Trace	$B_1\, P \cdot z$	$B_1'\, P^{\frac{1}{2}} \cdot z$
Flooding	$b_1 \cdot z$	$b_1 \cdot z$

$$B_1 = b_1 \cdot b_2^{-1} \cdot b_4$$
$$B_1' = b_1 \cdot b_2^{-1} (b_3 \cdot b_4')^{\frac{1}{2}}$$

of the external concentration supplied to tissue cultures and to mice are shown in fig. 3.2. The incorporation rate has been measured by the mean grain count over labelled cells after a 10-min labelling period in tissue cultures, or the median grain count over labelled cells in tissue sections after a single injection of H³Tdr in mice. These are only approximate estimates of the rate of incorporation of H³Tdr and no attempt has been made to relate the grain counts to the actual number of H³ atoms incorporated into DNA. Both the tissue cultures and the whole animal experiments show the whole range of incorporation rates from trace to flooding conditions, but the details of the results in the two systems are different. It appears that the results obtained from the whole animal are more accurately described by a four factor model without end-product inhibition (i.e. $L^* \propto P$) whereas the results of tissue culture experiments necessitate inclusion of such inhibition (i.e. $L^* \propto P^{\frac{1}{2}}$). The significance of this difference is not known, but a possible explanation may be proposed in terms of the different labelling conditions in the two systems. In the whole animal the concentration of Tdr which reaches the surface of those cells which are synthesising DNA increases and decreases gradually during the time following an injection and this may occur without major alteration in the internal pool size. In tissue cultures, Tdr is supplied to the immediate environment of the cells and this may result in major changes in the internal pool size such that end-product inhibition becomes an important factor. Cells in vivo are also subject to a larger set of controls than cells in culture, and these may include control of the availability of pre-

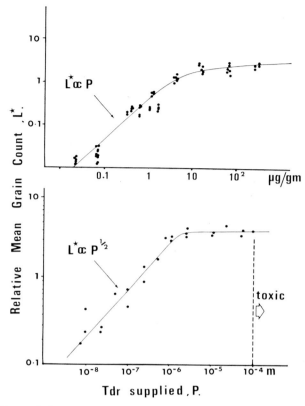

Fig. 3.2. Top: relative mean grain count (L*) over mouse intestinal crypt cells following a single injection of P µg/g of total Tdr (redrawn from STEWART et al. 1965).
Bottom: relative mean grain count over mouse L strain cells fixed immediately after
10 min exposure to P molar total Tdr (redrawn from CLEAVER and HOLFORD 1965).
Both diagrams have been redrawn using different units from the originals in order to
compare the two experiments directly.

cursors such that end product inhibition is not an important control
mechanism in vivo.

If H³Tdr is supplied continuously to tissue cultures, with repeated re-
plenishment of the labelled medium, the specific activity of thymine bases
in DNA should approach the same value as the specific activity of the TTP
pool that is represented by eq. (3.9). Consequently, under flooding condi-

tion, the specific activity of thymine bases in DNA will approach the value of the specific activity of the exogenous H^3Tdr. Under trace conditions the specific activity in DNA will approach a lower value on account of dilution by the endogenous pathways of TTP synthesis.

The maximum rate of incorporation in tissue culture in fig. 3.2 was reached at a concentration of about 3×10^{-6} M. This value may be compared with the concentration of Tdr that is required for optimum growth when cells are made totally dependent on external Tdr by the presence of the antimetabolite, amethopterin. HAKALA and TAYLOR (1959) found that a concentration of 2.3 to 5.5×10^{-6} M Tdr was required to maintain the growth of a number of cell types at about half of the maximum growth rates in the presence of amethopterin. GENTRY et al. (1965a) found that a concentration of 5×10^{-5} to 10^{-4} M Tdr was required to maintain maximum growth rates in Novikoff hepatoma cells in the presence of amethopterin. These values correspond to the range over which the rate of incorporation of H^3Tdr is a maximum and the exogenous Tdr completely satisfies the requirement for TTP.

The tissue culture and the in vivo results shown in fig. 3.2 could be compared further if the amounts of Tdr injected were expressed as a concentration of Tdr that is available to the particular cells under study. This cannot be done accurately, but an approximate estimate of the concentration can be made if it is assumed that the injected Tdr is distributed uniformly throughout the extracellular fluid of the mouse before incorporation into the cells. This will overestimate the actual concentration available to most tissues because a considerable amount of the H^3Tdr is degraded rapidly within the first few minutes of injection (see ch. 2 §§ 6, 7). The extracellular fluid in the mouse is, very approximately, 0.2 ml per g (PROSSER and BROWN 1961). The flooding conditions of labelling in vivo consequently occur at Tdr concentrations of roughly 10^{-4} M, and above. This concentration range is roughly similar to the range in tissue culture, but detailed comparisons between the in vivo and in vitro results are difficult because little is known about the distribution of Tdr in the extracellular fluid or its availability to individual cells and tissues.

Although the simple calculations for the incorporation rates as a function of concentration adequately describe the results of tissue culture experiments shown in fig. 3.2, the results for whole animal experiments over the range of concentrations which result in flooding require more detailed treatment. Over these concentrations the relationship between the incorporation of H³Tdr, after a single injection, and concentration is more accurately described by the following relationship (QUASTLER 1963; STEWART et al. 1965):

$$L^* = z \cdot (b_1/b_3) \cdot \ln P + \text{constant} \qquad (\ln = \log_e).$$

This relationship was obtained experimentally by STEWART et al. (1965) and its derivation is given in ch. 8 § 4.

3.4 Modifications and limitations of the four factor model

The simple form of the four factor model presented above, although giving reasonable agreement with experiment in the cases described, can only be applied under restricted conditions.

A detailed analysis and solution of the eqs. (3.1) to (3.6) for any particular experiment is difficult but can be achieved with the aid of a computer. Computer solutions have been attempted by STEWART et al. (1965) for whole animal experiments, and by HOLFORD (1965) for tissue culture. By making assumptions for the values of the four rate constants these workers have obtained reasonable agreement between experiment and theory.

If the simple end-product inhibition factor, $1/S$, is used in the analysis the model predicts that the incorporation rate into the pool at the start of labelling will be infinite, since S_0 is assumed to be zero in the simple model. This is obviously incorrect, and although the initial rate may be extremely rapid during establishment of the equilibrium pool size, it will be limited by the capacity of the incorporation pathways. To avoid an infinite value at the start of labelling, the correct expression for end-product inhibition must be used. For competitive inhibition of Tdr kinase by TTP (IVES et al. 1963) the term $b_4' P/S$ should be replaced by $b_4' P/K_i$ $(1 - P/K_m - S/K_i)$, in which K_m is the Michaelis constant for Tdr kinase and K_i the corresponding constant for end-product inhibition (DIXON and WEBB 1964). A similar factor for inhibition would also be required to allow for the effect of the pool on the internal synthetic pathways, b_2. An alternative modification which can be used to limit the initial incorporation rate is to assume that the natural pool size in the absence of external Tdr, S_0 is not negligible; b_2 is then slightly larger than b_1 and a small amount of degradation from the pool will occur continuously (STEWART et al. 1965; HOLFORD 1965). The initial incorporation rate of Tdr will then be $b_4' P/S_0$.

To pursue the analysis of the four factor model further would digress too far to be useful here. The main obstacle to a thorough analysis of the predictions of the four factor model is that a large amount of numerical data for numerous tissues over a wide range of concentrations, specific activites, incubation times etc., are required in order to obtain accurate results for comparison with the analytical and computer solutions. The principles of the model are useful, however, in providing a simple framework for the interpretation experiments in H^3Tdr kinetics.

3.5 Pool formation during pulse labelling experiments

A series of observations which indicate that a pool of H^3Tdr derivatives is formed during labelling in tissue culture have been described by CLEAVER and HOLFORD (1965). In these experiments cultures were labelled for 10 min with H^3Tdr and then allowed to continue growth for predetermined periods of time in medium which did not contain any Tdr. Cultures were fixed at intervals and the amount of H^3Tdr which had been incorporated into DNA was determined by grain counting in autoradiographs. The mean grain counts obtained in this experiment, and in a similar one in which the growth medium was supplemented with Tdr at a concentration of 10^{-5} moles/litre after the pulse of H^3Tdr, are shown in fig. 3.3. The latter procedure is commonly referred to as 'chasing' the pulse of H^3Tdr.

From the results shown in fig. 3.3, the following deductions can be made:

(a) In addition to the incorporation of H^3Tdr into DNA during the 10-min labelling period, a certain amount of H^3Tdr is incorporated into a pool which is removed by the fixative (acetic acid: alcohol, 1:3). The contents of this pool are then used as a source of precursors for DNA synthesis during the subsequent 3 to 4 hr of growth in medium not containing Tdr.

(b) After 10 min of labelling approximately twice as much H^3Tdr has

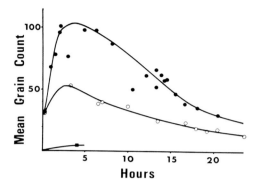

Fig. 3.3.   Mean grain counts over mouse L strain cells fixed at intervals after an initial 10 min in H³Tdr, 5 μCi/ml 2 Ci/mmole 2.5 × 10⁻⁶M.   The rise in grain counts between 0 and 5 hours is due to the incorporation of labelled derivatives of H³Tdr into DNA from an intracellular pool formed during the 10 min labelling. The decline from 5 hours onward is due to the division of labelled cells. ● grown in medium containing no added Tdr, ○ grown in medium supplemented with 10⁻⁵ M Tdr, ■ mean grain count in cultures added after the 10 min labelling period; these are labelled by the small amount of H³Tdr which remained in the medium (redrawn from CLEAVER and HOLFORD 1965; HOLFORD 1965).

been incorporated into the acid-soluble pool as has been incorporated into DNA. This follows from the grain counts in fig. 3.3; the amount of H³Tdr incorporated into DNA in 10 min is represented by a mean grain count of 30, and after the contents of the pool have been incorporated into DNA during the ensuing 3 to 5 hr the mean grain count has risen to 100.

(c) Although a large pool is formed in 10 min, this pool is not completely exhausted until 3 to 4 hr of growth have occurred. The rate at which the pool builds up must consequently be much more rapid than the rate at which it declines.

(d) If, after pulse labelling, the cultures are grown in medium containing Tdr at a concentration of 10⁻⁵ M, the contents of the pool are not incorporated into DNA to the same extent as occurs when the medium does not contain Tdr. The pool contents are consequently chased out of the cell through the degradation and excretion pathways.

The contents of the pool that are present in L strain cells after 10 min of labelling with H³Tdr were determined by extracting the pool with 2%

TABLE 3.2

H³ activity in perchloric acid extracts of L strain cells after 10 min of labelling with H³Tdr, 5 μCi/ml, 2 Ci/mmole (CLEAVER and HOLFORD 1965; HOLFORD 1965).

Chromatogram spot	Activity (counts/min, corrected for background of 98)
Thymidine	382
Thymidine monophosphate	258
Thymidine diphosphate	688
Thymidine triphosphate	14,127
0.25 μCi of orginal H³Tdr	11,472

perchloric acid at 4 °C for 2 hr without prior fixation of the cultures. The results are shown in table 3.2. The major constituent of the pool in these cells consists of H³TTP, but in other cell types, or in vivo, the relative proportions of the pool constituents may be different to these found in L strain cells.

A similar pool of labelled Tdr derivatives has been identified in a variety of cell types and the contents are in most cases readily soluble in acid or alcohol fixatives (HUGHES et al. 1958; FEINENDEGEN and BOND 1962; MILLER 1963; STONE and PRESCOTT 1964; COOPER et al. 1966). RIGAL (1961), however, found it necessary to use 10% formic acid to remove the pool, and CRATHORN and SHOOTER (1960) found the pool in ascites cells to be insoluble except in strong acids. In subsequent experiments the pool in ascites cells was soluble in 4% perchloric acid, 2% acetic acid or acetic acid-ethanol (1:3 v/v; CLEAVER 1966). On account of the solubility of the pool contents it has been necessary to devise a method of autoradiography in which a dry film is applied to the labelled cells in order to locate the pool. By this means it has been demonstrated that the labelled pool is located mainly in the nucleus of mammalian cells (FEINENDEGEN and BOND 1962) and of microorganisms such as *Tetrahymena*, that have clearly defined nuclei (MILLER 1963). In *Tetrahymena* the labelled pool is only formed during the S phase, and the pool that remains when DNA synthesis is completed remains in the nucleus until the next round of DNA synthesis occurs after cell division (STONE and PRESCOTT 1964; STONE et al. 1965). Sufficient material remains in the pool at completion of DNA synthesis to provide up to 20% of the thymine requirement during the subsequent round of DNA synthesis (STONE and PRESCOTT 1964). In the grasshopper neuroblasts, also, a pool of Tdr derivatives can remain in the cell after the end of S and be used for DNA synthesis in the following S phase after cells have completed mitosis (MCGRATH et al. 1965).

In the example shown in fig. 3.3, chasing in cold Tdr caused the contents of the pool to be lost from the cell and much less label entered DNA than in the absence of the chasing Tdr. In *Vicia faba*, however, only a small fraction of the pool is lost from the cells and chasing in cold Tdr merely delays the increase in labelled DNA without affecting the final level that is reached (EVANS 1964). Consequently, when pulse chase experiments are planned it is not always an advantage to chase in cold Tdr and the merits of this procedure must be weighed for each particular case.

3.6 Time taken for pool to reach equilibrium concentration

The pool that is formed during pulse labelling reaches a significant size in a very short period (fig. 3.3) and the time at which equilibrium is reached after addition of label can be determined by use of the pool size effects that have been described by HELL et al. (1960) and by NEWTON et al. (1962).

The principle of the method is that when unlabelled Tdr is administered to cells for a period of time before administering H^3Tdr, the unlabelled material will have formed a pool of TTP which will dilute the H^3Tdr which is phosphorylated subsequently. Less H^3Tdr will then be incorporated into DNA than would have been the case in the absence of the pool.

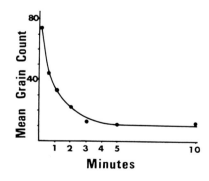

Fig. 3.4. Effect of the duration of pretreatment of mouse L strain cells with Tdr, 2.5×10^{-6} M, on the subsequent incorporation of H^3Tdr, 5 μCi/ml 2 Ci/mmole, also 2.5×10^{-6} M, into DNA during a 5 min labelling period (redrawn from HOLFORD 1965, see also CLEAVER and HOLFORD 1965).

Cultures were incubated with Tdr (2.5×10^{-6} M) for periods between 0.5 to 10 minutes in order to establish a pool. The cultures were briefly washed and then labelled with H³Tdr (also 2.5×10^{-6} M, so as to avoid concentration changes) for 5 min before fixation and subsequent auto-radiography. A control culture was also labelled without pretreatment with Tdr. The mean grain count for each culture is shown in fig. 3.4. On the basis of the four factor model appropriate for tissue cultures (fig. 3.2) the rate at which the pool is built up is extremely rapid (the initial rate of uptake of Tdr is infiinite, in the form of the model described with end-product inhibition, ch. 3 § 2) and from fig. 3.4 it is evident that the pool reaches equilibrium within about 3 min.

3.7 *Rate of decay of the pool*

The rate at which the pool decays depends both on the rate of DNA synthesis, b_1, and the rate of degradation b_4S. Although in the pulse chase experiment of fig. 3.3 it can be seen that the pool is completely exhausted within 3 to 4 hr, this may be an overestimate since some H³Tdr may still be present in the medium due to incomplete washing. In one experiment there was sufficient H³Tdr still present in the medium, or released from the cells, after the end of the pulse label to contribute significantly to further DNA synthesis (about 10 to 15% of the amount of label in DNA at

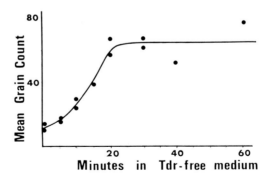

Fig. 3.5.   Effect of 45 minutes pretreatment of mouse L strain cells with Tdr, 2.5×10^{-6} M, followed by varying periods in Tdr-free medium, on the subsequent incorportation of H³Tdr, 5 μCi/ml 2 Ci/mmole, also 2.5×10^{-6} M, into DNA (redrawn from HOLFORD 1965).

the end of 10 min labelling, fig. 3.3). A more accurate estimate of the half life of the pool can be obtained using a similar method to that used to determine the rate of build-up of the pool.

In this experiment cultures were grown in Tdr (2.5×10^{-6} M) for 45 min to establish the unlabelled pool. They were then transferred to medium containing no Tdr and the pool was allowed to decay for a predetermined period of time. The cultures were then labelled for 5 min with H^3Tdr, fixed, and the grain counts in autoradiographs were determined. The mean grain counts are shown in fig. 3.5. It can be seen that as the time in Tdr-free medium increases the internal pool size decreases and there is progressively less dilution of the H^3Tdr used for labelling. The pool appears to be exhausted after about 20 to 30 min.

3.8 Pool size in relation to the external concentration

The pool size effects used in the two previous sections can also be used to determine the way in which the pool size varies with the external concentration of Tdr. This can be done by establishing a pool with external Tdr at one of a number of concentrations and then determining the extent to which a single concentration of H^3Tdr is diluted by the pool.

Cultures were incubated in Tdr for at least 10 min to establish a pool at an equilibrium level, washed briefly and then labelled with H^3Tdr (5μCi/ ml, 2 Ci/mmole). The cultures were fixed at intervals up to 15 min in H^3Tdr and the mean grain counts determined in autoradiographs, as before. The mean grain counts are shown in fig. 3.6. If the mean grain counts after 5 min in H^3Tdr are expressed as a fraction of control count the results may then be displayed as a function of the concentration of Tdr used for the pretreatment. The results from fig. 3.6, together with some additional results, are shown in fig. 3.7. The results shown in figs. 3.6 and 3.7 indicate that the size of the intracellular pool is dependent on the concentration of Tdr in the external medium. Even at as low a concentration as 10^{-9} M, a pool is formed which is sufficient to cause detectable dilution of the H^3Tdr (2.5×10^{-6} M) used for labelling. At higher concentrations, e.g. 10^{-6} M, the pool size is sufficiently large to make it difficult to detect any H^3Tdr incorporation into DNA during the 5-min labelling period.

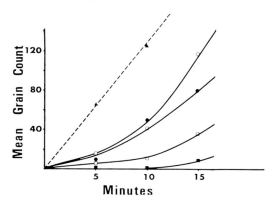

Fig. 3.6. Effect of pretreatment of mouse L strain cells for 10 min with various concentrations of Tdr on the subsequent incorporation H³Tdr, 5 μCi/ml 2 Ci/mmole 2.5 × 10⁻⁶ M, into DNA. ▲, control with no pretreatment; ○, 2.5 × 10⁻⁷ M; ●, 2.5 × 10⁻⁶ M; □, 2.5 × 10⁻⁵ M; ■, 2.5 × 10⁻⁴ M; (redrawn from CLEAVER and HOLFORD 1965).

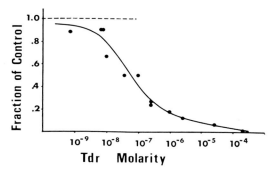

Fig. 3.7. Effect of pretreatment of mouse L strain cells with various concentrations of Tdr for 10 min, on the incorporation of H³Tdr, 5 μCi/ml 2 Ci/mmole, 2.5 × 10⁻⁶ M, into DNA during a subsequent 5-min labelling period (redrawn from CLEAVER and HOLFORD 1965).

To determine the relationship between the pool size and the external Tdr concentrations and analyse the previous experiments on the basis of the four factor model is a complex problem. It necessitates solving the differential equations for the pool size under non-equilibrium conditions when changes are made in the external Tdr concentration. However, an approximate estimate for the equilibrium pool size can be obtained which is useful in the interpretation of the formation of detectable pool sizes down to very low Tdr concentrations. From eq. (3.8) the equilibrium pool size in tissue cultures, S_e, is given by,

$$S_e = (b_4' P/b_3)^{\frac{1}{2}}.$$

Since this expression is derived without reference to the conditions of labelling (trace or flooding) a pool is to be expected throughout the concentration range and will vary according to this relationship. The results of fig. 3.7 show that a pool formed by incubation with Tdr at concentrations between 10^{-8} and 10^{-9} M is sufficient to reduce the incorporation of H^3Tdr in a 5-min labelling period by about 10%. The H^3Tdr concentration used was 2.5×10^{-6} M, about 1000 times the lowest concentrations used to establish a pool. Since the final pool size is proportional to the square root of the external concentration, the final H^3Tdr pool size will only be about 30 times the size of the unlabelled pool formed during the pretreatment. It is quite reasonable, therefore, that a pool formed by a concentration of Tdr as low as 10^{-9} M will cause a detectable change in the amount of label incorporated into DNA.

3.9 Estimation of the values of the rate constants in the four factor model for L strain cells

The experiments which have been described above can be used to obtain approximate estimates of the four constants, b_1, b_2, b_3, and b_4' in the four factor model. The first two, b_1 and b_2, are simply obtained from the rate of DNA synthesis in L strain cells and the fraction of thymine bases in DNA. The L strain cells used for these experiments have a telophase DNA content of 12×10^{-12} g/nucleus which is completely replicated in 13 hr (CLEAVER 1965), and about 30% of the bases in mammalian DNA are thymine (SUEOKA 1961). From these values b_1 and b_2 are equal to:

$$b_1, b_2 = 1.7 \times 10^{-17} \text{ moles/min or } 10^7 \text{ molecules/min.}$$

The rate of decay of the pool portrayed by fig. 3.5 gives a value for b_3, directly, as the time constant of the decay, $1/15$ min^{-1}. An alternative value for the time constant of the pool can be obtained from the data of fig. 3.3 in which the contents of a labelled pool are used as a source of precursors for DNA. This gives a different value of about $1/60$ min $^{-1}$, but this is a rather poor estimate for reasons already stated. More consistent estimates of b_3 can be obtained for these two types of experiment on pool decay if feedback effects from the TTP pool on both the external incorporation and the internal synthetic pathways are taken into consideration (HOLFORD 1965).

The two types of labelling conditions, trace and flooding, occurred below and above, respectively, a labelling concentration of about 2.5×10^{-6} M, fig. 3.2. These conditions were defined as ones where b_2 was either greater or smaller than $b_4' \, P/S$. Consequently, an estimate of b_4' can be obtained from the value of P at which b_2 is equal to $b_4' \, P/S$. Defining the concentration and the pool size at this particular point as P_1 and S_1 respectively, then the following relationship can be derived:

$$b_2 = b_4' \, P_1/S_1 = (b_3 \, b_4' \, P_1)^{\frac{1}{2}}, \text{ from eq. (3.8)}$$
$$\text{and } b_4' = (b_2)^2/b_3 P_1.$$

Taking $1/b_3$ as $1/15$ min $^{-1}$ and b_2 as 1.7×10^{-17} moles/min/cell the value for b_4' is then 1.7×10^{-27} moles/litres/min or 10^{-3} molecules litres/min/cell. The value of the pool size at this concentration of exogenous Tdr will be b_1/b_3 or 2.5×10^{-16} moles/cell. If this pool is concentrated in a nucleus of about $300 \, \mu^3$ in volume, the pool concentration will be about 10^{-3} M and if spread throughout the cell about 10^{-4} M.

The values of the constants in the four factor model in the case of mouse L strain cells, using a model which includes a feedback factor, are then

$b_1 = 1.7 \times 10^{-17}$ moles/min/cell or 10^7 molecules/min/cell

$b_2 = 1.7 \times 10^{-17}$ moles/min/cell or 10^7 molecules/min/cell (defined as equal to b_1)

$b_3 = 1/15$ min $^{-1}$

$b_4' = 1.7 \times 10^{-27}$ moles/l/min/cell or 10^{-3} molecules/l/min/cell

The corresponding values estimated by STEWART et al. (1965) in the case of mouse intestinal epithelium cells, in vivo, using a model which did not include a feedback factor, are

$b_1 = 10^7$ molecules/min/cell

$b_2 = 1.5 \times 10^7$ molecules/min/cell (defined as $1.5\,b_1$)

$b_3 = 1/15$ to $1/10$ min^{-1}

$b_4 = 15$ (a very approximate estimate, defined as a dimensionless constant by STEWART et al. 1965).

These values are characteristic for the particular cells studied, and also depend on whether the feedback factors are included in the four factor model. Other cell types may give different numerical values but it is likely that the values will be similar for most mammalian cells.

3.10 Natural pool size of thymine nucleotides in the absence of labelling

Three features of the natural pool of TMP, TDP and TTP, which exists in the cell, in the absence of exogenous Tdr, are important. These are, the location of the pool within the cell, the rate at which nucleotides pass through the pool, and the size of the pool under steady-state conditions. The location of the pool is uncertain, but is probably in the nucleus since the pool of labelled nucleotides that is formed during labelling with H^{3}Tdr is mainly nuclear (FEINENDEGEN and BOND 1962; MILLER 1963). The rate at which nucleotides pass through the pool can be simply estimated from the rate at which thymine bases are required for DNA synthesis. This rate has been given in the preceding section and is equal to b_1 in the four factor model. This has a value of about 10^7 molecules/min/cell or 1.7×10^{-17} moles/min/cell during DNA synthesis.

The steady state size of the pool is a more difficult quantity to estimate. The pool size cannot be obtained from the data for incorporation rates as a function of external Tdr concentration, which have been shown in fig. 3.2. In these results the change from trace to flooding conditions occurs when the rates of endogenous synthesis and of incorporation are equal, not when the internal pool and the external Tdr are of equal concentrations. A number of workers have estimated the amount of thymine nucleotides present in mammalian cells and some of these are shown in table 3.3. The pool sizes are quoted for the total of TMP, TDP and TTP, but in most cases the latter accounts for more than 70% of the pool (POTTER et al. 1957; CLEAVER and HOLFORD 1965; GENTRY et al. 1965a). These

TABLE 3.3

Natural pool sizes of thymine nucleotides. (These values have in some cases been estimated from published data and have also been summarised by HOLFORD (1965). Except where stated the pool size is quoted for the total of TMP, TDP and TTP but the latter accounts for more than 70% of the pool. In the first four cases the pool is assumed to be distributed throughout the cells of the tissue, but if it is confined to cells in DNA synthesis the pool size/cell will be considerably larger than listed here.)

Cell type	Molecules/cell	Moles/cell	Pool confined to a nucleus about 300 μ^3	Ref.
Calf thymus	1.8×10^7	3×10^{-17}	10^{-4} M	1
Rat thymus	4.8×10^7	8×10^{-17}	3×10^{-4}	2
Rat spleen	6×10^6	10^{-17}	3×10^{-5}	2
Novikoff hepatoma	$9\text{--}19 \times 10^6$	$1.5\text{--}3 \times 10^{-17}$	$5\text{--}10 \times 10^{-5}$ (TTP)	3
Mouse L strain (see also ch. 8 § 3)	2.4×10^6	4×10^{-18}	10^{-5}	4
Mouse intestinal crypt	$2.5\text{--}5 \times 10^7$	$4\text{--}8 \times 10^{-17}$	$1\text{--}3 \times 10^{-4}$	5
E. coli 15 T-A-U (grown in thymine)	1.4×10^4	2.4×10^{-19}	10^{-4} (assuming volume of 2.4 μ^3)	6

References:

1) POTTER et al. (1957)
2) POTTER and NYGAARD (1963)
3) GENTRY et al. (1965a)

4) HOLFORD (1965)
5) STEWART et al. (1965)
6) NEUHARD and MUNCH-PETERSEN (1966)

estimates were obtained either by direct biochemical methods (POTTER et al. 1957; POTTER and NYGAARD 1963; NEUHARD and MUNCH-PETERSEN 1966) or by indirect methods (GENTRY et al. 1965a; HOLFORD 1965; STEWART et al. 1965). The latter involved determining the optimum concentration of Tdr for maintaining growth of tissue cultures in the presence of amethopterin (GENTRY et al. 1965a) or making approximate estimates of the upper limit of the pool size from the kinetics of the four factor model (HOLFORD 1965; STEWART et al. 1965). These estimates can only be regarded as very approximate because the quantities of thymine nucleotides which have to be determined biochemically are very small, and the indirect methods are not based on sure theoretical foundations. However, the values obtained by several independent workers (table 3.3) are similar in magnitude and the total pool size of TMP, TDP and TTP may be considered to be within the range from 4×10^{-18} to 8×10^{-17} moles/cell. It is to be hoped that further experiments may make more accurate estimates possible.

The rate at which the pool turns over can be estimated from the natural pool size and the rate at which the contents pass through the pool. This turnover rate is very rapid and the whole contents of the pool turn over in about 5 min. A similar turnover rate of 3 to 5 min has been quoted by PELC and APPLETON (1965) and 0.5 min by POTTER and NYGAARD (1963) and these values agree reasonably well in view of the experimental errors involved.

3.11 Pitfalls of high and low specific activity experiments

In a number of experiments attempts have been made to follow changes in the natural intracellular pool size by variation of the concentration of H3Tdr or C14Tdr used for labelling. The particular experiments were described under the titles, 'Pitfalls of high specific activity tracer studies' (HELL et al. 1960) and 'A Pitfall of low specific activity radioactive thymidine' (PAINTER and RASMUSSEN 1964). These terms, however, are misleading because in these particular experiments the specific activity was not the only variable. In practice, the specific activity was varied by simply adding unlabelled thymidine, and the total activity per ml was unchanged, while both the total concentration and the specific activity were altered. Low specific activity meant high concentration, and vice-versa. This confusion in the terms 'high' and 'low' specific activity was repeated in certain radiation experiments (DENDY and CLEAVER 1964; CLEAVER 1964). The important fact in all of these experiments is that changes in the internal pool size were detectable only because two different concentrations of labelled Tdr were used. To attribute differences in the pattern of incorporation, as distinct from the general level of incorporation, to the changes in specific activity alone implies that the biological system discriminates between radioactive and non-radioactive molecules. This would be due to an isotope effect (BRODA 1960), on account of the different sizes of the two isotopes, for example, or to a radiation effect caused by the decays

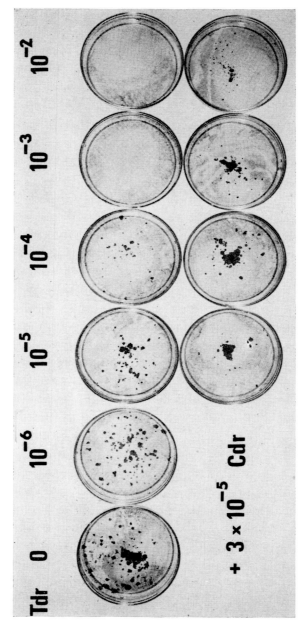

Fig. 3.8. Colonies of marsupial kidney strain PtK1 cells grown for 14 days in F10 (Tdr−) supplemented with 10 dialysed calf serum and various concentrations of Tdr. Left to right, increasing molar concentrations of Tdr. Top row, unsupplemented with deoxycytidine, bottom row, supplemented with 3×10^{-5} M deoxycytidine.

within the biological system. These effects can only be demonstrated unambiguously by means of experiments in which the total concentration is constant and only the specific activity varies.

In conclusion, each experiment in which the terms 'high' and 'low' specific activity are used should be read carefully to ascertain whether total concentration or specific activity or both are the relevant experimental variables.

3.12 Inhibitory effects of thymidine

Thymidine when supplied to tissue cultures at excessive concentrations can inhibit cell growth almost completely. The range of concentrations which is inhibitory is similar in most cell types, first appearing between 10^{-5} and 10^{-4} M and is complete above 10^{-4} M (BOOTSMA et al. 1964; CLEAVER and HOLFORD 1965; GALAVESI et al. 1966; MORRIS and FISCHER 1963; PAINTER et al. 1964; PUCK 1964; GENTRY et al. 1965b). An example of the inhibition of colony formation in marsupial kidney cells by Tdr is shown in fig. 3.8. The growth of the cultures appears to be the same over the range of concentrations from 0 to 10^{-5} M, but at higher concentrations there has been very little cell growth.

The biochemical mechanisms of this inhibition of cell growth involve the feedback pathways that regulate the activity of several of the enzymes on the pyrimidine pathways. In the presence of excess Tdr there is a high level of TTP within the cell which has an inhibitory effect on Tdr kinase, deCMP deaminase and CDP reductase (e.g. IVES et al. 1963). The latter inhibition is particularly important because it results in a deficiency in deCTP, one of the essential precursors of DNA. Cell growth in the presence of excess Tdr consequently slows or ceases, because the level of deCTP is unsufficient to maintain DNA synthesis at the normal rate. These effects can result in permanent damage to the chromosomes (YANG et al. 1966) and a reduction in cell survival (KIM et al. 1965) when growth is resumed after release of the block caused by high concentrations of Tdr. DNA synthesis can be maintained in high concentrations of Tdr by adding Cdr to the medium at concentrations between about 10^{-6} and 10^{-5} M. The addition of Cdr bypasses the inhibition of CDP deaminase which prevents DNA synthesis (MORRIS and FISCHER 1963; WHITTLE 1966; GENTRY et al.

1965b). In fig. 3.8, for example, the addition of 3×10^{-5} M Cdr has enabled cell growth to be maintained in much higher concentrations of Tdr than was possible in the absence of Cdr. Mammalian serum (SCHNEIDER 1955) and some tissue culture media normally contain Cdr and this may be one cause of variation in the exact concentration of Tdr at which inhibition can be demonstrated. In one case (WHITMORE and GULYAS 1966) L60T cells could be grown in 4×10^{-4} M Tdr due to the presence of Cdr in the tissue culture medium (1066 medium with 10 % horse serum).

The inhibitory effect of high concentrations of Tdr is not a unique property of this particular nucleotide. Any normal compound which enters into the pathways of cell metabolism and which regulates the activity enzymes or other important synthetic pathways by negative feedback is likely to be inhibitory at high concentrations. Deoxyadenosine and deoxyguanosine, for example, are precursors of DNA but both are inhibitory at concentrations above 10^{-3} M (XEROS 1962).

3.13 Synchronisation of tissue cultures with excess thymidine

Since excess Tdr inhibits DNA synthesis, those cells of the population which are not synthesising DNA when Tdr is first added are unaffected. Consequently, excess Tdr can be used to accumulate cells in a small region of the cell cycle and a useful degree of synchrony obtained by this technique.

The experimental procedure that is commonly employed to obtain synchronised cultures with Tdr consists of two successive treatments with a concentration of about 10^{-3} M (BOOTSMA et al. 1964; GALAVESI et al. 1966). When the Tdr is first added, cells engaged in DNA synthesis are blocked at the particular stage of the S phase which they had reached, while cells in other phases continue growth and accumulate at the beginning of S. After a period of about 16 hr the cell population has two components, one consists of cells which are all at the beginning of S and prevented from starting DNA synthesis by the excess Tdr, and the other consists of cells distributed throughout the S phase. Tdr is then removed so that the whole population can continue growth and pass through the S phase, which takes about 6 to 8 hr. If Tdr is added at this stage the whole population will then accumulate at the beginning of the S phase. This synchronous population can then be studied at various stages of the cell cycle by removing the Tdr block and allowing DNA synthesis to resume. An example of a synchronous tissue culture population in mitosis after release of a double Tdr block is shown in fig. 3.9.

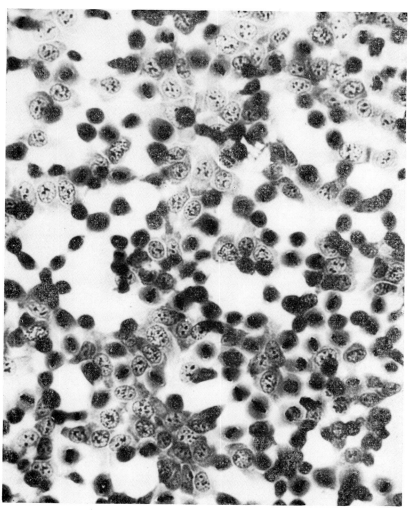

Fig. 3.9. Human epithelial adenocarcinoma cells 11 to 12 hr after release of a double Tdr block. Mitotic index in this culture is approximately 70% (KASTEN, unpublished).

This experimental procedure has been used for a number of experiments, and it has the advantage that only a normal metabolite is employed. In some respects it is preferable to use a normal metabolite for preparing a synchronous culture rather than antimetabolites such as amethopterin or fluorodeoxyuridine which may have undesirable side effects, although Tdr at high concentrations does have undesirable side effects itself. However, the growth of synchronised cultures may not be exactly the same as that of asynchronous cultures at all stages of the cell cycle, when either Tdr or antimetabolites have been used, and the durations of the phases of the cell cycle are not always identical in the two types of populations (GALAVESI et al. 1966; TILL et al. 1963).

3.14 *Radiobiological effects of labelled thymidine*

The radioactive disintegration of H^3 or C^{14} in labelled Tdr can cause a similar range of radiobiological effects to those caused by radiations which originate from external sources, such as X-rays or γ-rays (see review by WIMBER 1964). These effects may include growth delays (NATARAJAN 1961; WHITMORE and GULYAS 1966), chromosome aberrations (MCQUADE et al. 1956, MCQUADE and FRIEDKIN 1960, NATARAJAN 1961, WIMBER 1959, HSU and ZENZES 1965, BREWEN and OLIVIERI 1966), mutation (PERSON and LEWIS 1962; BATEMAN and CHANDLER 1962), and cell killing (DREW and PAINTER 1959, 1962; MARIN and BENDER 1963; PAINTER et al. 1958; PERSON and LEWIS 1962; WHITMORE and GULYAS 1966; APELGOT and LATARJET 1962; APELGOT 1966). In almost all cases, the disintegrations which occur within the nucleus are the main cause of the radiation damage (PAINTER et al. 1958; SANDERS et al. 1961; PERSON and LEWIS 1962). The presence of H^3-labelled thymine bases within the DNA molecule itself does not appear to enhance the radiation effect and similar effects may be produced with H^3-labelled H_2O if the concentration and specific activity within the nucleus is the same as for the incorporated H^3Tdr (WIMBER 1964, BOND and FEINENDEGEN 1965).

Several processes occur during radioactive disintegration. Radiation of some type is emitted (in this context it would be a β-particle) and transmutation of the emitting nucleus occurs. The product nucleus corresponds to a different element from the original radioactive nucleus and will have a different valency. It may also be in an excited state and possess a certain amount of recoil energy as a result of the disintegration (see table 1.1). Both the emission of a β-particle and the nuclear transmutation (H^3 to He^3, or C^{14} to N^{14}) may cause radiobiological effects when the labelled Tdr molecule has been incorporated into DNA, but the relative importance of the two processes is different for H^3 and C^{14} (APELGOT and LATARJET 1962). In the case of H^3 the emitted β-particle exerts the main biological effect, but in the case of C^{14} both the transmutation to N^{14} and the β-particle may produce important effects (STRAUSS 1958). The reason for this is that the transmutation of H^3 to He^3 merely leaves vacant sites for hydrogen atoms in the pyrimidine ring, and there is a plentiful supply of hydrogen atoms in living cells from which these sites may be filled. This transmutation consequently has negligible biological effect. The transmutation of C^{14}, however, results in the formation of N^{14} which cannot satisfy the valency requirements of the site originally occupied by carbon in the Tdr molecule. Consequently, the combined result of the nuclear transmutation and the recoil energy from the radioactive decay will be disruption of the pyrimidine ring, in the case of 2-C^{14}Tdr, or conversion to uracil, in the case of methyl-C^{14}Tdr. The transmutation would be expected to have the most drastic biological effect in the case of 2-C^{14}Tdr. The precise role of transmutation in the radiobiological effects of H^3 and C^{14}Tdr, however, is not clearly established and the main mechanism is probably through the ionisations caused by the emitted β-particles. Since the specific activities of commercially available H^{3}Tdr are usually about 1000 times that of C^{14}Tdr, radiation effects are more commonly encountered in experiments with H^3, and the remainder of this section will be mainly devoted to a description of some of these experiments.

The radiation effects depend quantitatively on the number of H^{3}Tdr molecules incorporated into DNA, and this is determined by the total thymidine concentration available (see fig. 3.2), its specific activity and the time for which H^{3}Tdr is available. In general, if the concentration is kept constant then a reduction in the specific activity will be correlated with a reduction in the radiation effects, when the concentrations are not high enough to saturate the incorporation pathways. Examples which illustrate these correlations in terms of the survival of HeLa cells labelled with H^{3}Tdr are given in tables 3.4 and 3.5. It can be seen that the sur-

Thymidine metabolism

TABLE 3.4

Percentage of colony-forming cells surviving after 15 to 16 hr exposure of HeLa cells to H³Tdr (from MARIN and BENDER 1963).

Specific activity	0.4 μCi/ml	0.1 μCi/ml
0.50 Ci/mmole	43	43
0.05 Ci/mmole	50	72

TABLE 3.5

Percentage of colony forming cells surviving after 24 hr exposure of HeLa cells to H³Tdr (calculated from DREW and PAINTER 1959).

Specific activity	2.5 μCi/ml	0.5 μCi/ml
1.88 Ci/mmole	5.1	10.8
0.47 Ci/mmole	17.3	21.3
0.23 Ci/mmole	21.3	47.0

vival of HeLa cells is considerably reduced as a result of the incorporation of H³Tdr over periods of 15 to 24 hr. When shorter labelling periods are used only those cells which are synthesising DNA during the labelling period are likely to be affected by H³Tdr, and survival is usually only significantly reduced when high specific activity material is used. For example, a 30-min labelling period with 2 μCi/ml, 1.9 Ci/mmole reduced the survival of HeLa cells by only 1.2%. A 3-hr labelling period reduced survival by 14% (DREW and PAINTER 1962). At a higher specific activity, a 1-hr labelling period with 1 μCi/ml, 6.7 Ci/mmole reduced the survival of L strain cells by 35% (WHITMORE and GULYAS 1966). An example of the gross morphological damage to tissue culture cells that results from growth in high specific activity H³Tdr is illustrated in fig. 3.10.

Various attempts have been made to relate the energy deposited in a nucleus by the tritium β-particle to an equivalent absorbed dose of radiation. On the assumption that all of the energy of a single disintegration is deposited with a sphere of radius 2 μ, the equivalent dose has been estimated to be about 1.1 rad/disintegration (GOODHEART 1961) and 2.4 rad/disintegration (KISIELSKI et al. 1964). In *E. coli* the number of H³ disintegrations which result in one lethal hit is approximately 2000 in a

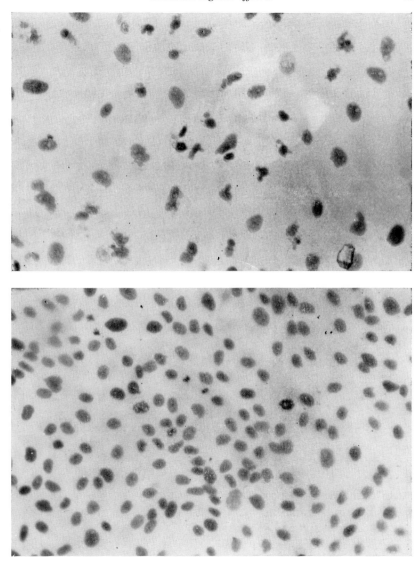

Fig. 3.10. Morphological changes in marsupial kidney strain PtK1 cells as a result of radiation damage from 4 days growth in high specific activity H³Tdr, 25 μCi/ml 13 Ci/mmole. Top, culture grown in H³Tdr; bottom, control culture grown in a similar concentration of unlabelled Tdr (approx. × 140).

radioresistant strain, or 200 in a radiation-sensitive strain, when the
disintegrations are allowed to occur at -196 °C (APELGOT 1966). When
the disintegrations occur at 0 °C the number of disintegrations per lethal
hit is reduced by a factor of about 10. The corresponding doses of X-rays
required for a single lethal hit at -196 °C was 26 krad or 8.9 krad
respectively. These figures lead to an equivalent dose of 13 rad/disinte-
grations in the resistant strain, or 4.4 rad/disintegration in the sensitive
strain. It is difficult to make a detailed comparison between radiation
from internal tritium and from an external source, however, on account
of the different special distributions of the ionisations.

In whole animal experiments, as opposed to tissue cultures, the quantities of H³Tdr normally employed for autoradiographic or other labelling
experiments is 1 to 2 μc/g body weight, and these have little radiation
effect (CRONKITE 1959; MENDELSOHN 1960; SMITH et al. 1962; JOHNSON and
CRONKITE 1966). The reason for this is probably that a large fraction of
the injected material is degraded and excreted from the body, and only a
relatively small number of cells incorporate H³Tdr into their DNA. If
large quantities of H³Tdr are injected it is possible to demonstrate some
radiation damage in proliferating systems. Damage to mouse spermatogonia can be detected after the injection of 5μCi/g (JOHNSON and
CRONKITE 1959) or 50 μCi/g (KISIELSKI et al. 1964), to the developing chick
embryo after injection of more than 10 μCi/g (SAUER and WALKER 1961),
and to the liver of young rats at about 1 to 2 μCi/g (GRISHAM 1961; POST
and HOFFMAN 1961). Lethal mutations have also been detected in mouse
embryos as a result of fertilisation with sperm labelled by injecting the
male donors with 5 μCi/g H³Tdr (BATEMAN and CHANDLER 1962). In these
cases it was estimated that only about 1 % of the tritium disintegrations in
the sperm gave rise to lethal mutation. In general, little radiation effect
appears to result from the use of H³Tdr or C¹⁴Tdr in tracer studies in
animals, although the possibility of long term effects such as carcinogenesis cannot be completely ruled out (LISCO et al. 1961; BASERGA et al.
1962, 1966; JOHNSON and CRONKITE 1967).

3.15 *Synchronisation of tissue cultures with H³Tdr*

The lethal effect of high specific activity H³Tdr has been employed as a
technique for selectively killing cells in the DNA synthetic phase (S phase)

of the cell cycle, leaving the remainder of the population as a viable synchronous population (WHITMORE and GULYAS 1966). When H^3Tdr is first added to a culture only the cells in the S phase incorporate the label, but as time passes more cells will become labelled as they enter the S phase (fig. 3.11). When H^3Tdr is continuously available at high specific activity (e.g. 1 $\mu Ci/ml$, 6.7 Ci/mmole) all of the labelled cells are killed by the internal tritium disintegrations, so that after a period of about 6 hr the only remaining viable cells are those which are unlabelled and within a small interval at the end of the G_1 phase as illustrated in fig. 3.11. These cells then constitute a useful synchronous population and further incorporation of H^3Tdr can be prevented by changing the growth medium or diluting the label with high concentrations of Tdr (100 $\mu g/ml$). If the latter procedure is adopted it is necessary to ensure that there is sufficient Cdr present to prevent growth inhibition by high Tdr concentrations.

Large synchronous populations can be obtained by using this method, and it has the advantage that the synchronous population has not been

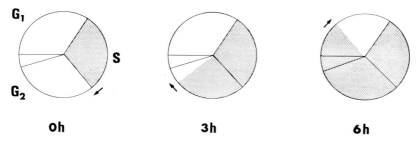

Oh   **3h**   **6h**

Fig. 3.11.   Scheme of the cell cycle of mouse L60T cells showing the fraction of the cycle occupied by labelled cells (shaded) after a short exposure, a 3 hour exposure, and a 6 hour exposure to H^3Tdr (redrawn from WHITMORE and GULYAS 1966).

subjected to any metabolic inhibitors which would cause unbalanced growth. However, the synchronised population is associated with a large population of labelled cells which, though unable to grow to any significant extent, may be able to carry on other biochemical functions. This means that the technique cannot be used for most biochemical studies but it is quite suitable for studying the effects of various agents on cell survival at different stages of the cell cycle.

References

APELGOT, S., 1966, Intern. J. Radiation Biol. *10*, 495

APELGOT, S., and R. LATARJET, 1962, Biochim. Biophys. Acta *55*, 40

BASERGA, R., H. LISCO, and W. E. KISIELSKI, 1962, Proc. Soc. Exp. Biol. Med. *110*, 687

BASERGA, R., H. LISCO, and W. E. KISIELSKI, 1966, Rad. Res. *29*, 583

BATEMAN, A. J., and A. C. CHANDLER, 1962, Nature *193*, 705

BOND, V. P., and L. E. FEINENDEGEN, 1965, in Biophysical aspects of radiation quality. International Atomic Energy Agency, Vienna

BOOTSMA, D., L. BUDKE, and O. VOS, 1964, Exp. Cell Res., *33*, 301

BREWEN, J. G., and G. OLIVIERI, 1966, Radiation Res. *28*, 779

BRODA, E., 1960, in Radioactive isotopes in biochemistry, Elsevier, Amsterdam

CLEAVER, J. E., 1964, Ph.D. thesis, University of Cambridge

CLEAVER, J. E., 1966, unpublished results

COOPER, R. A., S. PERRY, and T. R. BREITMAN, 1966, Cancer Res. *26*, 2267, 2276

CRATHORN, A. R., and K. V. SHOOTER, 1960, Nature *187*, 614

CRONKITE, E. P., 1959, in Kinetics of cellular proliferation, F. Stohlman, Jr., ed., Grune and Stratton, New York and London

DENDY, P. P., and J. E. CLEAVER, 1964, Intern. J. Radiation Biol. *8*, 301

DREW, R. M., and R. B. PAINTER, 1959, Radiation Res. *11*, 535

DREW, R. M., and R. B. PAINTER, 1962, Radiation Res. *16*, 303

DIXON, M., and E. C. WEBB, 1964, in Enzymes, 2nd ed., chap. 8, Longmans, London

EVANS, H. J., 1964, Exp. Cell Res. *35*, 381

FEINENDEGEN, L. E., and V. P. BOND, 1962, Exp. Cell Res. *27*, 474

GALAVESI, G., H. SCHENK, and D. BOOTSMA, 1966, Exp. Cell Res. *41*, 428, 438

GENTRY, G. A., P. A. MORSE, Jr., D. H. IVES, R. GEBERT, and V. R. POTTER, 1965a, Can. Res. *25*, 509

GENTRY, G. A., P. A. MORSE, Jr., and V. A. POTTER, 1965b, Can. Res. *25*, 517

GOODHEART, C. R., 1961, Radiation Res. *15*, 767

GRISHAM, J. W., 1960, Proc. Soc. Exp. Biol. Med. *105*, 555

HAKALA, M. I., and E. TAYLOR, 1959, J. Biol. Chem. *234*, 126

HELL, E., R. J. BERRY, and L. G. LAJTHA, 1960, Nature *185*, 47

HOLFORD, R. M., 1965, Ph.D. thesis, University of Cambridge

HSU, R. C., and M. T. ZENZES, 1965, in Cellular Radiation Biology, Williams & Wilkins Co., Baltimore, p. 404

HUGHES, W. L., V. P. BOND, G. BRECHER, E. P. CRONKITE, R. B. PAINTER, H. QUASTLER, and F. G. SHERMAN, 1958, Proc. Natl. Acad. Sci. U.S. *44*, 476

IVES, D. H., P. A. MORSE, Jr., and V. R. POTTER, 1963, J. Biol. Chem. *238*, 1467

JOHNSON, H. A., and E. P. CRONKITE, 1959, Radiation Res. *11*, 825

JOHNSON, H. A., and E. P. CRONKITE, 1966, Biophys. J. *27*, 64 (abstract)

JOHNSON, H. A. and E. P. CRONKITE, 1967, Rad. Res. *30*, 488

KIM, J. H., S. H. KIM, and M. L. EIDINOFF, 1965, Biochem. Pharm. *14*, 1821

KISIELSKI, W. E., L. D. SAMUELS, and P. C. HILEY, 1964, Nature *202*, 458

LISCO, H., R. BASERGA, and W. E. KISIELSKI, 1961, Nature, *192*, 571

MARIN, G., and M. A. BENDER, 1963, Intern. J. Radiation Biol. *7*, 221, 235

McGrath, R. A., W. M. Leach, and J. G. Carlson, 1965, Exp. Cell Res. *37*, 39

McQuade, H. A., and M. Friedkin, 1960, Exp. Cell Res. *21*, 118

McQuade, H. A., M. Friedkin, and A. A. Atchinson, 1956, Exp. Cell Res. *11*, 249, 256

Mendelsohn, M. L., 1960, J. Natl. Can. Inst. *25*, 485

Miller, O. L., 1963, J. Cell Biol. *19*, 50A (abstract)

Morris, W. R., and G. H. Fischer, 1963, Biochim. Bipohys. Acta *68*, 85, 93

Natarajan, A. T., 1961, Exp. Cell Res. *22*, 275

Neuhard, J., and A. Munch-Petersen, 1966, Biochim. Biophys. Acta *114*, 61

Newton, A., P. P. Dendy, C. L. Smith and P. Wildy, 1962, Nature *194*, 886

Painter, R. B., R. M. Drew, and W. L. Hughes, 1958, Science *127*, 1244

Painter, R. B., R. M. Drew, and R. E. Rasmussen, 1964, Radiation Res. *21*, 355

Painter, R. B., and R. E. Rasmussen, 1964, Nature *201*, 409

Pelc, S. R., and T. C. Appleton, 1965, Nature *205*, 1287

Person, S., and H. L. Lewis, 1962, Biophys. J. *2*, 451

Post, J., and J. Hoffman, 1961, Radiation Res. *14*, 713

Potter, R. L., 1960, Nucl. Acid outlines, Vol. 1

Potter, R. L., and O. F. Nygaard, 1963, J. Biol. Chem. *238*, 2150

Potter, R. L., S. Schlesinger, V. Buettner-Janusch, and L. Thompson, 1957, J. Biol. Chem. *226*, 381

Prosser, C. L., and F. A. Brown, Jr., 1961, in Comparative animal physiology, 2nd ed., Sanders, Philadelphia, London, p. 388

Puck, T. T., 1964, Science *144*, 565

Quastler, H., 1963, in Actions chimiques et biologiques des radiations, M. Haissinsky, ed., Masson et Cie, Paris, p. 147

Rigal, W. M., 1961, Nature *192*, 768

Sanders, P. C., D. F. Petersen, and W. H. Langham, 1961, Ann. N. Y. Acad. Sci. *95*, 969

Sauer, M. E., and B. E. Walker, 1961, Radiation Res. *14*, 633

Schneider, W. C., 1955, J. Biol. Chem. *216*, 287

Smith, W. E., G. Brecher, F. Stohlman, Jr., and J. Cornfield, 1962, Radiation Res. *16*, 201

Stewart, P. A., H. Quastler, M. R. Skougaard, D. R. Wimber, M. F. Wolfsberg, C. A. Perotta, B. Ferbel, and M. Carlough, 1965, Radiation Res. *24*, 521

Stone, G. E., O. L. Miller, and D. M. Prescott, 1965, J. Cell Biol. *25*, 171

Stone, G. E., and D. M. Prescott, 1964, J. Cell Biol. *21*, 275

Strauss, B. S., 1958, Radiation Res. *8*, 234

Sueoka, N., 1961, J. Mol. Biol. *3*, 31

Till, J. E., G. F. Whitmore, and S. Gulyas, 1963, Biochim. Biophys. Acta *72*, 277

Whittle, E. D., 1966, Biochim. Biophys. Acta *114*, 44

Whitmore, G. F., and S. Gulyas, 1966, Science *151*, 691

Wimber, D. E., 1959, Proc. Natl. Acad. Sci. U.S. *45*, 839

Wimber, D. E., 1964, in Advances in radiobiology, I, L. G. Augenstein, R. Manson and H. Quastler eds., Academic Press, New York and London, p. 85

Xeros, N., 1962, Nature 194, 682

Yang, S. J., G. M. Hahn, and M. A. Bagshaw, 1966, Exp. Cell Res. *42*, 130

CHAPTER 4

Interphase replication of DNA and the cell cycle

4.1 Introduction to the cell cycle

On the basis of light microscope observations, without the aid of radio-active precursors, mammalian cells were thought to pass through two main phases during their growth. During the longer phase, known as interphase or the resting phase, the nucleus of the cell was clearly visible and the cells were considered to be involved in the differentiated function of the tissue in which the cells were located. The shorter phase, mitosis, in which the chromosomes became visible and cell division occurred, was then considered to be the one in which both replication and division of the chromosomes occurred. It was not until after the introduction of quantitative cytological techniques and radioactive precursors that it became possible to distinguish between the replication of the chromosomes and their segregation at mitosis. WALKER and YATES (1952), for example, measured the optical density to ultraviolet light of individual living chick

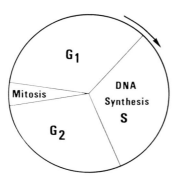

Fig. 4.1. The cell cycle in mammalian cells showing the four phases of the cycle. Arrow indicates the direction in which cells progress around the cycle.

cells in culture, and the Feulgen dye content of fixed cells, and their results clearly showed that the synthesis of nucleic acids occurred during interphase. HOWARD and PELC (1951, 1953), using autoradiography with S^{35}- and P^{32}-labelled precursors, and LAJTHA et al. (1954) using C^{14} and P^{32} also showed that the synthesis of DNA and chromosome material occurred during interphase. HOWARD and PELC (1953) suggested that the cell cycle could be represented in terms of progression around a clock face, and the various phases of the cycle represented as sectors on that face. This cycle is shown in fig. 4.1; M and S stand for mitosis and DNA synthesis respectively, while G_1 and G_2 are gaps during which no DNA synthesis occurs, although RNA and protein synthesis occurs throughout both gaps and the S phase.

The cell cycle of a population in tissue culture may conveniently be studied by exposing the cells to H^3Tdr. If a brief labelling period is used only the cells which are in the S phase incorporate H^3Tdr and these are clearly distinguished as labelled cells in autoradiographs (fig. 4.2).

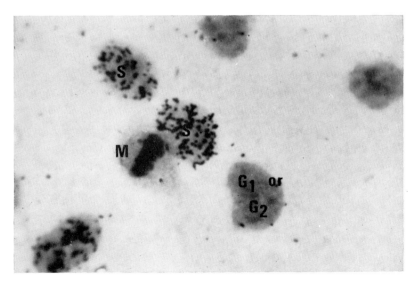

Fig. 4.2. Autoradiograph of human amnion FL strain cells labelled for 30 min with H^3Tdr, 1.25 μCi/ml 3 Ci/mmole stained with the Feulgen reaction and lightly counter stained so that the cytoplasm of interphase cells is not visible. Labelled cells are in the S phase, unlabelled cells in G_1 or G_2, M is a mitotic cell.

Although it is not possible to distinguish between G_1 and G_2 cells in autoradiographs, these two may be distinguished by means of Feulgen staining. The Feulgen dye content of G_2 cells, corresponding to cells in which DNA replication has been completed, is double that of G_1 cells in which DNA replication has not yet begun (see ch. 4 § 8, WALKER and YEATS 1952, DENDY and CLEAVER 1964).

The increase in nucleic acids and protein in the nuclei of mammalian cells during the cell cycle has been studied extensively using quantitative cytological methods and some of the results obtained are shown in a simplified form in fig. 4.3. In normal cells both DNA, RNA and protein

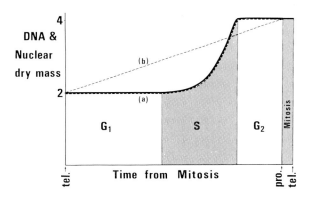

Fig. 4.3. Simple representation of the increase in DNA and nuclear dry mass of individual cells during the cell cycle (scale of DNA and nuclear dry mass shown for diploid cells in multiples of the haploid amounts). (a) DNA and nuclear dry mass in normal cells and DNA in malignant cells. (b) nuclear dry mass in malignant cells. (Nuclear dry mass is made up of 80 to 85% protein and 15 to 20% nucleic acids, see SEED 1963.)

synthesis are correlated closely in time, and most of the nuclear protein synthesis occurs during the S phase. In malignant cells, however, this close correlation is disturbed, and nuclear protein synthesis occurs throughout the whole of interphase (SEED 1963, 1966).

The assignment of cells in any particular population to one of the four phases described above assumes that these cells are involved in the continuous cycle of replication and cell division. This is true for most cases in tissue culture, but in most of the tissues of the body only a fraction of the total population is involved in this cycle and the remainder is involved in other functions. The fraction of the population that is involved in the cell cycle is defined as the Growth Fraction (G.F.) and methods for determining this parameter will be discussed in ch. 7 §§ 5, 13. It is convenient to refer to cells that are not in the cell cycle as being in a separate phase, G_0 (LAJTHA et al. 1962), although it is sometimes difficult to distinguish between cells in G_0 and those which are progressing very slowly around the cycle. Consequently, the G_0 phase is not always a totally distinct phase from those of the cell cycle. Cells in G_0 may be induced to enter the cell cycle by a number of stimuli and this phase contains cells which act as a viable reserve which begin replication and division in cases of injury and death in other cells of the population. The DNA content of G_0 cells usually corresponds to that of G_1 but in a few tissues there are also G_0 cells which correspond to the G_2 phase (e.g. skin epithelium, GELFANT 1962, 1963). It is difficult sometimes to make a rigid distinction between cells in G_0 and those for which G_1 is extremely long, either in the definition or in the experimental study of these phases. The role of the G_0 phase in tissue regeneration will be discussed in ch. 7, and this chapter will be restricted to the mitotic cell cycle.

4.2 Distinction between the cell cycle time and the population doubling time

In analysis of quantitative aspects of cell growth two similar parameters are commonly employed, the cell cycle time T and the population doubling time T_D. The former is the time taken for a cell to progress completely around the cell cycle once, i.e. the time taken for one cell to become two, at the same position of the cycle. The population doubling time is the time taken for the whole cell population to double in size and only has the same value as the cycle time when all cells are proliferating (G.F. = 1.0) and there is no cell loss or cell death. If division occurs at random in the population, the fraction of the population in division at any one time being constant, and each cell in the population has the same cycle time then the cell number increases exponentially (ENGELBERG 1961)

$$N(t) = N(0) \exp \ln 2 . t / T_D \quad \text{and} \quad T = T_D.$$

If the cells in the population do not all have the same cycle time the cell number still increases exponentially but T_D is then slightly shorter than the mean value of T (ENGELBERG 1961). In a number of cell populations encountered experimentally the growth fraction is less than 1.0, and in these cases T_D will be longer than T. Exponential growth is still maintained in such populations if the growth fraction and the rate of cell loss or cell gain remain constant over the period of observation (RIGAS 1958; PUJARA 1964; WHITMORE and TILL 1964). It is common to find that the growth fraction is less than 1 in many tissues and tumours and in some tissue cultures, and it is necessary to distinguish clearly between T and T_D. The distinction is particularly important when formulae such as those derived later in this chapter are used, because these are based on populations in which all cells are in the cell cycle.

A particularly clear example of the difference between the cell cycle time and the population doubling time is found in the growth of tissue culture cells in the presence of bromodeoxyuridine, BUdr (PUJARA 1964). In the absence of BUdr both the cell cycle time and the population doubling time for mouse L cells was 18 hr. After prolonged growth in BUdr, at 5 μg/ml (300 to 400 hr), the population doubling time was lengthened to 35 hr but the cell cycle time was only slightly changed, 21.5 hr. In this case a certain fraction of the growing part of the population was continually leaving the cell cycle and losing the ability to divide due to the incorporation of BUdr. Though the cell cycle time of the growing cells was only slightly affected by the BUdr, the fraction of non-growing cells caused a very marked change in the population doubling time.

Synchronous populations are sometimes used experimentally (see ZEUTHEN 1964) and in these the cell number increases in a stepwise manner and the doubling time is not a constant parameter as it is in asynchronous populations. In such populations it is useful to define an additional parameter, the degree of synchrony. The kinetics of synchronous populations have been described by ZEUTHEN (1958) and ENGELBERG (1961) and will not be discussed further here.

4.3 Determination of the duration of the phases of the cell cycle

Once the concept of the cell cycle had been established it was obviously necessary to determine the duration of the various phases, and to discover whether their durations showed any similarity in different cell types and how the phases varied under differing experimental conditions. The durations of the four phases can be determined by means of H^3 (and/or C^{14}) Tdr labelling and autoradiography and the remainder of this chapter will be devoted to a description of some of these methods, together with a simple mathematical analysis of cell population kinetics. The methods described here are restricted to those which enable rapid and accurate determination of all of the phases of the cell cycle.

4.4 Age distributions within the cell cycle

Most cell populations are not synchronised to any extent but contain cells distributed throughout the whole cycle. It is usually necessary to know, or make an assumption, about the form of this age distribution in order to determine the duration of the phases of the cell cycle. The two age distributions most commonly encountered are those in steady-state populations, in which the total cell number is constant, or in expanding populations, in which the total cell number is increasing exponentially. Other types of populations are encountered experimentally and include, for example, declining populations which are mainly the consequence of disease or irradiation. Expanding populations which do not grow exponentially are found in a number of tissues or tumours and these are often the result of variation in the duration of the phases of the cell cycle or changes in the fraction of the population which is proliferating (POST and HOFFMAN 1964; LALA and PATT 1966). These populations constitute special cases which can usually be analysed, approximately, by modifications of the methods used for steady-state or exponentially growing populations.

In tissue cultures there is no difficulty in defining the limits of the population under consideration, but the situation is different in whole tissues. A particular population in a tissue must be defined in terms of some easily identified histological criteria (morphology, staining, location in the tissue, etc.) and it may not always be possible to determine its precise limits, particularly when the growth fraction is less than 1 and both proliferating and non-proliferating cells are intermingled.

(a) *Steady state populations*. Within these populations there is a constant rate of cell gain by mitosis and/or by migration, and an equal rate of cell loss, by death or by migration. This situation is found in many tissues of an animal and in such populations the total cell number remains approximately constant. The distribution of cells around the cell cycle is uniform and the number of cells in any particular phase of the cycle is then proportional to the duration of that phase, and this type of distribution is shown in fig. 4.4(a).

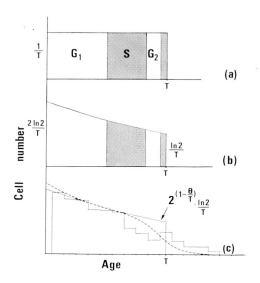

Fig. 4.4.   Age distribution of cells around the cell cycle, normalised to a total population size of unity. (a) steady state, (b) exponential growth, (c) exponential growth including the corrected distribution for a population in which the total cycle time varies between individual cells (–––––) and actual measured distribution for human amnion FL strain cells (histogram). (Redrawn from LENNARTZ and MAURER 1964; POWELL 1956, SISKEN and MORASCA 1965.)

The mitotic index is given by the relationship

$$\text{Mitotic index} = \frac{\text{duration of mitosis}}{\text{duration of cell cycle}} \tag{4.1}$$

and the labelling index (the fraction of the population labelled after a brief exposure to H^3Tdr or $C^{14}Tdr$) is given by

$$\text{Labelling index} = \frac{\text{duration of S phase}}{\text{duration of cell cycle}}. \tag{4.2}$$

(b) *Exponentially growing populations.* Ideal examples of these population are frequently encountered in tissue culture. Two cells are produced by each cell which enters mitosis, and these remain within the population with the result that there is always a preponderance of young cells. The mathematical expression for this distribution of cells around the cell cycle is derived in ch. 8 § 5 and has the form

$$dN/N(t) = [\exp{(1-\theta/T)}\ln 2]\, d\theta \, . \, \ln 2/T \tag{4.3}$$

where $dN/N(t)$ is the fraction of the total cell population $N(t)$ at time t which occupies the fraction $d\theta/T$ of the total cell cycle T. The full definitions of these terms will be found in ch. 8 § 5. In these formulae and the derivations in the Appendix, it is assumed that the duration of mitosis is short and is to be equally divided between the G_1 and G_2 phases, i.e.

$t_1 =$ duration of G_1 plus one half of mitosis t_m.
$t_2 =$ duration of G_2 plus one half of mitosis t_m.
$t_s =$ duration of S.

This age distribution for exponential growth is illustrated in fig. 4.4(b), and is derived on the assumption that the duration of the cell cycle is exactly the same for every cell in the population. If allowance is made for a distribution of cell cycle durations within the population, such as is found in practice, the age distribution is altered slightly. This alteration mainly affects the distribution of cells toward the older end of the cell cycle and an example of theoretical distribution, and an experimentally determined distribution for human amnion cells (SISKEN and MORASCA 1965), is shown in fig. 4.4(c). The theoretical distribution was based on a standard deviation of 13% in the cell cycle durations in the population, corresponding to the value obtained in the cultures of human amnion cells, and it can be seen that theoretical and experimental distributions agree fairly closely. For most purposes it is usually satisfactory to use the distribution quoted above (eq. (4.3)) and to neglect the variation in the durations of the cell cycle, rather than use the more rigorous, and more complex formulae derived by POWELL (1956).

Relationships equivalent to those for the mitotic index and labelling index in steady-state growth (eqs. (4.1) and (4.2)) may be obtained for exponential growth from the age distribution (eq. (4.3)) and these are,

$$\text{Mitotic index} = t_m \ln 2/T \qquad \text{(SMITH and DENDY 1962)} \qquad (4.4)$$

$$\text{Labelling Index} = [\exp t_s. \ln 2/T - 1] \cdot \exp t_2 \ln 2/T \qquad (4.5)$$
(CLEAVER 1965).

These are derived in detail in ch. 8 § 6. The duration of mitosis can be obtained directly from the mitotic index and the duration of the cell cycle by eqs. (4.1) or (4.4), so the experimental methods which will be described in the following sections will be mainly confined to methods for determining the durations of G_1, S and G_2 (i.e. t_1, t_s and t_2). For convenience, the methods will be described in terms of their application to tissue cultures, but in most cases they can be applied to in vivo studies with very little modification. To a first approximation, a pulse label in tissue culture is equivalent to a single injection of H^3Tdr into an animal, although the detailed shape of the pulse in the two systems is different. Continuous labelling in tissue culture is attained by adding excess H^3Tdr to the medium, and in vivo may be approximated by a continuous supply to the blood stream or by repeated injections at short time intervals.

4.5 Pulse chase method

If cultures are labelled with H^3Tdr during a brief pulse of 10 to 30 min only those cells which are in the S phase will be labelled. If these cultures are allowed to continue growth after the pulse, the labelled cells will pass through mitosis as a wave of labelled mitotic figures. It is often necessary to add unlabelled Tdr to the growth medium after the end of the pulse of H^3Tdr in order to dilute the pools of labelled molecules which are still present (see ch. 3 § 5). If this step is omitted, label continues to enter DNA until the pools are exhausted and this will extend the effective length of the pulse. By determining the time course of appearance and disappearance of the wave of labelled mitoses, in terms of the fraction of labelled mitotic figures at various times, the duration of the phases of the cell cycle can be measured. This technique was one of the earliest to be employed in studying the cell cycle (HOWARD and PELC 1953; PAINTER and DREW

1959) and it can be used to reveal a considerable amount of detail concerning the phase lengths and the variations between individual cells in a population (BARRETT 1966).

The results expected for an ideal case and an example of the application of the method to mouse L strain cells is shown in fig. 4.5. The successive waves of labelled mitoses correspond to successive divisions of the fraction of the population that was in S during the availability of H³Tdr. In

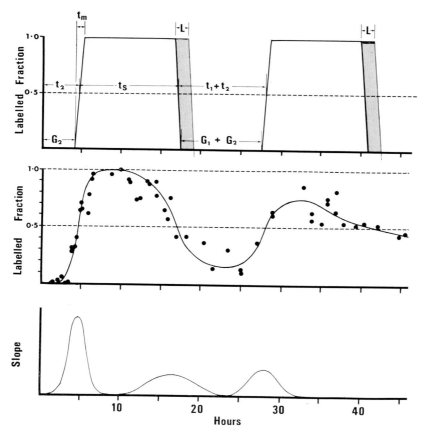

Fig. 4.5.   Fraction of labelled mitoses as a function of time after a pulse label of H³Tdr. Top: ideal case for population with no intercell variation, L = labelling duration. Center: actual case for mouse L cells labelled with H³Tdr 5 μCi/ml 2 Ci/mmole. G_1 5.7 hr, S 12.2 hr, G_2 4.4 hr, M 0.9 hr, T 23.2 hr. Bottom: slope of labelled mitoses curve.

the ideal case, in which there are no variations between individual cells, the fraction of labelled mitotic figures remains at zero until a period of time equal to the duration of G_2, and then rises rapidly to 1.0 in a period equal to the duration of mitosis. The labelled fraction then remains at 1.0 for a period equal to the duration of $(S-t_m)$ and subsequently falls to zero. The second wave of labelled mitotic figures appears after a further period of time equal to the durations of G_1 and G_2. If the duration of the labelling period is not negligible then cells which enter S during the availability of H^3Tdr will also be labelled and this will extend the length of the waves of labelled mitoses. This effect has been included in the ideal case in fig. 4.5, and the result of this is to overestimate t_s and under-estimate $t_1 + t_2$, by amounts equal to the duration of the labelling period. Ideal conditions such as these, however, are rarely observed. In most experimental situations, such as the one shown in fig. 4.5, the variations in the rate at which individual cells progress around the cell cycle reduced the definition of the successive wave of labelled mitotic figures. It is usually possible to obtain two waves and sometimes a third, but after longer periods of time the labelled cells are spread throughout the cycle and no further waves can be detected. The variations in G_2 alone cause the initial rise in the fraction of labelled mitotic figures to be more gradual than in the ideal case and it is not possible to estimate t_m from this portion of the curve. If all mitoses are scored, without discriminating between the various stages, and the duration of the labelling period is very short (i.e. about 5 to 10 min), then the time from the midpoint of the labelling pulse to that at which 0.5 of the mitoses are first labelled is equal to t_2, $(G_2 + \frac{1}{2}M)$. If the various phases of mitosis are recorded separately then the first appearance of labelled prophases will precede labelled metaphases which will in turn precede that of labelled telophases. The time interval between the initial rise in the labelled fraction in each of these phases of mitosis will give an estimate of the duration of the phases and the total mitotic time (ODARTCHENKO et al. 1964). This method is particularly useful for in vivo experiments because more direct estimates of mitotic time by time lapse photography are only suitable for tissue cultures (SISKEN and MORASCA 1965).

An additional curve may be constructed to show the variation in the slope of the labelled mitoses curve as a function of time (STANNERS and TILL 1960; CLEAVER 1964a). This has been included in fig. 4.5 and portrays the distributions in the rates of appearance and disappearance of labelled mitoses. From the width of these distributions the standard deviations of the lengths of the phases of the cell cycle amongst the population may be determined. In fig. 4.5, for example, the standard deviation of t_2 in the population is 1.0 hr. If the durations of t_2 in the population are normally distributed then the standard deviation can be read directly from the labelled mitoses curve and is equal to the time between the 0.16 and 0.5 points or the 0.5 and 0.84 points on the rising portion of the curve.

The durations of the phases of the cell cycle may be obtained from the labelled mitoses curve in the manner already described. It should be noted that since the 0.5 points give the times at which half of the cell population have reached certain stages of growth the phase durations obtained will be the median rather than the mean for the population. If the distributions of the phase durations are not symmetrical, as is commonly found in practice (STANNERS and TILL 1960) the distinction between the mean and median is an important one. Since the initial wave of labelled mitoses is not symmetrical, the rise in the curve being more rapid than the fall, there must be variation in the duration of S between individual cells of the population in addition to the variation in t_2. Also the slope of the second rising portion of the labelled mitoses curve is greater than the slope of the previous fall, which may be interpreted in terms of variability in G_1 and G_2 which compensates for the variability in S (SISKEN and MORASCA 1965).

This technique may be applied to any system in which the mitotic index is sufficiently high for the fraction of labelled mitoses to be determined accurately without the necessity of scoring an excessively large number of cells. The labour involved in determining the fractions of labelled mitoses at a large number of time intervals is probably the main disadvantage of this method. Also, the procedure of supplying and removing H³Tdr at the start of the experiment may disturb the cultures and introduce additional variations in the growth rate between individual cells that are not present in an undisturbed population. Despite these objections, this is one of the simplest methods to employ, and is the one which has been most frequently used.

4.6 Continuous labelling method

This method has the advantage that H³Tdr is added once to the growth medium, and the manipulation of cultures which is necessary in the previous method is avoided. However, to obtain the full information concerning the cell cycle it is necessary to determine several parameters as functions of the labelling time: the fraction of labelled mitoses, the fraction of labelled cells and the average grain count. Although this method is convenient to employ in tissue cultures, it is less so in the whole animal. To achieve continuous labelling in vivo it is necessary to subject the animal to the shock of repeated injections or continuous infusion of label and this may well result in disturbances at the cellular level which make cell cycle analysis difficult to interpret.

An example of the three parameters mentioned above is shown in fig. 4.7, from experiments with a strain of human skin epithelial cells (NCTC 2544). The curve showing the fraction of labelled mitoses is used to obtain a value for t_2 in the same manner as in the previous pulse labelling method. Since the H³Tdr is present continuously, however, the fraction of labelled mitoses does not fall once it has reached a value of 1.0.

The fraction of labelled cells increases steadily with the duration of labelling due to the steady entry of cells into the S phase. At first there is an increase in the number of unlabelled cells due to division of G_2 cells together with an increase in labelled cells due to entry of G_1 cells into S. Since cultures in exponential growth contain more young cells than old, the rate of entry into S is greater than the rate of cell division. The labelled fraction consequently increases steadily with time from the start of labelling. The rate of increase should itself increase slightly when labelled cells begin to divide but this can rarely be detected due to variations between individual cells. The labelled fraction will reach 1.0 after the cells which were in G_1, G_2 and mitosis at the start of labelling have all entered S, i.e. after a time equal to $t_1 + t_2$. From the two curves for the labelled fractions values can consequently be determined for both t_1 and t_2.

The maximum amount of H³Tdr that a cell can incorporate in one cycle corresponds to a single complete replication of the DNA of the nucleus. This takes the whole S phase to complete and the average grain count should consequently reach a constant level after a period of time approximately equal to t_s. However, after times longer than t_2 labelled cells will begin to divide and the grain counts of the daughter cells will be half the parental grain count. Also, the labelled population will contain cells which either began or completed DNA replication during the labelling period and these too will contain less than the maximum amount of label. Due to the presence of these cells, the average grain count reaches a constant level only when the labelled fraction of the population contains predominantly those cells which have replicated the whole of their DNA in the presence of H³Tdr. Consequently, the time taken for the average grain count to reach a constant level overestimates to a small extent the duration of the S phase.

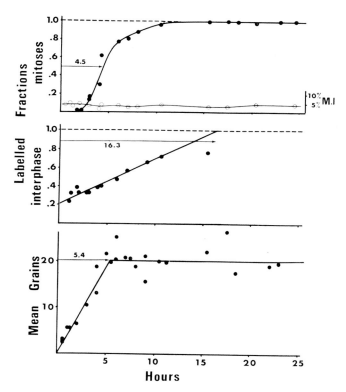

Fig. 4.6. Fraction of labelled mitoses, labelled interphase cells and mean grain counts as a function of time in H³Tdr, 2.5 μCi/ml 0.06 Ci/mmole, for human skin epithelium cells, strain NCTC 2544. G₁ 11.2 hr, S 5.4 hr, G₂ 3.9 hr, M 1.2 hr, T 21.7 hr.

To avoid these errors in the estimation of t_s an alternative parameter of the grain count distribution may be plotted instead of the average grain count (MALONEY et al. 1962). These workers arranged the labelled cells in order of increasing grain count and then took the grain count of the cell that was a certain predetermined number of cells before the one with maximum grain count. This grain count was plotted as a function of the time in H^3Tdr in the same manner as the average grain count in fig. 4.6, and a value similarly obtained for t_s. The value obtained for t_s in this way differs only slightly from that obtained from the average grain count and a refinement such as this is only necessary when exceptionally accurate determinations of t_s are required. Since there are unavoidable variations between individual cells in any population, there would seem to be little value in determining the mean duration of any of the phases of the cell cycle with exceptional accuracy. Of more value is an approximate estimate of the means (i.e. to within one place of decimals at the most, when the durations are expressed in hours) together with the standard deviation.

An alternative method for determining the rate of entry of cells into the S phase, which gives similar results to continuous labelling, is to give two pulse labels separated by a measured interval. This is often employed in whole animal studies, using H^3Tdr for one injection and C^{14}Tdr for the other, since it is easier to give two successive injections than continuous infusion (BASERGA and LISCO 1963; WIMBER and QUASTLER 1963; PILGRIM and MAURER 1965).

4.7 *Continuous labelling in the presence of colchicine (or colcemide)*

The two previous methods which have been described (ch. 4 § 5, 6), although adequate, have the major disadvantage that they necessitate frequent sampling of cultures over at least 24 hr. In cell cycle studies, as in most other studies, a short time at work is always preferable to a long one, if the end result is the same. The experimental method described in this section is one such shorter method which can be used to analyse the cell cycle. The procedure and its theoretical analysis have been developed extensively by one group of investigators (PUCK and STEFFEN 1963; PUCK et al. 1964) and the following description is based on their work.

The procedure involves the addition of colchicine and H³Tdr simultaneously to tissue cultures, and the determination of the rate at which unlabelled and labelled cells enter and are blocked in mitosis. Also, the rate of increase of all labelled cells with time yields additional information in a similar way as in the previous section. The analysis of the results of this procedure requires more mathematical analysis than either of the previous methods, and this is given in the following paragraphs and in ch. 8 § 7.

Suppose that colchicine is added at a particular time which will be taken as the starting point of the measurement, $t = 0$, and that it immediately blocks cell division in cells which are in mitosis and those which enter mitosis at later times. In this situation, the mitotic index will increase steadily with time. At a later time, t, the total number of cells in mitosis will be those which were in mitosis, initially, together with those which would have divided during the interval t.

During exponential growth the total cell number at time t may be expressed as:

$$N = N_0 \exp t \ln 2/T. \qquad (N = N_0 \text{ when } t = 0)$$

The number of cells which would have divided in the time t is equal to the increase in cell number which would have occurred in that interval, i.e. $N_0(\exp t \ln 2/T - 1)$.

Including also those cells which were in mitosis at $t = 0$, the fraction of cells blocked in mitosis after an interval t, will be given by:

Mitotic Index, MI, at time $t = \exp(t + t_m) \ln 2/T - 1$.

The expression for the mitotic index may be rearranged into the following more convenient form:

$$\log_{10}(1 + MI) = 0.301 \, (t + t_m)/T. \qquad (4.6)$$

The expression $\log_{10}(1 + MI)$ is known as the collection function for the mitotic index (PUCK and STEFFEN 1963). If colchicine is effective as soon as it is added to cultures, as has been assumed in deriving the collection function, then eq. (4.6) shows that this function should be linear with respect to time. The slope of the line obtained by plotting the collection function against time is then $0.301/T$ and the intercept $0.301 \, t_m/T$. Colchicine is only effective in this manner above a certain concentration, and at lower concentrations there is a lag in time before cells are blocked in mitosis. In the human cell strain KB, for example, colchicine blocks every cell in mitosis at concentrations above 2×10^{-7} M; at concentrations between 2×10^{-7} M and 5×10^{-8} M the cells which are in mitosis when colchicine is added are not blocked and there is a lag equal to t_m before cells begin to accumulate in mitosis. At lower concentrations colchicine is not completely effective in blocking cells in mitosis, and the collection function increases more slowly with time than at the higher concentrations (TAYLOR 1965).

At the intermediate concentrations, when cells in mitosis at the time colchicine is added are able to complete mitosis, but those entering mitosis are blocked, the collection function takes the form:

$$\log_{10}(1+\mathrm{MI}) = 0.301\, t/T. \tag{4.7}$$

Under these conditions the collection function should still have a slope of $0.301/T$, but should extrapolate to the origin. If the collection function for labelled mitoses is determined in addition to that for all mitoses, this will be zero until a time equal to the duration of the G_2 phase has passed. At later times the collection function for labelled mitoses will be parallel

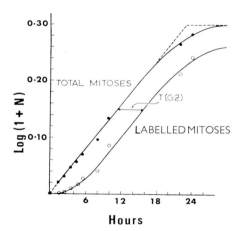

Fig. 4.7. Collection function, log $(1 + N)$, for total mitotic index and for labelled mitoses, where N is the appropriate MI, in a culture of HeLa S3 cells to which colcemide, 0.25 μg/ml, and H³Tdr, 0.025 to 0.04 μCi/ml, was added at the start of measurement (reproduced from PUCK and STEFFEN 1963).

to that for all mitoses and the time lag between them is equal to the duration of G_2. These collection functions are shown in fig. 4.7, and from them values can be obtained for the cell cycle time, the mitotic time and the duration of G_2. If the population is not exponential in growth, or growth is altered by the incorporation of H³Tdr the collection functions will not be linear or parallel and such effects are readily detected.

The collection functions reach a constant level after a period of time because the mitotic block is not perfect, and cells eventually pass through mitosis and enter G_1 as polyploid cells without undergoing cell division. This does not interfere with the determinations of the cell cycle time and G_2, unless the cultures are growing extremely slowly. In the latter case, cells will slip through mitosis without the collection function increasing sufficiently to enable an accurate determination of the cell cycle time to be made.

In the presence of H³Tdr in addition to colchicine, the fraction of the total population which is labelled, increases with time due to the entry of cells into the S phase. It is possible to define a collection function for labelled cells, similar to that for mitoses, and this may be derived by using the age distribution for cultures in exponential growth (eq. (4.3)) to determine the rate of entry into S.

If colchicine is used at a concentration which blocks mitosis immediately, there will be no increase in cell number, and the increase in labelled cells in a time interval, t, will be equal to the number of cells in that portion of G_1 of length t which ends at the start of S. The fraction of the population in this portion of the cell cycle is given by the integral of the age distribution (eq. (4.3)) between the limits of $t_1 - t$ and t_1:

$$\text{Increase in labelling index} = \int_{t_2}^{t_1} \frac{\ln 2}{T} [\exp (1 - \frac{\theta}{T})\ln 2] \, d\theta.$$

This integral is evaluated in ch. 8 § 7 and leads to the following relationship for the labelling index, LI, at a time t

$$\log_{10} [1 + \text{LI}/\exp (t_2 \ln 2/T)] = 0.301 \, (t_s + t)/T. \tag{4.8}$$

This expression has been plotted in fig. 4.8 using the values already determined for t_2 and T, and is similar to the collection function for mitotic figures (eq. (4.7)). The slope gives another estimate for the cell cycle time,

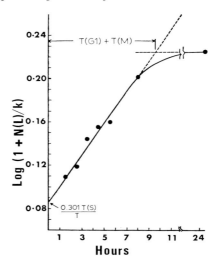

Fig. 4.8.   The collection function, log $(1 + N(\mathrm{L})/k)$ where $N(\mathrm{L})$ is the fraction of the total population labelled with H³Tdr and k is equal to exp (ln $2\, t\mathrm{G}_2/T$). Colcemide, 0.25 μg/ml, and H³Tdr, 0.025 to 0.04 μCi/ml, added at start of measurement for cultures of HeLa S3 cells (reproduced from PUCK and STEFFEN 1963).

and the intercept is equal to 0.301 t_s/T, but this not an independent estimate of T since a value has already been assumed in calculating the collection function. This collection function reaches a constant level when all of the cells in G_1 have entered S, and the time at which this occurs gives an estimate for the duration of G_1. The collection function does not level off sharply because of the variation in the lengths of G_1 between individual cells of the population. If a concentration of colchicine had been used which did not block those cells which were in mitosis initially, then the collection function does not level off until a time equal to the combined durations of G_1 and mitosis (see ch. 8 § 7).

Since the mitotic and the labelling indices increase steadily with time, these can be measured rapidly and accurately, and the method has been used to resolve events in the cell cycle to within precise limits (PUCK 1964). The method is particularly suitable for determining the times at which metabolic events occur within the cell cycle and the perturbations in the progress of cells through the cycle that are caused by antimetabolites or radiations (TOBEY et al. 1966).

4.8 *Combined microspectrophotometry and autoradiography*

This method is one by which the fraction of a cell population in each of the four phases of the cycle is determined directly, and under favourable circumstances this could be done using only a single culture. From the analysis of the age distributions around the cell cycle which have been described earlier, the fraction of the population in each phase of the cell cycle is related to the fraction of the cell cycle which is occupied by that phase. These relationships are given in table 4.1 (DENDY and CLEAVER

TABLE 4.1

Relationships between the fractions of the populations in each phase of the cell cycle and the relative durations of the phases.

Phase	Steady state*	Exponential growth*
Mitosis	$\dfrac{N_m}{N_0} = \dfrac{t_m}{T}$ (4.1)	$\dfrac{N_m}{N_0} = 0.693\,\dfrac{t_m}{T}$ (4.4)
G_1	$\dfrac{N(G_1)}{N_0} = \dfrac{t(G_1)}{T}$	$\dfrac{N(G_1 + \frac{1}{2}M)}{N_0} = 2\left[1 - \exp - \dfrac{t_1 \ln 2}{T}\right]$
S	$\dfrac{N(S)}{N_0} = \dfrac{t_s}{T}$ (4.2)	$\dfrac{N(S)}{N_0} = \exp\dfrac{t_2 \ln 2}{T}\exp\left[\dfrac{t_s \ln 2}{T} - 1\right]$ (4.5)
G_2	$\dfrac{N(G_2)}{N_0} = \dfrac{T(G_2)}{T}$	$\dfrac{N(G_2 + \frac{1}{2}M)}{N_0} = \left[\exp\dfrac{t_2 \ln 2}{T} - 1\right]$

*   For steady-state growth the formulae contain the true durations of each of the four phases of the cell cycle, i.e. $T = t_m + t(G_1) + t_s + t(G_2)$. For exponential growth the formulae are derived from the age distribution of eq. (4.3) in which mitosis was divided equally between the G_1 and G_2 phases, i.e. $T = t_1 + t_s + t_2$.

1964). Since this method only gives the relative duration of the phases of the cell cycle it is also necessary to determine the duration of the cycle or one of the phases in absolute terms by one of the methods described in the preceding sections.

The fraction of the population in each phase of the cycle can be determined by a combination of Feulgen staining and H³Tdr, and the unlabelled interphase fraction consists of both G_1 and G_2 cells which can be distinguished by their relative DNA content.

The experimental procedure of this method is to administer H³Tdr to a culture that is in the exponential phase of growth for a brief period (say, 10 min) before fixation, so as to label the S phase cells. The culture is then stained by the Feulgen reaction and an autoradiograph prepared. After development of the autoradiograph the Feulgen dye contents of the un- labelled cells are determined, using a microspectrophotometer. By this means, the unlabelled cells can be divided into two groups, those in G_1 and those in G_2; the Feulgen dye content of the latter being twice that of the former. Having determined the fractions of the population in each of the four phases of the cycle, the formulae of table 4.1 are then used to calculate the relative durations of each of the phases.

It may often be necessary to determine the Feulgen dye contents before preparation of the autoradiographs, particularly since clean preparations

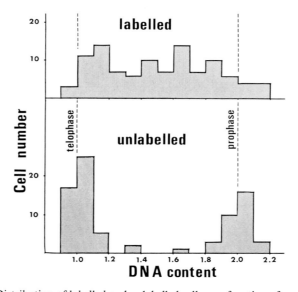

Fig. 4.9. Distribution of labelled and unlabelled cells as a function of DNA content in exponentially growing cultures of mouse L strain cells. Labelled for 10 min with H³Tdr (5 μCi/ml 2Ci/mmole) immediately before fixation and DNA contents determined from the Feulgen dye contents of individual cells and expressed in terms of the telophase content as 1.0 and the prophase content as 2.0 (CLEAVER 1964b).

are required for reliable microspectrophotometry. In such cases the locations of each measured nucleus may be recorded photographically at the start of the series of measurements and then identified in subsequent autoradiographs. Feulgen dye distributions that were obtained in one experiment are shown in fig. 4.9, and it is clear that there is no difficulty in this case in distinguishing the G_1 and G_2 populations. The results of the calculations of phase durations are given on the basis of a cell cycle time of 23.2 hr that had been determined independently.

This method is convenient since it requires only a single tissue culture preparation for the whole determination. The advantage, however, is deceptive. The labour involved in the microspectrophotometry is considerable, and also any degree of synchrony in the cell population will cause a bias in the relative proportions of the population in the various phases. It is also necessary to know whether all or only part of the particular population under study consists of cells actively progressing round the cell cycle. If only part of the cell population is actually in the cell cycle, the remainder will be unlabelled cells and these will make determination of the G_1 and G_2 populations difficult. In such cases this method may be less reliable than some of the earlier methods described.

4.9 *Constancy and variation in the duration of the phases of the cell cycle*

The duration of the phases of the cell cycle have been determined in numerous cell types using the methods that have been described in the earlier sections of this chapter and some of the values are shown in tables 4.2 and 4.3. Only experiments in which the durations of each of G_1, S and G_2 were determined have been used in compiling these tables. Numerous experiments have been performed in which the duration of S alone was determined and the values obtained are similar to those in the tables. In one series of experiments (KOBERG 1963) the duration of S in a number of rat and mouse tissues were determined and these all lay in the range from 5.6 to 9.6 hr, most of the values being about 7 to 8 hr. In ascites cells, BASERGA and LISCO (1963) claimed to observe a difference in the duration of S in male and female mice, 10.4 hr in the former and 12.4 hr in the latter. In mouse oocytes the duration of S is slightly longer than

TABLE 4.2

Durations of the phases of the cell cycle in vitro.

Cell type	G$_1$ Hours	G$_1$ Fract.	S Hours	S Fract.	G$_2$ Hours	G$_2$ Fract.	M (hr)	T (hr)	Ref.
Human embryonic fibroblasts	2.5	0.135	11.5	0.622	4.5	0.243	–	18.5	1
Human leucocytes	4.6	0.260	9.6	0.543	3.5	0.197	–	17.7	2
Human leucocytes (early growth)	>24	–	12	–	6.0	–	–	>42	3
Human kidney (asynchronous growth)	13.6	0.504	8.0	0.296	4.6	0.170	0.8	27.0	4
(synchronous growth)	10.1	0.474	7.6	0.357	2.8	0.131	0.8	21.3	4
HeLa	12–16.5	0.51	8.5	0.304	3–7.5	0.19	–	28	5
HeLa S3	12–16	0.56	8–10	0.36	1–3	0.04–12	–	25	5
HeLa S3	8.4	0.418	6.0	0.298	4.6	0.229	1.1	20.1	6
Human amnion	9.8	0.505	6.7	0.345	2.2	0.113	0.7	19.4	7
Human diploid	4.5–8	0.35	7.5	0.417	4.0	0.222	–	18	8
Human skin (fig. 4.7) (NCTC-2544)	11.2	0.517	5.4	0.249	3.9	0.180	1.2	21.7	9
Human fetal lung (18th passage)	6	0.357	6	0.357	4	0.238	0.8	16.8	10
(42nd passage)	>8	–	8	–	4–14	–	>0.5	>25	10
Mouse L60	9–11	0.50	6–7	0.325	3.0	0.15	–	20.0	8
Mouse L60T	4–5	0.281	8.0	0.50	3.0	0.188	–	16.0	8
Mouse L (fig. 4.6)	5.7	0.246	12.2	0.526	4.4	0.190	0.9	23.2	9
Mouse L (fig. 4.10)	4.0	0.173	13.5	0.582	4.8	0.207	0.9	23.2	9
Mouse L	8.1	0.45	6.3	0.35	3.6	0.20	–	18	11
Mouse fibroblasts	8.0	0.421	6.0	0.316	5.0	0.263	–	19	12
Mouse L5178Y	1.5	0.130	6.9–7.4	0.63	3.0	0.26	–	11.5	8
Chinese hamster	3.5	0.250	8	0.57	2.5	0.18	–	14	13
Chinese hamster	5–6	0.393	6.7	0.478	2.0	0.143	–	14	8
Chinese hamster	2.5	0.185	8.5	0.63	2.0	0.148	0.5	13.5	14

TABLE 4.2 (cont.)

Cell type	G₁		S		G₂		M	T	Ref.
	Hours	Fract.	Hours	Fract.	Hours	Fract.	(hr)	(hr)	
Chinese hamster	13.5	0.563	8.0	0.333	2.5	0.104	–	24	15
Chinese hamster CH24	6.2	0.413	6.3	0.420	0.5	0.167	–	15	16
Chinese hamster ovary	4.7	0.38	4.1	0.33	2.8	0.226	0.8	12.4	17
Hamster tumor	3.7	0.218	8.0	0.47	4.0	0.235	–	17	8
Rabbit kidney (early growth)	32–60	–	10	–	5.0	–	–	47–57	18

References:

1) MOORHEAD and DEFENDI (1963)	10) MACIERA-COELHO et al. (1966)
2) CAVE (1966 a, b)	11) MAK (1965)
3) BENDER and PRESCOTT (1962)	12) KILLANDER and ZETTERBERG (1965)
4) GALAVESI and BOOTSMA (1966)	13) TAYLOR (1960)
5) PAINTER and DREW (1959)	14) STUBBLEFIELD (1966)
6) PUCK and STEFFEN (1963)	15) CHU (1965)
7) SISKEN and MORASCA (1965)	16) DEWEY and HUMPHREY (1962)
8) DEFENDI and MANSON (1963)	17) PUCK et al. (1964)
9) CLEAVER (see this chapter)	18) LIEBERMAN et al. (1963)

In tables 4.2 and 4.3 the phase durations have been taken from the published values or estimated from published data. The fractional durations in table 4.2 are expressed in terms of the whole cycle duration. When the duration of mitosis has not been stated it is included in the durations of G_1 and G_2. This means that there is an uncertainty of about half the mitotic time in the quoted durations of G_1 and G_2, but this does not affect the discussions and conclusions based on these tables.

TABLE 4.3

Durations of the phases of the cell cycle in vivo.

Cell type	G₁ (hr)	S (hr)	G₂ (hr)	M (hr)	T (hr)	Ref.
Mouse intestinal epithelium	1–2	8	1.5	–	11.2	1
Mouse intestinal epithelium	9.0	7.5	1.5	1.0	19	2
Mouse intestinal epithelium (germ free)	18.5	14.5	3.0	2.0	38	2

TABLE 4.3 (cont.)

Cell type	G_1 (hr)	S (hr)	G_2 (hr)	M (hr)	T (hr)	Ref.
Mouse duodenum epithelium	4.5–5.5	5	<2.0	–	11.5	3
Mouse forestomach epithelium	14	13.5	1–2	1–2	20.5	4
Mouse uterine epithelium (castrated)	31.5	8.5	1.0	1.0	42	5
Mouse uterine epithelium (castrated and estrogen treated)	18.5	5.5	1.0	1.0	26	5
Mouse hair follicles	2.8	6.0	2.0	–	10.8	6
Mouse ear epidermis	>22 days	30	6.5	3.8	24 days	7
Mouse ear epidermis	7–80	18	3.5	2.0	30–100	8
Mouse spermatogonia type AII	7.5	7.5	14.0	–	28–30	9
Mouse spermatogonia type AIII	8.0	8.0	11.0	–	26–28	9
Mouse spermatogonia type AIV	9.5	13.0	8.0	–	30–31	9
Mouse spermatogonia type (intermediate)	8.5	14.0	6.0	–	26–28	9
Mouse spermatogonia B	10.5	18.0	4.5	–	29–30	9
Mouse embryonic tail	1.2	6.3	1.5	–	9	10
Mouse embryo neural tube	2.3	4.0	0.8	1.3	8.4	11
Mouse epithelial tumour	7.0	6.5	2.0	–	15.5	12
Mouse spindle tumour	3.0	12.0	1.0	–	16	12
Mouse mammary tumour	7hr-3 days	9–13	1–4	–	1–3.5 days	13
Mouse leukemia L5178Y	1.5	6.9–7.4	3	–	11.5	14
Mouse Ehrlich ascites	3	8.5	1.5	5.1	18	15
Mouse Ehrlich ascites	<1	12	6	–	18	16
Mouse Ehrlich ascites	2.5	8.5	7	–	18	16
Mouse Ehrlich ascites	<1	11	7	–	18	16
Mouse Ehrlich ascites	4–4.5	6.5–7	4	–	15	16
Mouse Ehrlich ascites	<18	13–14	6	–	<38	16
Mouse Ehrlich ascites (1 day)	0	6.0	2.0	–	8	17
Mouse Ehrlich ascites (4 days)	0	13	4.0	–	17	17
Mouse Ehrlich ascites (7 days)	0	18	4.0	–	22	17
Mouse Yoshida sarcoma	2	6.5	3–7	1	11–18	18
Rat liver (1 day old)	5.0	7.0	1.5	0.3	13.8	19
Rat liver (3 weeks old)	9.0	9.0	1.8	1.7	21.5	19
Rat liver (8 weeks old)	28.0	16.0	1.8	1.7	47.5	19
Rat liver (regenerating)	–	7.0	4.0	–	–	20
Rat duodenum epithelium	<1	8.2	1	–	9.4	21
Rat jejunum epithelium	<1	7.7	1	–	9.0	21

TABLE 4.3 (cont.)

Cell type	G_1 (hr)	S (hr)	G_2 (hr)	M (hr)	T (hr)	Ref.
Rat ileum epithelium	<1	7.8	1	–	8.9	21
Rat jejunum epithelium (crypt bottom, cells 1–6)	3.5	8.5	1	1	14	22
Rat jejunum epithelium (crypt center, cells 13–15)	2.0	6.5	1	1	10.5	22
Rat jejunum epithelium (crypt top, cells 22+)	1.5	6.5	1	1	10	22
Hamster pouch epithelium	128	10.2	1.6	2.6	142	23
Hamster pouch epithelium	8.7–11.9	6.1	2.2	0.5	17.5	23
Hamster jejunum epithelium	1–1.75	6.7	4.9	–	13.0	24
Hamster jejunum epithelium (necrotic)	1–1.25	6.0	4.7	–	11.8	24
Hamster jejunum epithelium (tumour)	1–1.5	6.1	4.6	–	12.0	24
Canine erythroid precursors	2	6	1	1	10	25
Canine myeloid precursors	2.5	5.5	1	1	10	26
Human colon epithelium	>10	11–14	1	–	24	27
Chicken duodenal epithelium	5.8	5.0	0.7	–	11.5	28
Chicken proventralis epithelium	–	5.3	1.2	–	10–15	28
Chicken embryo mesencephalon	6.2	5.8	3.0	1.0	16	29
Chicken embryo alar plate	9.0	4.0	2.0	1.0	16	29
Chicken embryo retina	4.0	4.0	2.0	–	10	29
Grasshopper neuroblast	0	1.5	0	2.0	3.5	30
Grasshopper spermatocytes	11.5	12	4.5	–	28	31
Bullfrog lens epithelium (24 °C)	79 d(appr)	100	11	–	83 d	32
Bullfrog lens epithelium (30 °C)	30 d(appr)	48	7	–	33 d	32
Tradescantia root tips	1	10.5	2.5	3	17	32
Tradescantia root tips	6.7	10.5	3.0	–	20.2	31
Onion root tips	10	7	3	5	25	32
Pisum root tips	6–10	6	3	–	15–19	33

References: see page 130.

in the somatic cells of the animal and is between 10.5 and 12 hr (CRONE et al. 1966). The duration of S in myelocytes in the dog bone marrow is about 5 hr (MALONEY et al. 1962) and the duration of S in erythropoietic and granulopoietic cells in man is between 13 and 14 hr (STRYCKMANS et al. 1966).

Although there are many tissues and cell types for which the cell cycle durations are unknown, a number of general conclusions can be reached on the basis of those which have been determined. These are as follows: (1) The durations of the corresponding phases of the cell cycle are *not* exactly the same for every cell type, either in terms of hours or when expressed as fractions of the total cycle duration. Similar cell types in culture grown under different conditions show differences in the cell cycle which are not due merely to experimental error.

(2) The range of variation for the G_1 phase is greater than that for the S or G_2 phases. From table 4.2, the duration of G_1 in tissue cultures can be between 1.5 and 60 hr, S between 4.1 and 13.5 hr (0.25 to 0.63 of the cycle), and G_2 between 1 and 7.5 hr (0.04 to 0.26 of the cycle). In vivo the range of values that have been found for G_1 is from less than 1 hr to many days, while the S and G_2 durations are similar to the in vitro values.

(3) There is a tendency for the duration of S, and in some cases also of G_1 and G_2, to lengthen with increase in the number of passages in culture or

References to table 4.3:
1) FRY et al. (1961)
2) MATSUZAWA and WILSON (1964)
3) LESHER et al. (1961)
4) WOLFSBERG (1964)
5) EPIFANOVA (1966)
6) GRIEM (1966)
7) SHERMAN et al. (1961)
8) PILGRIM et al. (1966)
9) MONESI (1962)
10) WIMBER (1963)
11) KAUFFMAN (1966)
12) GOLDFEDER (1965)
13) MENDELSOHN et al. (1960)
14) DEFENDI and MANSON (1963)
15) EDWARDS et al. (1960)
16) LENNARTZ and MAURER (1964)
17) LALA and PATT (1966)
18) CHIGASAKI (1963)
19) POST and HOFFMAN (1964)
20) SHEA (1964)
21) LORAN and CROCKER (1963)
22) CAIRNIE et al. (1965)
23) REISKIN and MENDELSOHN (1964)
24) BETTS et al. (1966)
25) LALA et al. (1966)
26) LALA (unpublished)
27) LIPKIN et al. (1962)
28) CAMERON (1964)
29) FUJITA (1962)
30) MCGRATH et al. (1965)
31) VAN 'T HOF (1966)
32) REDDAN and ROTHSTEIN (1966)
33) WIMBER and QUASTLER (1963)
34) MCQUADE et al. (1956)

with aging in vivo. The durations in embryonic or young tissues are often shorter than in the adult animal. In addition the duration of the phases differ between tissues depending on the metabolic state, hormones, location of the tissue, etc. In animals with a high body temperature, such as birds, the duration of S is shorter than in cases where the body temperature is low, such as amphibia.

(4) There is no clear and consistent difference between the phase durations in normal and malignant cells, and carcinogenesis must consequently involve other factors than merely an alteration in growth rate (see BASERGA 1965).

The similarity in the durations of the S and G_2 phases in a variety of cell types, in contrast to the wide variation in G_1 durations, has been described in the form of a general rule by DEFENDI and MANSON (1963), in which they state, 'Most mammalian cells of normal and tumour origin, in vivo and in vitro, spend a similar period of time in DNA synthesis and in mitosis irrespective of the generation time. Modifications of environmental factors such as pH and nutritional conditions appear to affect mostly the length of the G_1 period.' This view has very rapidly taken on the status of a dogma, often without concurrent recognition of the limits within which the dogma is valid. It is true that G_1 is the most variable of the phases but there are numerous examples in tables 4.2 and 4.3 in which S and G_2 also undergo characteristic variations. Not only does the mean duration of G_1 vary considerably from one cell type to another, but within one particular system it is the phase in which most of the variation between individual cells occurs (SISKEN and MORASCA 1965; TERASIMA and TOLMACH 1963). Growth of tissue cultures at temperatures below 37° C (SISKEN et al. 1965) or in serum concentrations below normal (HAHN and BAGSHAW 1966) also has a greater effect on the lengthening of the G_1 phase than on the other phases. In cultures of human diploid cells both G_1 and S increase, and particularly the former, after about 40 passages and at this stage the cultures are also very heterogenous as compared to younger cultures (MACIEIRA-COELHO et al. 1966).

In tissue cultures there is a strong selection pressure which favours the development of cell strains which have the fastest growth rates and few differentiated functions and it is consequently not surprising that in these systems the durations of the phases of the cell cycle are similar. In vivo, where a high growth rate is not predominantly important for the cells of a tissue, the durations of the phases vary considerably and some of these examples have been cited above (3). Other examples include cells of the basal layer of the mouse ear epidermis in which the G_1 and S phases are both exceptionally long, 22 days and 30 hr respectively (SHERMAN et al. 1961). This long duration may be on account of the lower temperature of this region of the body. During the maturation of spermatocytes both G_1 and S are increased in length in the more advanced spermatogonia, whereas G_2 is decreased such that the overall length of the cycle is similar at each stage (MONESI 1962). Hormones also appear to regulate the cycles in some tissues and these effects are most clearly observed with sex hormones. After castration the cell cycle in the mouse uterine epithelium is 42 hr long but may be reduced to 26 hr by injection of estrogen (EPIFA-NOVA 1966). This reduction is effected by a shortening of both G_1 and S, while G_2 is unaffected. Castration also affects the duration of S in the alveolar cells of the mouse mammary gland (BRESCIANI 1964). In these cells in normal mice, S is 20.7 hr long, but in castrated animals treated with 17-β-estradiol and progesterone S may be reduced to 10.7 hr.

Although there are these and other exceptions to the general rule of the constancy of S and G_2, these durations are similar in a large number of tissues and animals and the sequence from the start of DNA synthesis to the completion of mitosis may be considered as a single process. Most somatic cells in an adult animal have DNA contents which correspond to that of G_1 cells and stimuli which cause the onset of growth consequently result first in the initiation of DNA synthesis which is then followed by mitosis and an increase in cell number. The control of growth may then operate through the control of the onset and continuation of DNA synthesis (BASERGA 1965).

4.10 *The cell cycle in non-mammalian cells*

The cell cycle has been discussed exclusively with reference to mammalian cells in the preceding sections. However, every living organism passes through cycles of growth and reproduction and the cell cycle in mammalian cells is just one of a whole range of cyclic biological processes. Similar cell cycles may be described in other organisms, although the mammalian cycle is the one most frequently studied by means of H³Tdr techniques.

In *E. coli*, for example, the total cycle time is approximately 20 min under optimum conditions. Of this period 90 to 97% is spent in DNA synthesis and the remaining brief portion includes cell division but there are no periods that can be considered equivalent to G_1 or G_2 phases (MAALØE and HANAWALT 1961).

The cycle in *Tetrahymena* is of particular interest because this organism contains two nuclei which have different functions and different replication cycles. The macronucleus is polyploid and divides amitotically whereas the micronucleus passes through a recognisable mitosis. Although both nuclei divide at approximately the same time, DNA synthesis occurs at widely different times in the cycle in the two nuclei and there is no recognisable G_1 phase in the micronucleus (fig. 4.10, FLICKINGER 1965). Mitochondrial DNA in this organism is replicated throughout the cell cycle (PARSONS 1965).

In another microorganism, the slime mould *Physarum polycephalum*,

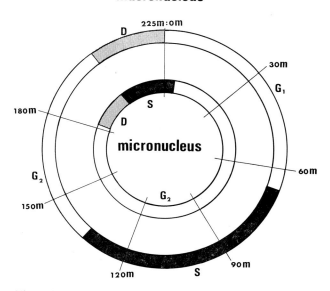

Fig. 4.10. The cell cycle in *Tetrahymena pyriformis*. D period of macro- or micro-nuclear division, S period of DNA synthesis in macro- or micronucleus. Time measured from the period of cell division (redrawn from FLICKINGER 1965).

there is a cell cycle of about 8 hours duration in which DNA synthesis is completed in the first 2 to 3 hr and the remainder of the cycle corresponds to a long G_2. In this organism, in contrast to *Tetrahymena*, mitochondrial DNA is replicated during a distinct period in the G_2 phase, a time quite separate from nuclear DNA replication (EVANS 1966).

DNA synthesis is extremely rapid during the early development of the sea urchin egg and the S phase is only 13 min at a temperature as low at 15 °C (HINEGARDNER et al. 1964). The complete cycle is 60 min long and the S phase begins as soon as the chromosomes have coalesced into a nucleus after mitosis, so that G_1 is negligible and G_2 is the longest phase of the cycle. In the grasshopper neuroblast on the other hand the longest phase is mitosis, the whole of interphase is occupied with DNA synthesis and there are no detectable G_1 or G_2 phases (GAULDEN 1956).

The interesting features that are common to all of the cell cycles, in both mammalian cells and microorganisms, are the control mechanisms which ensure the regularity of the cycles. Of these, very little is known at present, and this area is one in which studies should prove to be fruitful in the future.

References

BARRETT, J. C., 1966, J. Natl. Cancer Inst. *37*, 443

BASERGA, R., 1965, Can. Res. *25*, 581

BASERGA, R., and H. LISCO, 1963, J. Natl. Can. Inst. *31*, 1559

BENDER, M. A., and D. M. PRESCOTT, 1962, Exp. Cell Res. *27*, 221

BETTS, A., E. L. SEWALL, and R. TANGUAY, 1966, Cancer Res. *26*, 898

BRESCIANI, F., 1964, Science *146*, 653

CAIRNIE, A. B., L. F. LAMERTON, and G. G. STEEL, 1965, Exp. Cell Res. *39*, 528

CAMERON, I. L., 1964, J. Cell Biol. *20*, 185

CARLSON, J. G., and A. HOLLAENDER, 1948, J. Cell Comp. Physiol. *31*, 149

CAVE, M. D., 1966a, Hereditas *54*, 338

CAVE, M. D., 1966b, J. Cell Biol. *29*, 209

CHIGASAKI, H., 1963, Brain and Nerve *15*, 767

CHU, E. H. Y., 1965, Mutation Res. *2*, 75

CLEAVER, J. E., 1965, Exp. Cell Res. *39*, 697

CLEAVER, J. E., 1964, Ph.D. thesis, University of Cambridge

CRONE, M., E. LEVY, and H. PETERS, 1966, Exp. Cell Res. *39*, 678

DEFENDI, V., and L. A. MANSON, 1963, Nature *198*, 359

DENDY, P. P., and J. E. CLEAVER, 1964, Intern. J. Radiol. Biol. *8*, 301

DEWEY, W. C., and R. M. HUMPHREY, 1962, Radiation Res. *16*, 503

EDWARDS, J. L., A. L. KOCH, P. YOUCIS, H. L. FREESE, M. B. LAITE, and J. T. DONALD-SON, 1960, J. Biophys. Biochem. Cytol. *7*, 273

ENGELBERG, J., 1961, Exp. Cell Res. *23*, 218

EPIFANOVA, O. I., 1966, Exp. Cell Res. *42*, 562

EVANS, T. E., 1966, Biochem. Biophys. Res. Commun. *22*, 678

FLICKINGER, C. J., 1965, J. Cell Biol. *27*, 519

FRY, R. J. M., S. LESHER, and H. I. KOHN, 1961, Nature *191*, 290

FUJITA, S., 1962, Exp. Cell Res. *28*, 52

GALAVESI, G., and D. BOOTSMA, 1966, Exp. Cell Res. *41*, 438

GAULDEN, M. E., 1956, Genetics *41*, 645

GELFANT, S., 1962, Exp. Cell Res. *26*, 395

GELFANT, S., 1963, Exp. Cell Res. *32*, 521

GOLDFEDER, A., 1965, in Cellular Radiation Biology, Williams & Wilkins, Baltimore, p. 537

GRIEM, M. L., 1966, Nature *210*, 213

HAHN, G. M., and M. A. BAGSHAW, 1966, Science *151*, 459

HINEGARDNER, R. T., B. RAO, and D. E. FELDMAN, 1964, Exp. Cell Res. *36*, 53

HOF, J. VAN 'T, 1966, Exp. Cell Res. *41*, 274

HOWARD, A., and S. R. PELC, 1951, in Isotopes in biochemistry, G. E. W. Wolsten-holme, ed., Churchill, London, p. 138

HOWARD, A., and S. R. PELC, 1953, Heredity (suppl.) *6*, 261

KAUFFMAN, S. L., 1966, Exp. Cell Res. *42*, 67

KILLANDER, D., and A. ZETTERBERG, 1965, Exp. Cell Res. *38*, 272

KOBERG, E., 1963, in Cell proliferation, L. F. Lamerton and R. J. M. Fry, eds., Black-well, London, p. 62

LAJTHA, L. G., R. OLIVER, and F. ELLIS, 1954, Brit. J. Cancer *8*, 367

LAJTHA, L. G., R. OLIVER, and C. W. GURNEY, 1962, Brit. J. Haematol. *8*, 442

LALA, P. K., personal communication, unpublished results

LALA, P. K., and H. M. PATT, 1966, Proc. Natl. Acad. Sci. *56*, 1735

LALA, P. K., H. M. PATT, and M. A. MALONEY, 1966, Acta Haematol. *35*, 311

LENNARTZ, K. J., and W. MAURER, 1964, Z. Zellforsch. *63*, 478

LESHER, S., R. J. M. FRY, and H. I. KOHN, 1961, Exp. Cell Res. *24*, 334

LIEBERMAN, I., R. ABRAMS, N. HUNT, and P. OVE, 1963, J. Biol. Chem. *238*, 3955

LIPKIN, M., P. SHERLOCK, and B. M. BELL, 1962, Nature *195*, 175

LORAN, M. R., and T. T. CROCKER, 1963, J. Cell Biol. *19*, 285

MAALØE, O., and P. C. HANAWALT, 1961, J. Mol. Biol. *3*, 144

MACIEIRO-COELHO, A., J. PONTER, and L. PHILLIPSON, 1966, Exp. Cell Res. *42*, 673

MAK, S., 1965, Exp. Cell Res. *39*, 286

MALONEY, M. A., H. M. PATT, and C. L. WEBER, 1962, Nature *193*, 134

MATSUZAWA, T., and R. WILSON, 1964, in Mammalian radiation lethality, V. P. Bond, T. M. Fleidner, and J. O. Archambeau, eds., 1965, Academic Press, New York and London, p. 43

MCGRATH, R. A., W. M. LEACH, and J. A. CARLSON, 1965, Exp. Cell Res. *37*, 45

McQUADE, H. A., M. FRIEDKIN, and A. A. ATCHINSON, 1956, Exp. Cell Res. *11*, 249

MENDELSOHN, M. L., F. C. DOHAN, and H. A. MOORE, 1960, *25*, 447

MONESI, V., 1962, J. Cell Biol. *14*, 1

MOORHEAD, P. S., and V. DEFENDI, 1963, J. Cell Biol. 16, 202

ODARTCHENKO, N., H. COTTIER, and L. E. FEINENDEGEN, 1964, Exp. Cell Res. *35*, 402

PAINTER, R. B., and R. M. DREW, 1959, Lab. Invest. *8*, 278

PARSONS, J. A., 1965, J. Cell Biol. *25*, 641

PILGRIM, C. H., W. LANG, and W. MAURER, 1966, Exp. Cell Res. *44*, 129

PILGRIM, C. H., and W. MAURER, 1965, Exp. Cell Res. *37*, 183

POST, J., and J. HOFFMAN, 1964, Exp. Cell Res. *36*, 111

POST, J., and J. HOFFMAN, 1964, Exp. Cell Res. *37*, 183

POWELL, E. O., 1956, J. Gen. Microbiol. *15*, 492

PUCK, T. T., 1964, Cold Spr. Harb. Symp. Quant. Biol. 29, 167

PUCK, T. T., P. SAUNDERS, and D. PETERSEN, 1964, Biophys. J. *4*, 441

PUCK, T. T., and J. STEFFEN, 1963, Biophys. J. *3*, 379

PUJARA, C. M., 1964, Ph.D. thesis, University of Toronto

REDDAN, J. R., and H. ROTHSTEIN, 1966, J. Cell. Comp. Physiol. *67*, 307

REISKIN, A. B., and M. L. MENDELSOHN, 1964, Cancer Res. *24*, 1131

RIGAS, D. A., 1958, in Kinetics of cellular proliferation, F. Stohlman, Jr., ed., Grune and Stratton, New York and London, p. 408

SEED, J., 1963, Nature *198*, 147

SEED, J., 1966, J. Cell Biol. *28*, 233, 249, 257, 263

SHEA, S. N., 1964, Exp. Cell Res. *36*, 325

SHERMAN, F. G., H. QUASTLER, and D. R. WIMBER, 1961, Exp. Cell Res. *25*, 114

SISKEN, J. E., and L. MORASCA, 1965, J. Cell Biol. *25*, 179

SISKEN, J. E., L. MORASCA, and S. KIBBY, 1965, Exp. Cell Res. *39*, 103

SMITH, C. L., and P. P. DENDY, 1962, Nature *193*, 555

STANNERS, C. P., and J. E. TILL, 1960, Biochim. Biophys. Acta *37*, 406

STRYCKMANS, P., E. P. CRONKITE, J. FACHE, T. M. FLIEDNER, and J. RAMOS, 1966, Nature *211*, 717

STUBBLEFIELD, E , personal communication, see fig. 4.8

TAYLOR, E. W., 1965, J. Cell Biol. *25*, 145

TAYLOR, J. H., 1960, J. Biophys. Biochem. Cytol. *7*, 455

TERASIMA, T. and L. J. TOLMACH, 1963, Exp. Cell Res. *30*, 344

TOBEY, R. A., D. F. PETERSEN, E. C. ANDERSON, and T. T. PUCK, 1966, Biophys. J. *6*, 567

WALKER, P. M. B , and H. B. YATES, 1952, Proc. Roy. Soc. *B 140*, 274

WHITMORE, G. F., and J. E. TILL, 1964, Ann. Rev. Nucl. Sci, *14*, 347

WIMBER, D. E., 1963, in Cell proliferation, Vol. 1, L. F. Lamerton and R. J. M. Fry, eds., Blackwell, London

WIMBER, D. E., and H. QUASTLER, 1963, Exp. Cell Res. *30*, 8

WOLFSBERG, M. F., 1964, Exp. Cell Res. *35*, 119

ZEUTHEN, E., 1958, Advan. Med. Biol. Physics *6*, 37

ZEUTHEN, E., 1964, Synchrony in cell division and growth, J. Wiley and Sons, New York, London and Sydney

CHAPTER 5

The replication of DNA during interphase

5.1 Introduction

The S phase in mammalian cells which has been introduced in the preceding chapter is a phase in the cell cycle during which the whole genome of the cell is replicated, but this replication does not procede uniformly throughout the nucleus at a steady rate. DNA molecules are replicated at definite locations in the nucleus and at definite times in S, and the rate of replication varies according to location and the time in question. Details of this fine structure in the S phase will be discussed in this chapter, after an initial description of some of the contributions that H³Tdr studies have made to theories of the mechanism of DNA replication.

5.2 Replication of bacterial and mammalian DNA

Some of the most dramatic and visually satisfying studies of DNA replication that used H³Tdr or H³-thymine are those of CAIRNS (1961–1963). *E. coli* (CAIRNS 1962, 1963) DNA was fully labelled by growing the bacteria for several generations in H³-thymine. The cells were then lysed gently by dialysis against sodium dodecyl sulphate in order to release all of the DNA gently, without subjecting the molecule to damaging shear forces. From the lysate, CAIRNS obtained intact labelled DNA molecules and an example of an autoradiograph of one of these molecules is shown in fig. 5.1. Several conclusions were reached concerning the structure and manner of replication of the bacterial DNA molecule from such autoradiographs:

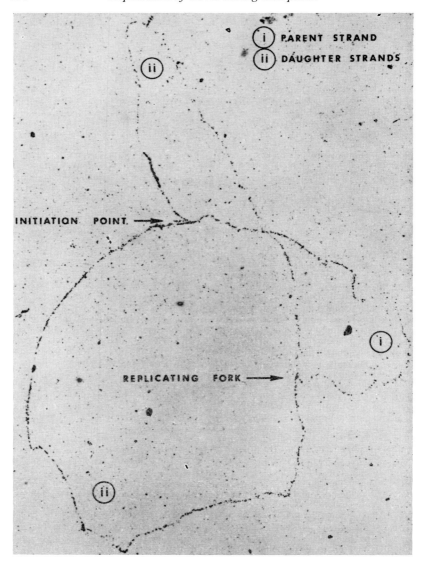

Fig. 5.1. Autoradiograph showing a duplicating chromosome from the bacterium *Escherichia coli* which had been labelled for two generations in H³-thymine, × 480 (reproduced from CAIRNS, Scientific American, January 1966).

(1) The bacterial chromosome consists of a single piece of DNA that is 700 to 900 μ in length.

(2) The chromosomes of both *E. coli* B3 and K12(Hfr) are circles.

(3) DNA replicates by means of a single fork and the ends of the molecule are joined during replication.

(4) In *E. coli* which normally has a generation time of 20 min, the replication fork must traverse the molecule at a rate of between 20 and 30 μ per min. Since the polynucleotide chains of the DNA helix make one complete turn for every 34 Å along the axis of the molecule it is necessary for the molecule to rotate at about 7,000 rpm at this rate of replication.

These observations supported the original Watson and Crick model for DNA replication which postulated a simultaneous unwinding and replication of the DNA at a site that progresses along the molecule (WATSON and CRICK 1953a-c). Since the distal ends of the molecule are joined during replication in *E. coli*, CAIRNS (1963) has suggested that this region, at which replication both starts and finishes, has a special role in controlling replication. It is envisaged as being analogous to a swivel mechanism that drives the rotation of the molecule, but the molecular mechanism involved is unknown.

Following these experiments of Cairns, similar experiments have been performed successfully which used mammalian cells. HUBERMAN and RIGGS (1966) obtained autoradiographs of DNA extracted from Chinese hamster cells and some of these revealed labelled molecules up to 1.8 mm in length. CAIRNS (1966) obtained autoradiographs of HeLa cell DNA in which the molecules were at least 0.5 mm in length after 24 hr in H^{3}Tdr. The replication rate in these cells was found to be approximately 0.5 μ per min, a rate considerably slower than that of *E. coli* (see (4) above). This rate of replication is too slow for replication to be completed within the 6 to 8 hr of the S phase by means of a single replication site on each chromosome. From CAIRNS' (1966) data, at least 100 separate replication sites on each chromosome are required throughout the S phase.

An estimate of the number of replication sites in mammalian cells has also been made by PAINTER et al. (1966) who used a technique completely different from that of Cairns. Painter et al. first labelled HeLa cells with H^{3}Tdr and subsequently labelled the cells with C^{14}BUdr. At the end of the C^{14}BUdr labelling period the cells were disrupted and the DNA extracted in fragments. Of these fragments, those which had densities

intermediate between hybrid and normal DNA and were labelled both with
H³ and C¹⁴ were the ones which contained the replication sites at the
time of the change from H³Tdr to C¹⁴BUdr. From the fraction of the
total DNA which was double-labelled and of intermediate density the
number of replicating sites per nucleus was estimated at between 10³ to
10⁴ per nucleus. If each replicating unit of DNA contains only one replication site then the upper limit of the molecular weight is about 10¹⁰ daltons.
The replicating units of DNA may be referred to as 'replicons', after the
definition employed in *E. coli* by JACOB and BRENNER (1963), and although
this term is useful it refers to an entity which is only vaguely defined and
not clearly identified experimentally in mammalian cells.

5.3 Mechanism of DNA replication

The observations of Cairns (fig. 5.1) in *E. coli* have been interpreted in
terms of a single replication site that proceeds in a single direction along
the molecule. The chemical bonds involved in the individual polynucleotide chains, however, confer distinct chemical directions to both chains

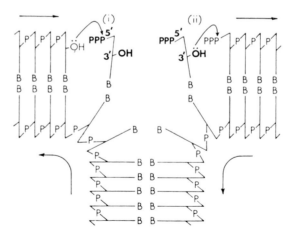

Fig. 5.2. Scheme of DNA replication indicating the two mechanisms involved in
synthesis of the antiparallel polynucleotide chains. B purine or pyrimidine base, P
phosphate group, PPP-OH-B nucleoside triphosphate, arrows indicate the direction of
the polynucleotide chains (reproduced from KEIR 1965).

which are antiparallel to one another (fig. 5.2, JOSSE et al. 1961). Replication in a single physical direction consequently necessitates replication of
the two chains in opposite chemical directions. One chain is synthesised
from the 5′ to the 3′ end (reaction (i)) whereas the other is synthesised from
the 3′ to the 5′ end (reaction (ii)). This poses certain problems in attempts
to understand the mechanism of replication in vivo, because the enzyme
DNA polymerase only appears to be able to perform one of these reactions
in vitro. When DNA synthesis occurs in vitro using the enzyme, substrates
and primer DNA, the action of DNA polymerase is commonly considered
to be by means of the attachment of a nucleoside 5′ triphosphate to the 3′
hydroxyl end of a polynucleotide chain with the release of pyrophosphate
(reaction (i) in fig. 5.2, see for example KORNBERG 1962; SMELLIE 1965).
Because of the apparent inadequacy of DNA polymerase for both of the
reaction steps required for DNA replication there is a possibility that a
totally different, and unknown, enzyme or set of enzymes is responsible
for DNA replication in vivo. The DNA polymerase that is known at present
may then be the enzyme that synthesises pieces of single-stranded poly-
nucleotides during repair of damaged DNA and recombination (HOWARD-
FLANDERS and BOYCE 1964; MESELSON 1964). At present, however, these
speculations have little substance, and DNA polymerase is the only DNA
synthesizing enzyme that has been identified.

The mechanisms involved in the synthesis of the two polynucleotide
chains are not, however, fundamentally different. Both mechanisms result
in the formation of a phosphodiester bond between the 5′ and 3′ positions
on the deoxyribose portions of the nucleosides. The difference is that in
one case the 5′ side of the bond originates from the free nucleoside triphosphate (reaction (i), fig. 5.2), and in the other from the terminal
nucleoside triphosphate of the polynucleotide chain (reaction (ii), fig. 5.2).
If one enzyme can perform the former reaction (i), then it would seem that
the same or a similar enzyme should also be able to perform the latter (ii).
This would not be true if there were, for example, stereochemical restrictions in the region of replication or in the active site of DNA polymerase
that favoured one reaction at the expense of the other. An alternative
possibility may be that reaction (ii), involving a 5′ triphosphate, does
not occur in vivo. In its place, there may be a reaction between an 3′
nucleoside triphosphate and a 5′ OH terminal of the polynucleotide chain
(SMELLIE 1965). The existence of 3′ nucleoside triphosphates has been

discussed in ch. 2 § 2, and although very little is known about them at present they may play an important role in DNA replication.

Since the sites of synthesis of the two polynucleotide chains are very close to one another the replication of the DNA molecule may be achieved by a single enzyme system. This system may then include a polymerase that has several similar subunits with at least two active centers such that both polynucleotide chains can be replicated at the same time. The DNA polymerase that has been extracted from bacterial and mammalian cells may be a subunit of this in vivo enzyme (KEIR 1965). In bacteria the enzyme system responsible for replication is attached to a point on the inside of the cell membrane (JACOB et al. 1963, 1966; GANESAN and LEDERBERG 1965). The site of replication is consequently stationary with respect to the cell and the DNA molecule passes through this site during replication. In insect and mammalian cells the DNA is attached to many points on the inside of the nuclear membrane (DUPRAW 1965a,b, 1966) but it is not yet possible to identify the sites of replication with these points or any other specific locations within the nucleus.

5.4 *Structural and temporal organisation of interphase DNA replication*

The interphase nucleus is far less rich in structural detail than the cytoplasm, and studies in its structure by light and electron microscopy have been much less informative than similar studies on the cytoplasm. Several major regions of the nucleus can be identified at both the light and electron microscope levels and H³Tdr autoradiography has contributed to our understanding of the replication of DNA in these regions.

The typical interphase nucleus contains a clearly defined organelle, the nucleolus, which contains predominantly RNA and protein and only a small amount of DNA. The DNA and nucleoprotein in the nucleus itself is organised in a extremely complex manner which is quite unknown at present. In a study of H³Tdr labelling in the regenerating limb buds of amphibian larvae, with electron microscope autoradiographs, REVEL and HAY (1961) and HAY and REVEL (1963) have been able to distinguish two components of the nucleus (see fig. 1.5). One component consisted of finely textured material which was distributed throughout the nucleus, around the nucleolus, around the inside of the nuclear membrane, and in mitotic chromosomes. This material had dimensions of 50 to 75 Å and was labelled with H^{3}Tdr and consequently contained the DNA. The other component of the nucleus was coarser in structure, with dimensions of 300 to 400 Å, was not labelled with H^{3}Tdr, and consequently contained nuclear RNA and protein.

Two different states of DNA in the nucleus have been recognized for over half a century, those of euchromatin and of heterochromatin (see review by BROWN 1966). These states differ in their staining reactions, in their degree of coiling, and also in their functions and replication. Euchromatin is active in supporting RNA synthesis and contains genes that actively express their information content. It stains relatively lightly with basic dyes and the Feulgen reaction during interphase and consists of loosely coiled fibres. Heterochromatin, on the other hand, appears to contain DNA in which the genetic information is repressed; it supports RNA synthesis to a lesser extent than euchromatin, stains relatively darkly with basic dyes and the Feulgen reaction during interphase, and consists of tightly coiled fibers. The distinction between these two states of DNA is not absolute, since heterochromatin contains a few active genes, though far fewer than euchromatin (HANNAH 1951). Some of the genetic information in heterochromatin may be required for embryonic development and is repressed in all the cells of the adult animal (BROWN 1966). In addition, different parts of the genome may be repressed in cells with different functions in the adult animal, and only the DNA containing the genetic information relevant to a particular tissue would be euchromatic.

Euchromatin and heterochromatin are replicated during the S phase at distinct times in many organisms. In the spermatocytes of the grasshopper, *Melanoplus*, for example, there is a distinct region of the nucleus that is heterochromatic. The euchromatin is replicated early in the S phase whereas the heterochromatic region is replicated late (LIMA-DE-FARIA 1959). During the middle part of S the replication periods of the two types of chromatin overlap. A similar replication sequence can also be observed in the leaf nuclei of *Secale* (LIMA-DE-FARIA 1959), in *Vicia* root tips and in cells of the mouse bone marrow and thymus (EVANS 1964). In cells of most female mammals one of the X chromosomes is completely heterochromatic throughout the cell cycle and is identified as the Barr body in interphase (BARR 1949, 1959; see reviews in MOORE 1966). The Barr body

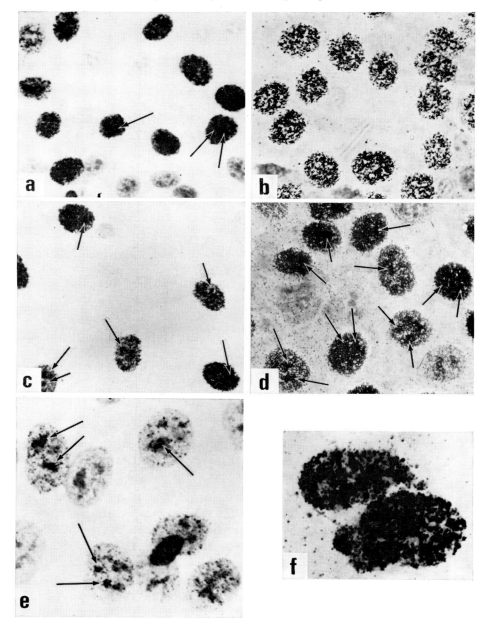

replicates at the end of the S phase (ATKINS et al. 1962) and the role of this body and the X chromosomes will be discussed in detail in the following chapter (ch. 6 §§ 2, 3; fig. 6.1).

In tissue cultures both euchromatin and heterochromatin are usually distributed throughout the nucleus and it is difficult to distinguish them clearly in autoradiographic studies of DNA replication. Some heterochromatin is associated with the nucleolus and with the nuclear membrane, and these regions are replicated late in the S phase, in the same way as the more distinct regions of heterochromatin in *Melanoplus*, *Secale* and *Vicia*, referred to above. In human leucocyte cultures, for example, three patterns of H³Tdr incorporation have been observed (RIBAS-MUNDO 1966), depending on the stage in S of the labelled cell. DNA replication during the early part of S was observed as diffuse labelling over the whole nucleus with the exception of the nucleolus. In the middle of S labelling was over both nucleus and nucleolus, and at the end of S heterochromatin in the nucleus and around the nucleolus was labelled.

In a study made by KASTEN and STRASSER (1966) the use of synchronised cultures enabled them to resolve details of the DNA replication sequences in greater detail than was possible in many of the experiments described

---

Fig. 5.3. Untreated or synchronised CMP cells exposed to H³Tdr at 12.5 μCi/ml, 6.7 Ci/mmole, for 1 hr, fixed in acetic alcohol 1:3 (v/v) and washed in 5% TCA at 5 °C for 15 min. Developed AR10 autoradiographs stained with haematoxylin and eosin and photographed by bright field (a to d × 480, e and f × 800).
(a) Randomly growing control cells, intense H³Tdr incorporation into nuclear DNA. A few nucleoli also appear labelled (arrows) in addition to nucleolar associated chromatin.
(b) Synchronised cells in the very early S phase (1 to 2 hr) demonstrate uniform DNA synthesis throughout the nucleus. There is no apparent DNA synthesis in nucleoli (phase contrast).
(c) During early S (3 to 4 hr) the first nucleolar DNA fraction is synthesised (arrows) and this synthesis is superimposed on extranucleolar DNA synthesis.
(d) Preferential H³Tdr incorporation is demonstrated into a second intranucleolar DNA fraction (5 to 6 hr) (phase contrast).
(e) Specific and exclusive replication of the second intranucleolar DNA fraction and its associated chromatin is revealed in several nuclei (6 to 7 hr).
(f) Synthesis of heterochromatin is indicated in these nuclei where prominent heteropyknotic blocks are heavily labelled in the late S phase (7 to 8 hr). (From KASTEN and STRASSER 1966).

above. Cultures of human epithelial adenocarcinoma (CMP) cells were synchronised with a double block of excess Tdr (see ch. 3 § 13). After release of the block, cultures were labelled for 1 hr at intervals through the S phase and then fixed immediately. Some examples of the labelling patterns that were obtained at various stages of S are shown in fig. 5.3 and are summarised in table 5.1. DNA replication in the nucleus and nucleolus occurred in two waves separated by a short interval about midway through S when replication almost ceased (fig. 5.4). At the end of S replication declined slowly and label tended to be localised over hetero-chromatic regions. RNA synthesis was also studied at different stages of S by labelling similar cultures with H³-uridine for 1 hr immediately before fixation. RNA synthesis in the nucleus remained at a uniformly high level throughout S except for a sharp drop at the time of the first wave of DNA replication. In the region of the nucleolus, RNA synthesis stopped com-pletely during the first wave of nucleolar DNA replication but was un-affected by the second wave. KASTEN and STRASSER (1966) interpreted these two waves of DNA replication in terms of the early replication of euchromatin and late replication of heterochromatin. The fall in RNA

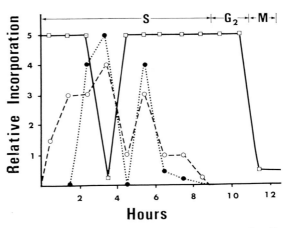

Fig. 5.4. Graphical summary of the relative incorporation of radioactive specific precursors into RNA and DNA of synchronised cells. Data are based on visual estimates of developed grains in autoradiographs and are presented to illustrate the dramatic changes in nucleic acid patterns. —□—□— RNA (H³ uridine), --○--○-- chromatin DNA (H³Tdr), ---●---●--- nucleolar DNA (H³Tdr). (KASTEN and STRASSER 1966, redrawn).

TABLE 5.1

Labelling patterns in regions of the nucleus and nucleolus of synchronised CMP cells (labelled with H^3Tdr for 1 hr at 12.5 μCi/ml 6.7 Ci/mmole or H^3 uridine for 1 hr at 20 μCi/ml 4.42 Ci/mmole KASTEN and STRASSER 1966).

Time from start of S (hr)	Labelling patterns	
	RNA (uridine)	DNA (thymidine)
0–2	Uniform	Uniform over whole nucleus except for nucleolus, intensity increasing with time.
2–3	Low	Uniform labelling of nucleus, nucleoli slightly labelled.
3–4	Very low (nucleus) unlabelled (nucleolus)	Uniform labelling of nucleus, nucleoli strongly labelled. Intensity of nucleolar labelling higher than nuclear.
4–5	Uniform	Nuclear labelling decreased from that at earlier times, nucleolus unlabelled.
5–6	Uniform	Increase in both nuclear and nucleolar labelling and synthesis of a second distinct nucleolar DNA fraction.
6–7	Uniform	Uniform labelling of nucleus, decline of nucleolar labelling.
7–8	Uniform	Slow decline in DNA synthesis at end of S and labelling especially marked over heterochromatin, as judged by clumping of silver grains over heteropyknotic blocks of chromatin.

synthesis during the first wave of DNA replication then occurs because individual molecules of DNA in euchromatic regions of the nucleus cannot replicate and support RNA synthesis at the same time. Since DNA in heterochromatic regions is repressed the second wave of DNA replication has no effect on RNA synthesis. In this interpretation the first wave of nucleolar DNA replication consequently represents the replication of intranucleolar DNA molecules which support RNA synthesis in the nucleolus, whereas the second wave represents mainly the replication of nucleolar associated heterochromatin.

The distinction between early and late replicating DNA in tissue cultures is maintained through several successive divisions. Those molecules which replicate early in S during one cell cycle replicate early in every cycle; those which replicate late in one cycle replicate late in every cycle (MUELLER and MATHIEU 1966; BRAUN et al. 1965). This means that DNA of cells in culture maintains its euchromatic or heterochromatic state through many divisions. In other systems this is not always the case, because the processes of differentiation involve the controlled activation or repression of various regions of the genome. In *Melanoplus*, for example, one of the X chromosomes of the female is repressed just before the final premeiotic interphase and becomes late labelling at this stage (NICKLAS and JACQUA 1965).

The giant chromosomes found in *Diptera* are a unique example of chromosomes that are visible as structural units during interphase and these contain DNA in alternate dark and light bands. In the dark bands, the DNA is tightly coiled while in the light bands the DNA is stretched in parallel arrays along the axis of the chromosome (MACINNES and URETZ 1966). During the development of polyteny there is little replication of heterochromatin (RUDKIN 1965) and the chromosomes increase in size by successive rounds of replication in euchromatin alone, without the intervention of heterochromatin replication or mitosis. The replication of DNA occurs at numerous sites simultaneously and the chromosomes appear to consist of linear array of independent replicons (PLAUT 1963; PLAUT and NASH 1964; PLAUT et al. 1966; see also references cited by the latter workers). In one set of experiments, PLAUT et al. (1966) identified approximately 30 replicons in about 15% of the chromosome length in *D. melanogaster*, but there is no reason to assume a uniform distribution of replicons throughout the whole set of chromosomes, or that autoradiograph methods can resolve them all completely.

Since heterochromatic DNA is repressed it might be expected that damage to this portion of the genome would have less effect on cell survival than similar damage to euchromatic DNA. Although many experiments have been performed which demonstrate a variation in the sensitivity of cells to irradiation as a function of the stage in the cell cycle at which they were irradiated, the results are conflicting and do not allow a simple comparison to be made between the sensitivity of early and late replicating DNA (see discussions by TOLMACH et al. 1963). One experiment, involving the effect of substituting BUdr for Tdr as a DNA precursor on cell survival, does appear to demonstrate that damage to late replicating DNA is less harmful to a cell than damage to early replicating DNA (KAJIWARA and MUELLER 1964). In these experiments synchronised HeLa cells were allowed to incorporate BUdr into DNA either during the early part of S or during late S. Cell survival was reduced if BUdr was incorporated during the early part of S but not when incorporated during late S.

5.5 *Variations in the rate of DNA replication during the S phase*

It is a common experience that the grain counts in autoradiographs of mammalian cells labelled with H^3Tdr varies widely among the cells of the population (see ch. 1 § 10, fig. 1.7). This was first clearly stated by LAJTHA et al. (1960) in an analysis of grain count distributions produced by a number of different radioactive isotopes. These workers showed that if the rate of incorporation of an isotope into the cells of a population was the same for each cell then the main source of variation in grain counts would be the randomness of radioactive decay and the distribution of grain counts would be close to a Poisson distribution. If there was a variation in the rate of incorporation of the isotope then the grain count distribution would be wider than a Poisson distribution. Human lymphocytes labelled with S^{35} gave a grain distribution which was close to a Poisson distribution, but in the case of basophilic normoblasts labelled with Fe^{59}, human bone marrow cells labelled with C^{14} formate, and mouse ascites cells and thymocytes labelled with H^3Tdr the distributions were considerably wider than a Poisson distribution. On the basis of the grain count distributions obtained with cells labelled with C^{14} formate or H^3Tdr LAJTHA et al. (1960) concluded that the rate of incorporation of these precursors into DNA varied by a factor of 5 between individual cells in the populations. Asynchronous cell populations were used in these studies and the results were interpreted in terms of a varying rate of DNA replication as individual cells progressed through the cell cycle.

Since there are numerous sites of DNA replication in the nucleus (see ch. 5 § 2) the rate of replication that is measured by the grain count over a nucleus will be an average value which represents the rate of increase of DNA per nucleus per unit time. A variation in the number of sites or in the rate of replication at individual sites will in either case give rise to a variation in the average rate of DNA replication in the nucleus as a whole. These two alternatives cannot be distinguished at present and in the remainder of this chapter experiments will be described in which the average rate of replication in the nucleus has been studied as a function of the position of cells in the S phase. Techniques that have been used to determine the position of cells in S in such experiments include time lapse photography (SEED 1962, 1963), determination of the DNA content of individual cells from their Feulgen dye content (DENDY and CLEAVER 1964), determination of the time taken for labelled cells to reach mitosis after a pulse of H³Tdr (KOBERG and MAURER 1962; CLEAVER 1964) and the use of synchronised cultures (KASTEN and STRASSER 1966). Two of these methods will be described in detail in the following sections.

5.6 Combined autoradiography and Feulgen staining

The typical experimental procedure in this method is to label cultures for a brief period (say 10 to 30 min), fix immediately, and after staining with the Feulgen reaction the grain count over individual cells can be correlated with the Feulgen dye content of the same cell (DENDY and CLEAVER 1964). The latter can be determined with a microspectrophotometer (see also ch. 4 § 8) and is proportional to the DNA content of the cell measured, while the former is proportional to the rate of DNA replication (see ch. 8 § 1). If the rate of DNA replication varies as cells progress through the S phase then the position of a cell in S as determined by its Feulgen dye content (i.e., in terms of the fraction of DNA synthesised) is not exactly comparable to the position determined by time lapse photography (i.e., in terms of the time spent in S). The middle of S in time, for example, may not correspond exactly to replication of half of the DNA of the cell. However, although it is necessary to keep this difference in mind, it does not result in any conflict between the sequence of the events detected by Feulgen staining and time lapse photography.

An example of results obtained by this method with cultures of mouse L strain cells is shown in fig. 5.5. In fig. 5.5 (top) the grain count over individual cells has been plotted against their DNA content, and in fig. 5.5 (bottom) the grain counts have been averaged at intervals through the range of DNA values. In this experiment the cultures were labelled with H³Tdr for 10 min and the fixed immediately, so each grain count represents the rate of DNA replication at the position in the S phase corresponding to the DNA content of the fixed cell. These results indicate that there is an increase in the rate of DNA replication as cells progress toward the end of S, and in this case the maximum rate is between 2 and 3 times the initial rate. Although it appears that replication begins at a slow rate but

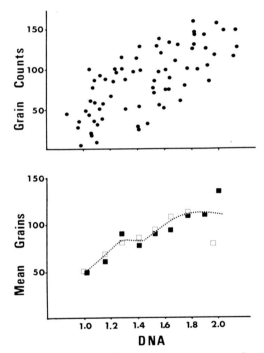

Fig. 5.5.   Grain counts over individual mouse L strain cells as a function of their DNA content (expressed in terms of the telophase DNA content as 1.0, the prophase DNA content as 2.0). Cultures were labelled with H³Tdr for 10 min immediately before fixation. Top: ● 5 μCi/ml, 2 Ci/mmole; bottom: ▣ 5 μCi/ml, 2 Ci/mmole, □ 50 μCi/ml, 0.2 Ci/mmole, grain counts averaged at intervals through S phase (CLEAVER 1964).

then cuts off sharply at the end of S this method does not resolve changes in rate clearly at either end of S because the DNA content of cells at these times are very close to the G_1 or G_2 DNA contents. The resolution of changes in the rate of replication at these times can be improved by using time lapse photography to determine the position of cells in S. In such experiments with HeLa, L or human fibroblasts, SEED (1962) observed that the onset of replication occurred gradually, reached a maximum rate in the latter half of S and cut off sharply at the end. (These conclusions are reached on examination of the published data but were not stated explicitly by Seed). A similar increase in the rate of replication has been observed in a number of cell types by this method and include, in vitro, rat heart fibroblasts (CLEAVER 1964), human lymphocytes, normal leuco-cytes and leukemic leucocytes (HALE et al. 1965) and, in vivo, cells of the mouse seminal vesicle (GALL and JOHNSON 1960) and the regenerating rat liver (HALE et al. 1965).

As may be seen in fig. 5.5 (top) there is considerable variation in grain counts even for cells with the same DNA content. Although in some cases this variation is due only to random radioactive decay and corresponds to a Poisson variation (see ch. 8 § 2), the variation is often wider than a Poisson and may indicate a variation in the rate at which individual cells progress through the S phase in addition to the trend to higher rates in cells in the latter half of S. The variation between individual cells is occasionally so great as to preclude any correlation being made between the rate of replication and the position of cells in S (HALE et al. 1965; SEED 1962).

5.7 *Pulse chase experiments and mitotic grain counts*

This experimental method is identical to that used in determining the durations of the phases of the cell cycle (see ch. 4 § 5) and affords a simple way of estimating the rate of replication in various parts of S. The grain counts over labelled mitotic figures of cells fixed at various times after a brief exposure to H^3Tdr, can be used as a measure of the rate of replica-tion at the time when those particular cells incorporated H^3Tdr. Cells in mitosis at time t, say, will be those which were exposed to H^3Tdr at a time $t-(G_2+\frac{1}{2}t_m)$. Several precautions are necessary in this method in order to obtain reliable results. First, the pulse of H³Tdr must be short and not prolonged by a labelled pool that remains in the cells after the removal of the external label (see ch. 3 § 5) and second, the mitotic figures must be flattened to minimize the self absorption of H³ β-particles. The latter is particularly important in tissue cultures because mitotic cells are spherical and have a very high self absorption unless flattened. This flattening can be achieved by a slight modification of the normal method for karyotype analysis, such as a treatment of the cultures with colchicine and a hypotonic solution for the 10 or 15 min immediately before fixation and air drying (CLEAVER 1964).

Some results that were obtained with mouse L strain cells are shown in fig. 5.6. This is the same cell type as was used with the previous method (ch. 5 § 6, fig. 5.5) and it can be seen that these results also show that there is an increase in the rate of DNA replication as cells progress through the S phase, with the maximum rate being reached in middle and late S. In this case a labelled pool did remain in the cells for a few hours after the end of the 10-min pulse of H³Tdr and caused an increase in the mean interphase grain count. The effect of this pool on the grain counts over mitoses is to overestimate the replication rate in those cells which were in S during the whole life time of the labelled pool and to under estimate the rate of replication in early and late S and in those cells which started or completed replication during the life time of the pool. This effect will alter the details of the mitotic grain count curve and tend to smooth out any variations which occur within S. This does not, however, alter the general conclusion of an increase in the rate of replication as cells progress through the S phase.

A pulse chase experiment performed using a single injection of H³Tdr may also be employed to study the rate of DNA replication in vivo since the availability time of H³Tdr is less than 1 hr and there will be no complications owing to a long-lived pool (see ch. 2 § 7). KOBERG and MAURER (1962) obtained results with this method which indicate that the rate of replication in the mouse intestinal epithelium is constant throughout the S phase, while in cells of the human bone marrow the rate varies and reaches maximum at about the middle of the S phase (STRYCKMANS et al. 1966). In cells of the root tip of *Vicia faba*, however, two maxima in the replication have been observed, one in early S and the other in late S, with a decreased rate in mid S (HOWARD and DEWEY 1961). Similar variations in

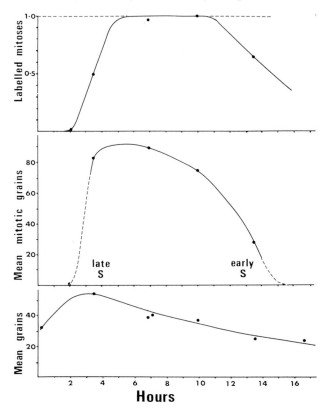

Fig. 5.6. Fraction of labelled mitoses (top), mean grain counts over spread mitoses (centre), and mean interphase grain count (bottom) as a function of time after a 10-min pulse label with H³Tdr (5 μCi/ml, 2 Ci/mmole) for mouse L strain cells. Cultures were grown in unlabelled Tdr at 10⁻⁵ M after the pulse label. Different exposure times were used in the autoradiographs for the centre and bottom diagrams (CLEAVER 1964).

the rate of replication have been observed with synchronized cultures. TERASIMA and TOLMACH (1963) using HeLa cells and KASTEN and STRASSER (1966) using CMP-strain cells both observed a variation in the replication rate with the maximum occurring about midway through the S phase. The latter experiments have already been described earlier in this chapter (ch. 5 § 4) and the rate of replication was found to fall sharply to a low value for a brief interval in mid S, with maxima in the replication rate before and after this fall. The method used for synchronisation in this experiment involved the double Tdr block (ch. 3 § 13) and after release of the block DNA replication begins in the presence of a large unlabelled pool of Tdr phosphates, so details in the variations of H³Tdr incorporation into DNA shown in fig. 5.4 may initially be confused by this pool (DREW and COMMERFORD 1967). This effect however does not invalidate the general conclusions concerning the fluctuating rate of DNA replication after the initial hours of S have passed and the pool declined to a negligible value.

5.8 A replicon model for the DNA in mammalian cells

Although the results obtained in the studies of DNA replication vary from one another in details, two main conclusions may be reached on which there is little disagreement. First, euchromatin is replicated early and heterochromatin late in the S phase and, second, the rate of DNA replication varies as cells progress through the S phase, in a manner that may depend on the cell type. There seems to be no obvious a priori for the replication of these two chromatin types in the observed sequence rather than the reverse. The tight coiling of heterochromatin may require a longer time to unwind than euchromatin, and this could cause heterochromatin to be later replicating than euchromatin. This explanation, however, assumes that DNA must be extended and uncoiled during replication and the state of DNA during replication has not yet been established. At the very least it is clear from the observations that not all possible sites in the nucleus undergo replication simultaneously. Consequently, it seems easier to envisage a mechanism by which the rate of replication in the nucleus as a whole varies on account of a variation in the number of sites which are replicating at each moment, rather than a variation in the actual rate of DNA replication along individual replicons. An illustration of this mechanism is shown in fig. 5.7 for a hypothetical nucleus with only 4 identical replicons. A mammalian cell nucleus described by a model with 10^3 to 10^4 replicons (PAINTER et al. 1966) is obviously capable of extensive variations of the type illustrated and could easily result in variations in the rate of replication in the nucleus, as a whole, as cells progress through the S phase. There is no experimental basis for assuming that all of the replicons are identical in size and additional asynchrony in

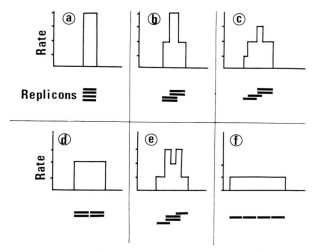

Fig. 5.7. A model of DNA replication in a nucleus containing 4 identical replicons. In each case the lower illustration shows the replication sequence and the upper the rate of replication in the nucleus as a whole at times during the S phase. The duration of S depends on the degree of synchrony between the replicons, each of which replicate in a time t. (a), (d), and (f) synchronous replication, S $= t$, $2t$, or $4t$ respectively (e.g. mouse intestinal epithelium). (b) asynchronous replication, S lies between t and $2t$, maximum replication rate in mid S (e.g. human bone marrow). (c) asynchronous replication, S $= 2t$, maximum replication rate in last half of S (e.g. mouse L strain). (e) asynchronous replication, S lies between $2t$ and $3t$, replication rate passes through two maxima (e.g. *Vicia* root tips, human CMP strain). See text, ch. 5 § 7 for examples cited.

replication could then arise on account of the different times required for replication. In some regions of the giant polytene chromosomes of *Chironomus* (PELLING 1966) or *Drosophila* (PLAUT et al. 1966), for example, replication appears to begin on a number of bands simultaneously but end at different times for each band, and these may be examples in which there are replicons of various sizes within the same nucleus. The asynchrony between different replicons that is assumed in the model in fig. 5.7 would be observed as asynchronous replication between segments of chromosomes and this is discussed in ch. 6 § 2. The major problem raised by a model such as this is the means whereby each replicon is controlled. The discovery of specific control proteins in *E. coli* (LARK and LARK 1963) is an indication of the type of control mechanism that may be anticipated in mammalian cells.

References

ATKINS, L., P. D. TAFT and K. P. DALAL, 1962, J. Cell Biol. *15*, 390
BARR, M. L., 1959, Nature *163*, 676
BARR, M. L., 1959, Science *130*, 679
BRAUN, R., C. MITTERMAYER and H. P. RUSCH, 1965, Proc. Natl. Acad. Sci. *53*, 924
BROWN, S. W., 1966, Science *151*, 417
CAIRNS, J., 1961, J. Mol. Biol. *3*, 756
CAIRNS, J., 1962, J. Mol. Biol. *4*, 407
CAIRNS, J., 1963, J. Mol. Biol. *6*, 208
CAIRNS, J., 1966, J. Mol. Biol. *15*, 372
CLEAVER, J. E., 1964, Ph. D. thesis, University of Cambridge
DENDY, P. E., and J. E. CLEAVER, 1964, Intern. J. Radiation Biol. *8*, 301
DREW, R. M., and S. L. COMMERFORD, 1967, Rad. Res. *30*, 455
DUPRAW, E. J., 1965a, Proc. Natl. Acad. Sci. *53*, 161
DUPRAW, E. J., 1965b, Nature *206*, 338
DUPRAW, E. J., 1966, Nature *209*, 577
EVANS, H. J., 1964, Exp. Cell Res. *35*, 381
GALL, J. G., and W. W. JOHNSON, 1960, J. Biophys. Biochem. Cytol. *7*, 657
GANESAN, A. T., and J. LEDERBERG, 1965, Biochem. Biophys. Res. Commun. *18*, 824
HALE, A. J., E. H. COOPER, and J. D. MILTON, 1965, Brit. J. Haematol. *11*, 144
HANNAH, A., 1951, Advan. Genet. *4*, 87
HAY, E. D., and J. P. REVEL, 1963, J. Cell Biol. *16*, 29
HOWARD, A., and D. L. DEWEY, 1961, Exp. Cell Res. *24*, 623
HOWARD-FLANDERS, P., and R. P. BOYCE, 1964, Genetics *50*, 256
HUBERMAN, J. A., and A. D. RIGGS, 1966, Proc. Natl. Acad. Sci. *55*, 599
JACOB, F., and S. BRENNER, 1963, C. R. Acad. Sci. Paris *256*, 298
JACOB, F., S. BRENNER, and F. CUZIN, 1963, Cold Spr. Harb. Symp. Quant. Biol. *28*, 329
JACOB, F., A. RYTER, and F. CUZIN, 1966, Proc. Roy. Soc. *B 164*, 267
JOSSE, J., A. D. KAISER, and A. KORNBERG, 1961, J. Biol. Chem. *236*, 864
KAJIWARA, K., and G. C. MUELLER, 1964, Biochim. Biophys. Acta *91*, 486
KASTEN, F. H., and F. F. STRASSER, 1966, Nature *211*, 135
KEIR, H. M., 1965, in Progress in nucleic acid research and molecular biology *4*, J. N. Davidson and W. E. Cohn, eds., Academic Press, New York and London, p. 81
KOBERG, E., and W. E. MAURER, 1962, Biochim. Biophys. Acta *61*, 229
KORNBERG, A., 1962, Enzymatic synthesis of DNA, Wiley, New York
LAJTHA, L. G., R. OLIVER, R. J. BERRY, and E. HELL, 1960, Nature *187*, 919
LARK, C., and K. G. LARK, 1963, J. Mol. Biol. *10*, 120
LIMA-DE-FARIA, A., 1959, J. Biophys. Biochem. Cytol. *6*, 457
MACINNES, J. W., and R. B. URETZ, 1966, Science, *151*, 689
MESELSON, M., 1964, J. Mol. Biol. *9*, 734

MOORE, K. L., ed., 1966, The sex chromatin, W. B. Saunders and Co., Philadelphia and London

MUELLER, G. C., and M. LE MATHIEU, 1966, Biochim. Biophys. Acta *114*, 108

NICKLAS, R. B., and R. A. JAQUA, 1965, Science, *147*, 1041

PAINTER, R. B., D. A. JERMANY, and R. E. RASMUSSEN, 1966, J. Mol. Biol. *17*, 47

PELLING, C., 1966, Proc. Roy. Soc. *B 164*, 279

PLAUT, W., 1963, J. Mol. Biol. *7*, 632

PLAUT, W., and D. NASH, 1964, in The role of chromosomes in development, Academic Press, New York and London, p. 113

PLAUT, W., D. NASH, and T. FANNING, 1966, J. Mol. Biol, *16*, 85

REVEL, J. P., E. D. HAY, 1961, Exp. Cell Res. *25*, 474

RIBAS-MUNDÓ, M., 1966, Exp. Cell Res. *41*, 210

RUDKIN, G. T., 1965, Genetics *52*, 470

SEED, J., 1962, Proc. Roy. *B 156*, 41

SEED, J., 1963, Nature *198*, 147

SMELLIE, R. M. S., 1965, Brit. Med. Bull. *21*, 195

STRYCKMANS, P., E. P. CRONKITE, J. FACHE, T. M. FLIEDNER, and J. RAMOS, 1966, Nature *211*, 717

TERASIMA, T., and L. J. TOLMACH, 1963, Exp. Cell Res. *30*, 344

TOLMACH, L. J., L. G. LAJTHA, C. L. SMITH, N. K. DAS, and E. ZEUTHEN, 1963, J. Cell. Comp. Physiol. *62* (suppl. 1), 141

WATSON, J. D., and F. H. C. CRICK, 1953a, Nature *171*, 737

WATSON, J. D., and F. H. C. CRICK, 1953b, Nature *171*, 964

WATSON, J. D., and F. H. C. CRICK, 1953c, Cold Spr. Harb. Symp. Quant. Biol. *18*, 123

CHAPTER 6

Replication and segregation of DNA in chromosomes of higher organisms

6.1 Introduction

In the previous chapter, DNA replication has been discussed without reference to the chromosomes. If, however, the distribution of labelled DNA is studied at mitosis, after labelling with H³Tdr during interphase, information can be obtained about the time of replication of DNA in various segments of the chromosomes. If cells are allowed to pass through several mitoses after labelling, information can also be obtained about chromosome subunits and the segregation of labelled DNA to daughter chromosomes. One of the first published reports of the preparation and use of H³Tdr involved a study of the segregation of labelled DNA at mitosis in *Vicia faba* (TAYLOR et al. 1957). This study established, from the very start, the manner in which newly replicated DNA segregated at mitosis and the results have been confirmed in numerous studies in other organisms. Although the historical order would begin with these experiments of TAYLOR et al. (1957) chromosome replication will be discussed first in this chapter.

6.2 Chromosome replication

If cells that have been labelled briefly during interphase are studied at the first mitosis after labelling, the regions of the chromosomes that were replicated in the presence of H³Tdr will be detected as labelled regions in autoradiographs. The first labelled cells to pass through mitosis will be those that were at the end of the S phase during exposure to H³Tdr; those

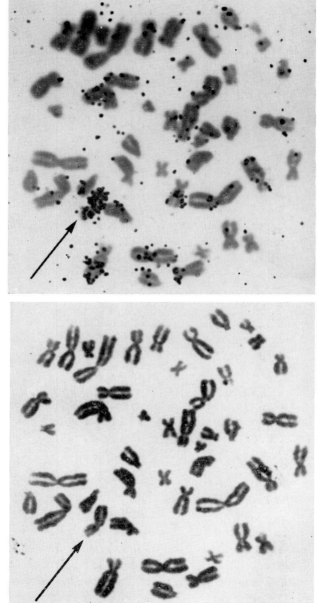

Fig. 6.1. Chromosome complement and autoradiograph of human female skin epithelium from cultures fixed within 6 hr of adding H³Tdr, showing heavily labelled X chromosome (arrow) and other late labelling regions of the chromosomes. Left photograph shows the same cell before application of the autoradiograph emulsion. (L. ATKINS, unpublished photographs).

which pass through mitosis later will be those that were labelled earlier in S (see also ch. 4 § 5, and ch. 5 § 7). In this manner it should be possible to analyse the whole replication cycle of each chromosome, but technical problems make the replication of chromosome segments at the beginning of S more difficult to study accurately than those later in S. The main limitation is the variability in the rate at which individual cells in a single population progress through the mitotic cycle. Cells labelled at a given point in S will pass through mitosis during an extended interval of time; the earlier in S that the cells were labelled the greater will be this interval. There will consequently be more error inherent in the study of the early replication sequences and these are poorly known at present, but the the method has proved very satisfactory in studying events at the end of the S phase.

In practice, the replication of chromosomes at the end of the S phase has been studied by adding H³Tdr and colchicine, or colcemide, to cultures and then making fixed chromosome preparations at times slightly longer than the duration of G_2. The only labelled mitotic figures seen at this time are those in cells which took up label at the end of S. A typical example is shown in fig. 6.1, taken from a culture of human female skin epithelium. On the basis of autoradiographic experiments similar to the one illustrated by fig. 6.1, a number of general conclusions can be reached concerning the distribution and intensity of label. The conclusions may be summarised as follows:

(1) The distribution of label is not uniform, and DNA replication occurs at discrete positions along the chromosomes and not throughout their lengths.

(2) DNA replication can occur at several positions on one chromosome simultaneously, at least during the availability time of H³Tdr.

(3) Chromosome replication is asynchronous. Homologous chromosomes may sometimes be observed to have different replication patterns and each particular chromosome may have its own characteristic replication pattern.

(4) Chromosomes have regions which consistently replicate late in the S phase, and an extreme case of late replication is found in the whole of one of the X chromosomes in the XX female in mammals.

These general conclusions are agreed upon by most workers, but details of the replication pattern in individual chromosomes throughout the S phase have proved difficult to elucidate in most cases. These difficulties have arisen mainly on account of the large number of chromosomes in most mammalian species, the difficulty of unambiguously identifying each chromosome routinely, and the problem of statistical analysis of autoradiographs of structures as small as individual chromosomes. Only a few species are available in which individual chromosomes can be identified with little ambiguity and replication studies have mainly been confined to the hamster, man, a number of plants including *Vicia*, *Crepis*, *Allium*, *Bellevalia* and *Tradescantia*, and recently the marsupial *Potorus* (see LIMA-DE-FARIA 1964; HSU et al. 1965; PEACOCK 1965; SWANSON and YOUNG 1965; WALEN 1963). Of these species, the human karyotype is the most difficult to analyse and human chromosomes cannot all be unambiguously identified. Because of the relatively large size of autoradiograph grains in comparison to the dimensions of the chromosomes, only small numbers of grains can be located over any particular segment of the chromosome. The statistical significance of the number of grains counted over particular segments is consequently low, and segments that appear to be unlabelled may merely show no grains for statistical reasons. One obvious way to improve the statistical significance of the grain numbers is to analyse a large number of separate mitotic cells that were labelled identically. STUBBLEFIELD (1965) has used an alternative method in which he made repeated autoradiographs of the same mitotic cell. In this technique, Stubblefield coated chromosome preparations of Chinese hamster cells with a thin Formvar film for protection, and was then able to make successive autoradiographs of the same slide with AR10 emulsion by removing the exposed emulsion after each autoradiograph had been developed. The grain distribution over the chromosomes of a single cell was recorded for 10 successive autoradiographs and by pooling these Stubblefield was able to identify the labelled and unlabelled segments of the chromosome unambiguously.

On the basis of H³Tdr labelling studies, the replication sequence of the chromosomes appears to be a characteristic property of each species. In the plants *Crepis* (TAYLOR 1958a), *Scilla*, and *Frittilaria* (PELC and LaCOUR 1960), for example, replication begins at the chromosome ends and finishes near the centromere, whereas in *Tradescantia* the chromosome ends are among the last regions to replicate (WIMBER 1961). In *Vicia* replication starts in euchromatic regions of the chromosomes and finishes in the heterochromatic regions (EVANS 1964). In the Chinese hamster chromosomes 10, 11, Y, and the long arm of the X all replicate at the end of the S phase, although there are some regions on each of these chromosomes that replicate early in S (STUBBLEFIELD 1965). The homologues of chromosomes 2, 5, 6, 7, and 8 in this species have replication patterns that are different from one another, whereas the homologues of chromosomes 10 and 11 have replication patterns that are indistinguishable from one another. Cultures of human leucocytes have been used extensively for studies of chromosome replication, and numerous regions on many of the chromosomes have been identified in terms of their early or late replicating behaviour (LIMA-DE-FARIA 1964; MUKHERJEE and SINHA 1965; BIANCHI and BIANCHI 1965). As in the case of the Chinese hamster, which has already been mentioned, homologous chromosomes in the human karyotype do not all have identical replication patterns to one another. Homologues of chromosomes 1, 2, 3, and 18, for example, have different replication patterns. In addition to the regions in which extensive early replication occurs, most of the chromosomes in the human karyotype, with the exception of the heterochromatic X in the female, incorporate H^{3}Tdr in a few small regions at the beginning of the S phase (PETERSEN 1964). The last to begin replication are single chromosomes in the groups 6 to 12+X, 13 to 15, 16 to 18, and the last of all 21 to 22 (MUKHERJEE and SINHA 1965).

These early and late replicating regions in the chromosomes correspond to the early and late replicating regions of the interphase nucleus which have been discussed in ch. 5 § 4. Replication appears to be organized in terms of the function of chromosome regions during interphase, euchromatic genetically active regions starting replication first, and heterochromatic repressed regions last although there is extensive overlap in S when both chromatin types are replicated together. The labelling patterns observed at mitosis are then a consequence of the way in which the DNA molecules are coiled into a larger chromosomal structure. The most interesting problem that arises from these studies is consequently not the elucidation of complete replication patterns for each species, but rather the means by which the replication patterns are controlled and the DNA molecules arranged in the chromosomes. This will be discussed further in ch. 6 § 7.

6.3 *The Lyon hypothesis and the late labelling X chromosome*

In cells from females of several mammalian species, one of the X chromosomes consistently replicates most of its DNA at the end of the S phase. This late labelling behaviour has been identified in tissue cultures of female cells from man (GERMAN 1962; GILBERT et al. 1962, 1965; MORISHIMA et al. 1962), cow (MUKHERJEE and SINHA 1963), horse, donkey, mule (MUKHERJEE and SINHA 1964), goat, pig (EVANS 1965), and marsupials (MARSHALL 1966). In addition, a late-labelling X chromosome has been identified in the female mouse in vivo (EVANS et al. 1965) and in the insect *Tenebrio molitor* (BAER 1965). An example of the late-labelling X chromosome in man is shown in fig. 6.1. At the end of the S phase the rate of DNA replication in the late-labelling X chromosome of man may be about 3 times the rate of replication in the other chromosomes (GILBERT et al. 1965). The homologous X chromosome, that is not late-labelling, has a replication pattern that is similar to the autosomes. In certain cases of human congenital abnormalities individuals are found who have an abnormal complement of sex chromosomes. Their sex chromosome complements include, for example, XO,XXX,XXXY, and XXXXX. In these cases one of the X chromosomes replicates during the S phase over a similar interval to the autosomes, whereas the remainder all replicate at the end of S. In general, if there are N X chromosomes then there are $(N-1)$ late-labelling X chromosomes (ROWLEY et al. 1963; GRUMBACH et al. 1963; MUKHERJEE et al. 1964). In the normal female the late-labelling X chromosome gives rise to the densely staining Barr body in the interphase nucleus (BARR 1949) and in cases where there are N X chromosomes there are $(N-1)$ Barr bodies in the interphase nucleus. Since heterochromatic regions of the chromosomes, and in particular, the Barr body, are regions of the chromosomes in which gene action has been repressed (ch. 5 § 4) it can be concluded that only one of the X chromosomes of the sex chromosome complement is required, in conjunction with the autosomes, for the functioning of the interphase cell.

The inactivation of all except one of the X chromosomes is a mechanism which ensures that the female with 2 X chromosomes and the male with 1 X have the same number of active X chromosome genes (dose compensation). This mechanism had been suggested on genetic evidence by LYON (1961) and by RUSSELL (1961) a few years before the replication sequences of the X chromosome were discovered, and has become known as the Lyon hypothesis. There were three lines of genetic evidence, derived mainly from the genetics of mice, that were put forward by Lyon and by Russell to demonstrate that only a single X chromosome could be active. These have been summarized by RUSSELL (1964) as follows:

(1) Females whose genotype lacks an X chromosome, i.e. XO, are phenotypically normal and fertile.

(2) Sex linked mutations appear as a mosaic phenotype in the heterozygous female. Coat colour, for example, may appear as a mixture of two types, some patches with the colour, expected from the maternal genes and the remainder of the patches with the colour expected from the paternal genes.

(3) A translocation of an autosomal fragment to an X chromosome results in a variegated phenotype in the female (but not the male) due to the repression of the genes on the translocated fragment when it is attached to the inactive X, but not when it is attached to the active X.

In addition to indicating that only one X is genetically active, (2) and (3) indicate that it is not necessarily the same X which is active in every cell of one individual. A mottled phenotype, (2) for example, would result if inactivation of one X chromosome occurred at random at some stage during the development of the animal. One X would then be active in one part of the body and the other X in another. Several other clear cases have been found that demonstrate random inactivation of one of the X chromosomes. These cases include the study of the activity of a sex linked gene on the X chromosome, the gene for glucose-6-phosphate dehydrogenase (G-6-PD), by DAVIDSON et al. (1963), and the study of the replication pattern of the X chromosomes in the female mule by MUKHERJEE and SINHA (1964). In the former study the parental X chromosomes could be distinguished by the biochemical activity of their products, and in the latter by their cytological appearance. If inactivation of the X chromosomes in human females is at random, then the heterozygous female should be a mosaic for sex linked genes. DAVIDSON et al. (1963) tested this hypothesis by growing colonies from single cells in tissue cultures of skin biopsies from a human female. They found that either of the alleles for G-6-PD was active, but only one of them active in any one colony. In the case of chromosome replication in the mule MUKHERJEE and SINHA (1964) found that either of the parental X chromosomes could be the late labelling X, and the maternal and paternal X's were late labelling with approximately equal frequency.

Although these examples make it probable that the choice of which X chromosome is to be inactivated during the development of the individual is a random one, in cases where one of the X chromosomes is abnormal the choice does not appear to be at random. In these cases the abnormal X is the one which is inactive and late labelling (GRUMBACH et al. 1963). This could be either due to a preferential inactivation of the abnormal X, or to random inactivation and loss of viability in those cells in which the normal X has been inactivated. These two alternatives have not yet been resolved.

Little is known about the details of the control mechanisms which selectively inactivate all except one of the X chromosomes, or those which regulate the period during interphase when the chromosomes replicate. The X chromosomes are inactivated very early during development and the Barr body is detectable at the late blastocyst stage in mammals (BARR 1966). Both of the X chromosomes remain active in mammalian reproductive cells and either may be transmitted to progeny. In some insects, however, one X is also inactive in the reproductive cells, e.g. *Tenebrio molitor* (see BROWN 1966). The selective inactivation of an X chromosome is a particular case of the more general phenomena of differentiation, heterochromatin, and the control of gene action in higher organisms. The late-labelling X chromosome may provide a useful tool for elucidating these problems.

6.4 Chromosome segregation at mitosis

The pioneer experiment on chromosome replication, and the segregation of chromosome subunits was that of TAYLOR et al. (1957) in which they studied H^3Tdr labelling of chromosomes in *Vicia* root tips. In this experiment the chromosomes were fully labelled with H^3Tdr by growing root tips in the label for approximately 8 hours. Immediately after the completion of this labelling period all of the chromosomes were labelled throughout their length in both chromatids. From this point onwards the root tips were grown in non radioactive water and the distribution of label in the chromosomes was analysed at successive mitoses. Taylor et al.

used colchicine in the water in which they grew the root tips at a concentration which completely blocked anaphase and cell division, but did not prevent the reorganisation of the chromosomes into an interphase nucleus and subsequent DNA replication. By this means, it was possible to determine unambiguously the number of divisions that a cell had passed through since the labelling period by counting the number of chromosomes that it contained. Cells at the first mitosis contained the diploid number of chromosomes, 12; cells at the second mitosis were tetraploid with 24 chromosomes; cells at the third mitosis were octaploid with 48 chromosomes. Whereas all of the chromatids were labelled at the first mitosis, at the second mitosis each chromosome contained one labelled and one unlabelled chromatid. Similar observations were made by PRESCOTT and BENDER (1963) in experiments that they performed with Chinese hamster cells and human leucocytes, but in these experiments colchicine was used merely to accumulate cells in mitosis for karyotype analysis and not to artificially induce polyploidy. An illustration of the distribution of labelled chromosomes and chromatids at the first, second, third, and fourth mitosis after labelling is shown in fig. 6.2. From these illustrations, it is clear that after the second mitosis the label in the chromatid is conserved and not distributed among the successive chromatids at later mitoses, except for occasional sister chromatid exchanges. These exchanges probably occur by breakage and reunion at homologous loci on sister chromatids and in almost every case there is still a labelled segment of a chromatid opposite to an unlabelled segment. Chromatid exchanges will be discussed in more detail in the following section.

TAYLOR et al. (1957) concluded, on the basis of their studies in *Vicia*, that the chromosome must be a double structure before replication, and one half must go to each chromatid at mitosis. The obvious analogy that was drawn was that the double structure of the chromosome is similar to the double strands of the DNA molecule which separate during semiconservative replication (ch. 5 §§ 2, 3). After replication in the presence of H^{3}Tdr both chromatids receive one old strand and one new, labelled, strand (see fig. 6.3). The chromosome at the first mitosis after labelling consequently appears labelled in both chromatids. During the subsequent interphase, replication in the absence of H^{3}Tdr results in one chromatid containing a labelled and an unlabelled strand and the other containing two unlabelled strands. At the next mitosis the chromosome consequently

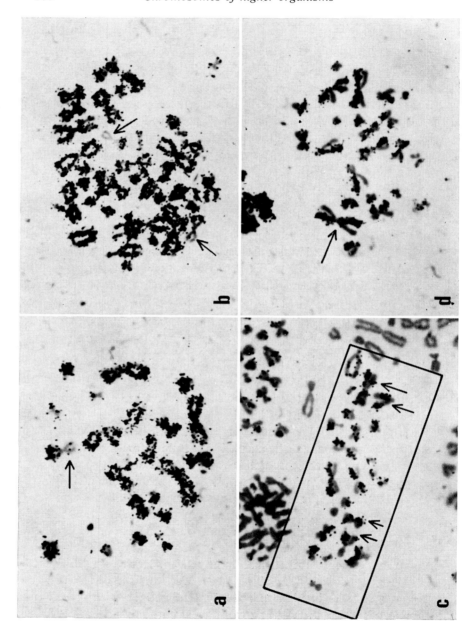

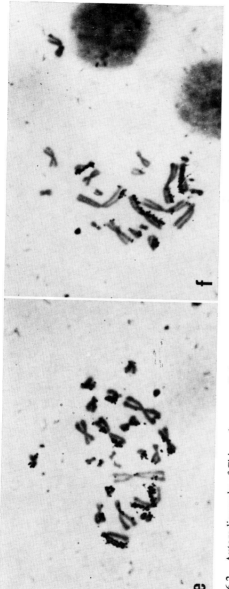

Fig. 6.2. Autoradiographs of Chinese hamster cell chromosomes freed of cytoplasm. (a) A complete complement of chromosomes at the first metaphase following DNA labelling. Both chromatids of every chromosome are radioactive although four of the smallest chromosomes are only lightly labelled and the short arms of the X chromatids (arrow) show no significant label. (b) A tetraploid set of chromosomes at the first division after labelling of DNA. Only the short arms of the two X chromosomes (arrows) have unlabelled chromatids. (c) A full complement of chromosomes at the second division metaphase following DNA labelling. Only one chromatid length of each chromosome contains labelled DNA. Several chromosomes show sister chromatid exchanges (arrows). The single large chromosome shows two small interstitial exchanges. (d) A complete set of chromosomes at the second division following labelling. The DNA is more heavily labelled than in (c). A switch of label from one chromatid to the other at the kinetochore is in most cases probably not an exchange but rather the result of 180° twist at this point (arrow). (e) A complete set of chromosomes at the third division following DNA labelling. Just over half of the chromosomes contain labelled DNA in one chromatid. (f) A complete complement of chromosomes at the fourth division after DNA labelling. One or two chromosomes were lost during fixation. Seven chromosomes have a labelled chromatid. In three of these only very short segments of chromatid are labelled. Close to 1/8 of the total chromatid length of the complement is labelled (reproduced from PRESCOTT and BENDER 1963).

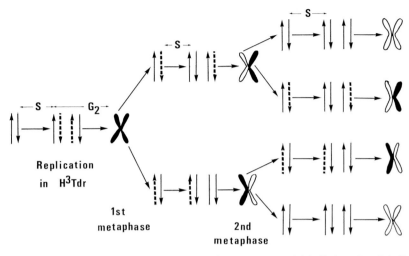

Fig. 6.3. Semiconservative replication and segregation of labelled and unlabelled chromosome subunits after one cycle of growth in H³Tdr and successive cycle of growth in non-radioactive medium. Labelled chromosome subunits indicated by dashed lines and complementary subunits indicated by antiparallel arrows. Labelled chromatids are shown shaded, and chromosomes show the observed distribution of label at the first, second and third mitoses after labelling.

appears labelled in only one chromatid. In subsequent cycles of replication and division the labelled strand is conserved and labelled chromosomes in all subsequent mitoses are labelled in one chromatid, apart from those in which sister chromatid exchanges occur. The chromosome subunits consequently replicate semiconservatively and on the basis of their replication and segregation behaviour are identical to the polynucleotide chains of the DNA molecule, but it has yet to be proved that the subunits are the polynucleotide chains (see ch. 6 § 7).

In addition to observing the distribution of label among chromatids merely in terms of the location of label, grain counts were made by TAYLOR (1958b) in experiments with *Bellevalia*. Grain counts were made over daughter chromosomes after they had separated at mitosis, and Taylor concluded that the difference in the number of grains over homologous chromosomes was due to random variation, and that the chromatids segregated randomly to daughter cells at mitosis. In an experiment in which they used C¹⁴Tdr, PLAUT and MAZIA (1956) obtained a grain distribution in *Crepis* which was not random, and they attempted to attribute this to a conservative mode of replication for the chromosomes. These results of Plaut and Mazia have generally been disregarded, though not satisfactorily explained, on account of the greater resolution that was obtained by TAYLOR et al. (1957) and TAYLOR (1958a,b) with H³Tdr, and the attractive correlation between semiconservative replication of DNA and the semiconservative replication of the chromosome that could be based on Taylor's results. The experimental results of PRESCOTT and BENDER (1963) may also be interpreted in terms of random segregation of daughter chromosomes at mitosis. They observed that at the second mitosis after labelling each chromosome was labelled in one chromatid, at the third mitosis approximately half of the chromosomes were labelled in each cell, and at the fourth mitosis approximately one quarter of the chromosomes in each cell were labelled. The exact number of chromosomes that were labelled at the third and fourth mitoses was slightly higher than one half and one quarter, respectively, on account of sister chromatid exchanges. These results are consistent with a random segregation of daughter chromosomes at mitosis, since there appears to be no

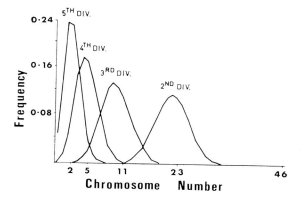

Fig. 6.4. Distribution of labelled chromosomes in daughter cells at the second and subsequent mitoses after labelling in man in the absence of sister chromatid exchanges. Segregation of daughter chromosomes is assumed to be at random and results in a binomial distribution of labelled chromosomes among the cells of the population. Horizontally, the number of labelled chromosomes; vertically, the fraction of cells receiving the number of labelled chromosomes at division (reproduced from CRONKITE et al. 1962).

systematic difference between the segregation of labelled and unlabelled subunits. Random segregation, however, has not been thoroughly established and there are some situations, particularly in vivo, in which a non random segregation may occur (LARK et al. 1966). In the case of stem cells (ch. 7 § 4), for example, the two daughter cells from a mitotic division eventually develop into different cell types from one another and part of this asymmetry may involve a non-random segregation of the daughter chromosomes.

On the basis of a random distribution of labelled and unlabelled subunits to daughter cells at mitosis, the distribution of the number of labelled chromatids per cell, at the second and subsequent mitosis after labelling, should follow a binomial distribution, in the absence of sister chromatid exchanges (CRONKITE et al. 1962). This distribution is illustrated in fig. 6.4. This ideal case is not observed in practice because frequent sister chromatid exchanges occur which result in a more widespread distribution of label. These exchanges can be used to obtain further information about the nature of the subunits which make up the double structure of the chromatid, or daughter chromosome, and will be discussed in the following section.

6.5 Types of chromatid exchange and the polarity of chromosome subunits

After Taylor had observed chromatid exchanges in the original experiments with *Vicia* (TAYLOR et al. 1957), additional experiments were performed with a different plant, *Bellevalia*, to determine the frequency types of the exchanges (TAYLOR 1958b). Since *Bellevalia* contains 4 chromosome pairs, that can be easily distinguished from one another, the analysis of chromatid exchanges was considerably easier and more accurate than if *Vicia* had been used. In the experiments with *Bellevalia* colchicine was again used so that the cells were tetraploid at the second mitosis after labelling. At this stage all of the chromosomes that were derived from the initial labelled complement were together in the same cell and exchanges that occurred in the first and second replication cycles could both be analysed.

Bellevalia root tips were grown in H^{3}Tdr for 6 to 10 hr, and in mitotic cells fixed at the end of the labelling period the chromosomes were fully labelled along their whole lengths. If an exchange occurred between a labelled strand on one chromatid and an unlabelled strand on the other, then at the first mitosis after labelling there would be an unlabelled seg-

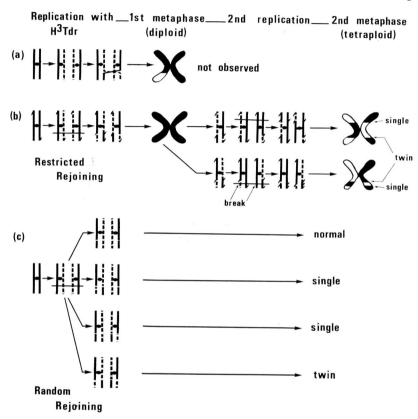

Fig. 6.5. The results of chromatid exchanges during and after one cycle in H³Tdr; labelled strands are represented by dashed lines and labelled chromatids by shading. The sites of breakage and rejoining are signified by a horizontal line across the whole chromosome. Centromere region shown diagrammatically in the mid region of the chromosome. (a) Half chromatid exchange during the first replication cycle, this was never observed by TAYLOR (1958b). (b) Result of sister chromatid exchanges when rejoining is restricted by a difference between the two strands of the chromatid. The difference is represented by a polarity analogous to the polarity of the DNA molecule. (c) Result of exchanges when rejoining is unrestricted and occurs at random. Four types of rearrangement are possible after each break (redrawn from TAYLOR 1958b).

ment on one chromatid of a chromosome (see fig. 6.5). Since this was not observed then the exchange of labelled strands probably did not occur. All exchanges observed must have been the consequence of breakage of whole chromatids and the exchange of segments of the double chromatid structure.

In the tetraploid cells TAYLOR (1958b) noted that there were two types of sister chromatid exchange. In addition to sister chromatid exchanges that involved only the chromatids of one chromosome, there were also exchanges at the same locus of two separate homologous chromosomes. These two types of exchange were defined as single chromatid exchanges and twin chromatid exchanges, respectively. Since the two chromosomes involved in a twin exchange were separate after the first colchine metaphase, a twin exchange must represent an event that occurred before this separation. Single exchanges may represent events that occur either before the first or between the first and the second colchicine metaphase. Restrictions on the rejoining process will affect the relative proportions of single and twin exchanges, and the ratio of singles to twins was used by Taylor to determine whether there were any restrictions.

In the preceding section ch. 6 § 4 the results of chromosome segregation studies were used to demonstrate that the chromosome has a double structure prior to replication. If sister chromatid exchanges, both singles and twins, arise by the breakage and rejoining of the subunits of the chromatids during or after replication of the chromosome, then the number of rearrangements of the subunits that are possible will depend on whether rejoining can occur at random or only with certain restrictions. A restriction on rejoining would exist, for example, if the subunits of the chromatid were the complementary strands of the DNA molecule which have opposite chemical polarity (see ch. 5 § 3). This restriction would imply that after replication a new labelled subunit would have the same polarity as the old unlabelled subunit on the sister strand (see fig. 6.3). An exchange would then require new subunits to rejoin with old subunits, and vice-versa. Every exchange during the first replication cycle would then appear as a twin exchange at the second metaphase in tetraploid cells (see fig. 6.5). Any exchange that occurred during the second replication cycle, when only one chromatid is labelled, would appear as a single exchange at the second metaphase. Since there are twice as many chromosomes present in the cell during the second replication cycle, colchicine having prevented cell division, the ratio of single to twin exchanges will be 2:1. This assumes that the probability of an exchange is the same throughout the duration of the experiment and is not affected by the duration of exposure to colchicine or H^3 disintegrations.

If there are no restrictions on rejoining then some exchanges which occur during the first replication cycle will appear as single exchanges instead of twins at the second metaphase. Random rejoining during the first replication cycle is illustrated in fig. 6.5. There are four different types of rearrangement that are possible, one of these will appear normal at the second metaphase, two will appear as single exchanges, and one will appear as a twin exchange. The ratio of singles to twins, that arise from events in the first replication cycle, will consequently be 2:1. During the second replication cycle each exchange will appear as a single exchange and, since there are twice as many chromosomes present during this cycle as there are during the first cycle, there will be eight possible rearrangements. At the second metaphase single exchanges will be observed that arise in the first and in the second replication cycles, and if each rearrangement can occur with equal probability the ratio of singles to twins will be 10:1.

In the experiments reported by TAYLOR (1958b) for *Bellevalia* the ratio of singles to twins was determined for each of the four chromosome pairs and the pooled ratio for the whole karyotype was 30 singles to 81 twins, or 1:2.7. This ratio is different from the ratios expected either on the basis of restricted rejoining (2:1) or random rejoining (10:1). TAYLOR (1958b) concluded that since the frequency of twins was higher than would be expected on the basis of random rejoining, some form of restriction must be invoked. The difference between the predicted and the observed ratios of singles to twins was explained in terms of a lower frequency of exchange during the second replication cycle than during the first. In the original interpretation Taylor assumed that the sister chromatid exchanges were spontaneous events, but the observed ratio of twin to single exchanges can be explained more satisfactorily of the sister chromatid exchanges are restricted and radiation induced (WIMBER 1959; MARIN and PRESCOTT 1964; WOLFF 1964). Since the amount of H^3 in a chromosome is halved after the first colchicine metaphase the radiation dose received per chromosome will be less during the second replication cycle than during the first. The frequency of radiation induced exchanges during the second cycle will then be less than during the first. This effect may contribute to the lower frequency of exchange during the second cycle that Taylor postulated in explanation of his results. On the basis of sister chromatid exchanges as radiation induced exchanges Wolff predicted a ratio of 1:2 for the ratio of singles to twins in an experiment such as Taylor's. This prediction is closer to the observed value of 1:2.7. Although the observed ratio of single to twin exchanges is not explained exactly by any of the hypotheses that have been mentioned, the frequency of twin exchanges is much greater than can be accounted for by random rejoining. It is most likely that rejoining is restricted and the subunits of the chromatids behave as if they were complementary strands of a DNA molecule.

A third type of exchange, in addition to single and twin sister chromatid exchanges, was also detected in Taylor's experiment but this was too rare to be analysed in any detail and was consequently ignored. At the second metaphase after labelling occasional chromosomes were detected in which sister chromatids were both labelled (isolabelling). PEACOCK (1963, 1965) observed that isolabelling was usually along the entire length of corresponding arms of sister chromatids, or near the tips of the chromatids. Occasional labelling of chromatid segments which did not reach to the tips of the chromatids (intercalary labelling) was also observed, but at a much lower frequency than the other types of isolabelling. Among 241 cases of isolabelling PEACOCK (1963) recorded only 17 cases of intercalary isolabelling. PEACOCK (1963, 1965) has suggested that isolabelling cannot be produced by sister chromatid exchange, but only by exchange between units that are smaller than the chromatids (subchromatid exchanges), which could occur if the chromatid were multi-stranded. A possible explanation of isolabelling might be that a labelled pool of H^3Tdr derivatives remains in the cells from the end of S until the beginning of the subsequent S. The existence of such a pool has been reported in a number of organisms and has been discussed in ch. 3 § 5. A long lived pool, however, would result in the labelling of early replicating regions of each chromosome in the second S phase, and this would not produce the observed pattern of isolabelling along whole arms or tips of sister chromatids. An alternative mechanism that could give rise to isolabelling has been suggested by WOLFF (1964), which does not necessarily involve a multi-stranded chromosome. If sister chromatid exchanges are radiation-induced, then occasional interchromosomal exchanges may also be induced by H³ disintegration. An interchromosomal exchange between homologous chromosomes during the second replication cycle would be observed as isolabelling of sister chromatids. Wolff considered that, if interchromosomal exchange between homologous chromosomes were more likely than between non homologous chromosomes, the rare intercalary isolabelling could be explained in terms of two interchromosomal exchanges. If this interpretation of isolabelling is correct then iso-unlabelling should also occur. Although iso-unlabelling is evident in some of the published photographs of PEACOCK (1963) and MARIN and PRESCOTT (1964), this is negative evidence that could also be due to one of many autoradiographic artefacts. The explanation of isolabelling as interchromosomal exchange, although plausible, has not been proved, and this type of labelling is one of the strongest pieces of evidence that the chromosomes are multi-stranded.

6.6 Chromosome replication and crossing over in meiosis

The final period of DNA replication, before meiosis, is completed during the last premeiotic interphase and is separated from meiotic prophase by a G_2 period which is analogous to the G_2 period which precedes mitotic prophase (TAYLOR and MCMASTER 1954; LIMA-DE-FARIA 1961; WIMBER and PRENSKY 1963; TAYLOR 1965). The premeiotic DNA replication shows the familiar semiconservative distribution of labelled DNA and chromosome subunits that has already been discussed for interphase replication of DNA between mitotic divisions. When cells are labelled with H³Tdr during the S period of the final premeiotic interphase the cells arrive at meiosis with labelled DNA in all of the chromatids; when cells are labelled during the interphase prior to the final premeiotic interphase then they arrive at meiosis with the equivalent of one chromatid labelled, although exchanges tend to distribute the label between chromatids (TAYLOR 1965). The frequency and distribution of visible chromatid exchanges (i.e. between one labelled and one unlabelled chromatid) at meiosis in the grasshopper *Romalea*, in cells which had been labelled with H³Tdr during the penultimate premeiotic interphase was also studied by Taylor. Although the frequency of exchange of labelled chromatids was approximately equal to the frequency of chiasmata, the sites of exchange were distributed at random along the chromatids whereas the distribution of chiasmata was not random. If these exchanges were produced by crossing over at chiasma then the observed random distribution of the exchanges may have been the result of terminalisation of the chiasma (see e.g. DARLINGTON 1965). Taylor, however, concluded that there were probably a significant number of exchanges that were not revealed by H^{3}Tdr labelling which occurred between homologous chromatids that were either both labelled or both unlabelled. Sister chromatid exchanges also contributed to the number of visible chromatid exchanges observed, but in contrast to mitotic divisions, sister chromatid exchange appears to be relatively infrequent in meiosis.

A small amount of DNA replication has also been detected during the period of crossing over in pachytene and zygotene. WIMBER and PRENSKY (1963), for example, detected the incorporation of H^{3}Tdr, autoradiographically, into the DNA of meiotic chromosomes of the male newt, *Triturus*, although the major portion of the DNA had completed replication approximately 13 days earlier. HOTTA et al. (1966) also detected the incorporation of H^{3}Tdr and P^{32} into the DNA of meiotic chromosomes in the plants *Lilium longiflorum* and *Trillium erectum* by means of chemical extraction, but in these cases the incorporation was too small to detect autoradiographically. The amount of DNA that was replicated during the period of crossing over only amounted to a small fraction of the total DNA of the cell and this period of DNA replication was separated from the premeiotic S phase by a definite G$_2$ period. Two alternative interpretations of the small amount of meiotic DNA replication were suggested by WIMBER and PRENSKY and HOTTA et al. (1966). Since the DNA replication was clearly associated in time with visible crossing over, then it may represent either repair replication as a result of a breakage and rejoining process during cross over, or the replication of small segments of the chromosomes that had not been replicated during the premeiotic S phase. These two alternatives could not be clearly distinguished in either of the experiments cited, although HOTTA et al. (1966) favoured the latter interpretation.

Apart from the replication of this small amount of DNA during meiosis, replication of most of the DNA of the cell is completed long before meiosis begins. Replication of most of the DNA of the cell is consequently a distinct process from the pairing of chromosomes and crossing over during meiosis, although not necessarily distinct from sister chromatid exchange which can occur during or after replication.

6.7 *Reflections on chromosome structure*

To review adequately all of the experiments that have some bearing on chromosome structure would be to digress too far from the main theme of this work. However, the H³Tdr studies that have been described in this chapter do provide some hints for possible chromosome structures. There are two main controversial themes around which much of the current discussion of chromosome structure circulates. The first concerns the exact size and chemical nature of the basic chromosome fibre, the second concerns the number of these fibres that are present in the chromosome.

The sizes of the chromosome fibres that have been described vary widely with the different techniques employed. The sizes range from 30 to 500 Å in diameter, but the size that is most frequently observed is between 100 to 200 Å (HYDE 1965; DUPRAW 1965, a, b, 1966; RIS 1966). On the basis of whole mount studies, in which the chromosome material is extracted from the interphase or mitotic cell and studied intact in the electron microscope, the fibres are quite uniform and are often branched to form a complex three dimensional network (Dupraw; Ris). Some branches in this network have a Y configuration which resembles the Y configuration that a DNA molecule may have in the region of the replication site (see figs. 5.1 and 5.2). These branched structures are not necessarily replication sites, however, because the same Y configurations have been seen in chromosome preparations from sperm and from salamander erythrocytes in which there is no DNA replication (Ris). The coiling of chromosome fibres must be very tight and complex because the total DNA content of a human diploid cell nucleus, for example, has a length of approximately 180 cm, all of which must be packed into 46 chromosomes that are only a few microns in length (MACHATTIE and THOMAS 1964; DUPRAW 1965b).

The two alternatives that are considered with reference to the number of fibres that are present in each chromosome are those of a single-stranded or a multi-stranded structure. If a chromosome could be held at opposite ends and then stretched to remove all of the coiling, a single-stranded structure would stretch to a single fibre, a multi-stranded structure would stretch to a number of parallel fibres. In the case of a multistranded structure, there is also the problem of whether the strands would be identical to one another or would carry completely different genetic information.

Several conclusions concerning chromosome structure can be reached on the basis of the autoradiographic results discussed in the preceding sections, and these may be listed as follows:

(1) H^3Tdr is incorporated into DNA in a chromosome as part of subunits of the chromosome that remain intact during succeeding replications and divisions, except for occasional sister chromatid exchanges.

(2) The chromosome, prior to replication, has two different subunits which may be complementary to one another in a manner similar to the individual strands of the DNA double helix.

(3) The chromosome, after replication, has four subunits which divide so that each chromatid (daughter chromosome) regularly receives an old and a new subunit.

(4) During replication the chromosome appears to behave like a linear aggregate of individual DNA molecules, each of which replicates independently.

These conclusions are little more than a restatement of experimental results, and there can be little disagreement over their validity. The precise identity of the chromosome subunits, however, is a matter for considerable argument and conjecture. A single stranded model of the chromosome would fit each of the four conclusions listed above extremely well, and the chromatid subunits would then be the individual strands of the DNA molecule. The results of GALL (1963) on the kinetics of DNAse degradation of lampbrush chromosomes are also consistent with a single stranded chromosome that contains double helical DNA molecules linked end to end along the chromosome axis. The genetics of higher organisms are described in terms of linear genetic maps and the simplest molecular basis for these maps would be single stranded chromosomes. In bacteria and DNA viruses there is an exact correspondence between the linear or circular genetic maps and the linear or circular DNA molecules that these organisms contain (see e.g. WATSON 1965). It would be an attractive generalisation if genes in higher organisms, as well as in microorganisms and DNA viruses, were simply segments of single DNA molecules. A multi-stranded chromosome is more difficult to interpret genetically, because if the strands contain repetitions of the same genetic information there will be multiple sites for mutagenesis. A mutation on one strand must then be assumed to affect all of the corresponding strands identically.

The single-stranded model, however, is not completely satisfactory. In particular, it is difficult to reconcile the single stranded model with observations of subchromatid exchanges (PEACOCK 1963, 1965), half and quarter chromatid structures seen in the light microscope in fixed (LOPEZ-SAEZ and GONZALES-FERNANDEZ 1963; TROSKO and WOLFF 1965) and living cells (BAJER 1965, HOLM and BAJER 1966), and subchromatid aberrations produced by radiations (LEA 1946; SAX and KING 1955; WILSON et al. 1959; WILSON and SPARROW 1960; CROUSE 1961). All of these observations constitute evidence in favour of a multistranded model for the chromosome although some of the observations may be interpreted in terms of the behaviour of extensively coiled single stranded chromosomes. The evidence for single-stranded or multi-stranded chromosomes is, consequently, fairly equally balanced and both models have their ardent supporters. The definitive experiments that will shift the balance have yet to be performed.

References

BAER, D., 1965, Genetics *52*, 275

BARR, M. L., 1949, Nature *163*, 676

BARR, M. L., 1966, Intern. Rev. Cytol. *19*, 35

BAJER, A., 1965, Chromosoma *17*, 291

BIANCHI, N. O., and M. S. A. DE BIANCHI, 1965, Chromosoma *17*, 273

BROWN, S. W., 1966, Science *151*, 417

CRONKITE, E. P., T. M. FLIEDNER, S. A. KILLMAN, and J. R. RUBINI, 1962, in Tritium in the physical and biological sciences II, International Atomic Energy Agency Vienna, p. 189

CROUSE, H. V., 1961, Chromosoma *12*, 190

DARLINGTON, D. C., 1965, Cytology, Churchill, Oxford

DAVIDSON, R. G., H. M. NITOWSKY, and B. CHILDS, 1963, Proc. Natl. Acad. Sci. *50*, 481

DUPRAW, E. J., 1965a, Proc. Natl. Acad. Sci. *53*, 161

DUPRAW, E. J., 1965b, Nature *206*, 338

DUPRAW, E. J., 1966, Nature *209*, 577

EVANS, H. J., 1964, Exp. Cell Res. *35*, 381

EVANS, H. J., 1965, Exp. Cell Res. *38*, 511

EVANS, H. J., C. E. FORD, M. F. LYON, and J. GRAY, 1965, Nature *206*, 900

GALL, J. G., 1963, Nature *198*, 36

GERMAN, J. L., 1962, Trans. N. Y. Acad. Sci. *24*, 395

GILBERT, C. W., S. MULDAL, L. G. LAJTHA, and J. ROWLEY, 1962, Nature *195*, 869

GILBERT, C. W., S. MULDAL, and L. G. LAJTHA, 1965, Nature *208*, 159

GRUMBACH, M. M., A. MORISHIMA, and J. H. TAYLOR, 1963, Proc. Natl. Acad. Sci,
    49, 58

HOLM, G. and A. BAJER, 1966, Hereditas *54*, 357

HOTTA, Y., M. ITO, and H. STERN, 1966, Proc. Natl. Acad. Sci. *56*, 1184

HSU, T. C., W. SCHMID, and E. STUBBLEFIELD, 1965, in The role of chromosomes in
    development, M. Locke, ed., Academic Press, New York and London, p. 83

HYDE, B. B., 1965, Progr. in biophys. and molec. biol. *15*, 129

LARK, K. G., R. A. CONSIGLI, and H. C. MINOCHA, 1966, Science, *154*, 1202

LEA, D. E., 1946, Actions of radiations on living cells, Cambridge University Press,
    p. 201

LIMA-DE-FARIA, A., 1964, in Mammalian cytogenetics and related problems in radio-
    biology, C. Pavan, C. Chagas, O. Freta-Pessoa, L. R. Caldas, eds., Pergamon
    Press, Oxford, p. 31

LIMA-DE-FARIA, A., 1961, Hereditas *47*, 674

LOPEZ-SAEZ, J. F., and A. GONZALES-FERNANDEZ, 1963, Cytologia *28*, 381

LYON, M. F., 1961, Nature *190*, 372

MACHATTIE, L. A., and C. A. THOMAS, 1964, Science *144*, 1142

MARIN, G., and D. M. PRESCOTT, 1964, J. Cell Biol. *21*, 159

MARSHALL, J. A., 1966, Science *151*, 417

MORISHIMA, A., M. M. GRUMBACH, and J. H. TAYLOR, 1962, Proc. Natl. Acad. Sci.
    48, 756

MUKHERJEE, B. B., and A. K. SINHA, 1963, Can. J. Genet. Cytol. *5*, 490

MUKHERJEE, B. B., and A. K. SINHA, 1964, Proc. Natl. Acad. Sci. *51*, 252

MUKHERJEE, B. B., and A. K. SINHA, 1965, J. Med. Genet *2*, 192

MUKHERJEE, B. B., O. J. MILLER, W. R. BREG, and S. BADER, 1964, Exp. Cell Res. *34*,
    333

PEACOCK, W. J., 1963, Proc. Natl. Acad. Sci. *49*, 793

PEACOCK, W. J., 1965, in Intern. Symp. genes and chromosomes structure and function,
    Natl. Cancer Inst. monograph *18*, J. I. Valencia and R. F. Grell, eds., p. 101

PELC, S. R., and L. F. LACOUR, 1960, in The cell nucleus, J. S. Mitchell, ed., Butter-
    worth, London, p. 232

PETERSEN, A. J., 1964, J. Cell Biol. *23*, 651

PLAUT, W., and D. MAZIA, 1956, J. Biophys. Biochem. Cytol. *2*, 573

PRESCOTT, D. M., and M. A. BENDER, 1963, Exp. Cell Res. *29*, 430

RIS, H., 1966, Proc. Roy. Soc. *B*. *164*, 246

ROWLEY, J., S. MULDAL, C. W. GILBERT, L. G. LAJTHA, J. LINDSTEIN, M. FRACCARO, and K. KAIJSER, 1963, Nature *197*, 251

RUSSELL, L. B., 1961, Science *133*, 1795

RUSSELL, L. B., 1961, Trans. N.Y. Acad. Sci. *26*, 726

SAX, K., and E. D. KING, 1955, Proc. Natl. Acad. Sci. *41*, 150

STUBBLEFIELD, E., 1965, J. Cell Biol. *25:3*, 137

SWANSON, C. P., and W. J. YOUNG, 1965, in Reproduction: molecular, subcellular and cellular, M. Locke, ed., Academic Press, New York and London, p. 107

TAYLOR J. H., 1958a, Exp. Cell Res. *15*, 350

TAYLOR, J. H., 1958b, Genetics *43*, 415

TAYLOR, J. H., 1965, J. Cell Biol. *25:2*, 57

TAYLOR, J. H., and H. McMASTER, 1954, Chromosoma *6*, 489

TAYLOR, J. H., P. S. WOODS, and W. L. HUGHES, 1957, Proc. Natl. Acad. Sci. *43*, 122

TROSKO, J. E., and S. WOLFF, 1965, J. Cell Biol. *26*, 125

WALEN, K., 1963, Genetics Today *1*, 106

WATSON, J. D., 1965, Molecular biology of the gene, W. A. Benjamin Inc., New York and Amsterdam

WILSON, G. B., and A. H. SPARROW, 1960, Chromosoma *11*, 229

WILSON, G. B., A. H. SPARROW, and V. POND, 1959, Am. J. Bot. *46*, 309

WIMBER, D. E., 1959, Proc. Natl. Acad. Sci. *45*, 839

WIMBER, D. E., 1961, Exp. Cell Res. *23*, 402

WIMBER, D. E., and W. PRENSKY, 1963, Genetics *48*, 1731

WOLFF, S., 1964, Mutation Res. *1*, 337

CHAPTER 7

Population kinetics in animal tissues

7.1 Introduction

The introduction of H³Tdr as a specific label for DNA has provided a powerful tool for the study of cell populations in animal tissues. With this tool it has been possible to label cells that are synthesising DNA in preparation for division and study their subsequent growth, maturation function, and death on a quantitative basis with greater precision than had previously been possible. A number of assumptions have to be made about the specificity and stability of H²Tdr in such studies and these were stated explicitly by CRONKITE et al. (1959a,b, 1960).

(1) H³ label does not exchange from its position in the pyrimidine ring under biological conditions.

(2) Thymine does not exchange after it has been incorporated into DNA.

(3) DNA turnover is due solely to mitosis and death.

(4) Incorporation of H³ labelled breakdown products into DNA from dead cells is insignificant.

(5) Incorporation of large pieces of DNA as breakdown products is unlikely in most cell systems.

(6) DNA synthesis destines a cell to divide.

(7) H³Tdr is uniformly distributed throughout the body after administration and is promptly incorporated into DNA or degraded.

(8) The time for which H³Tdr is available is short with respect to the duration of DNA synthesis.

(9) There is no significant radiation injury to the cells on account of the H³ β-particles.

(10) In vitro labelling determines the proliferative potential.

(11) In vivo labelling makes it possible to determine the kinetics of proliferation.

The evidence for most of these assumptions have been discussed in detail in previous chapters and, although they are not all completely true for every tissue, the exceptions are small and can be avoided or allowed for in any particular experiment. Radiation injury occurs when large doses of H³Tdr are used (ch. 3 §§ 14, 15). POST and HOFFMAN (1965a, 1967), for example, have found that the normal kinetics of tissue growth in the liver of the young rat are permanently altered by injections of more than 2 μCi/g of H³Tdr. There is also substantial evidence for a small, but significant, amount of salvage of H³ labelled breakdown products in vivo (see ch. 2 § 8) and the effect that this has on the interpretation of experiments will be discussed later (ch. 7 § 10). A small amount of DNA synthesis may occur that is related to repair and does not destine a cell to divide. Some of the evidence for such repair is discussed at the end of this chapter (ch. 7 § 14). An implicit assumption in all labelling studies is that the cells which are labelled with H³Tdr behave in a way that is representative of the growing cell population. Although this is probably true in most cases, it should be realised that the presence of label in a strand of a DNA molecule implies that this is a newly synthesised strand. The behaviour of molecules with a newly synthesised strand may not necessarily be identical in all respects to molecules that were synthesised at other times. The assumptions listed above are, however, sufficiently well founded for H³Tdr to be an exceptionally reliable label for the study of cell proliferation. Some of the principles and results of such studies will be discussed in this chapter.

7.2 Types of cell populations

The term 'population' has been introduced in ch. 4 § 4 and is used to refer to any group of cells of one or more types which can be defined in terms of its extent in space and time (GILBERT and LAJTHA 1965). The definition of a population depends on the particular experimental problem that is under investigation, but if the nature and limits are known this need not cause any ambiguity. A population may be, for example, the cells of a solid tumour which are clearly defined spatially, or leukemic cells which are distributed in the blood stream but defined in terms of their atypical morphology, or the erythrocyte or leucocyte precursors in the bone marrow. In the latter example, the bone marrow consists of a mixture of a large number of morphologically distinct cell types. Each type may be considered as a population which is defined in terms of cell morphology, and the numerous populations of the marrow are then intermingled with one another. Alternatively, the cells of the bone marrow may be regarded as one single population defined in terms of its location.

Two types of population have been discussed in ch. 4 § 4, the steady-state and the exponentially growing populations. The latter is a closed population with no cell gain or loss from other populations and one in which all of the cells are growing continuously. The steady-state population, on the other hand, also contains cells which are continuously growing, but in addition cells are gained and lost at a rate which maintains the total cell number constant. These types of population are two examples of many that can exist, and the nature of a population will in general be determined by the relative importance of three parameters: the rate of cell gain from other populations, the rate of cell loss to other populations, and the rate of cell division within the population itself (GILBERT and LAJTHA 1965). The possible types of population with various combinations of these parameters are shown in fig. 7.1. In examples (a) to (d) of fig. 7.1 there is no cell division within the populations but only inputs or outputs, and in examples (e) to (h) there is also cell division. A simple transit population, for example, is found in the reticulocytes of the bone marrow or the cells in the upper regions of the villi in the intestinal epithelium. A decaying population is found in the adult ovary, since in this tissue cells are continuously released during adult life and no cell division occurs after birth. The neurons of the central nervous system do not divide in the adult animal, and die at a very slow rate, so these may be regarded as a closed static population. The dividing and maturing cells of the bone marrow, the intestinal crypts, and the skin epithelium are examples of dividing transit populations. The stem type is a population which is able to maintain itself at a constant size by cell division and also act as the source of cells for some of the other population types. An example of this type of population is found in the stem cells of the bone marrow. Tissue cultures, the liver during regeneration and tumours from which there is no loss by metastasis or cell death are examples of closed dividing populations (fig. 7.1h). Although the case of tissue cultures has been discussed in ch. 4 § 4 in terms of exponential growth, a closed dividing population may follow any of a number of growth laws, depending on the nature of the population and the conditions of growth. Ascites cells for example may be described under some conditions by the relationship

Cell number = constant (time)^3.   (KLEIN and REVESZ 1953)

Solid tumours such as Jensen's sarcoma (MAYNEORD 1932) or mouse mammary tumours (MENDELSOHN 1964) may be described in terms of a similar growth law in terms of tumour volume:

Tumour volume = constant (time)^3.

In these closed dividing populations the growth law is determined by a large number of parameters, including the durations of the phases of the cell cycle and the growth fraction. All of these parameters may vary as functions of the age of the tumour and it is often extremely difficult to distinguish them even in such an apparently simple system (see, for example, MENDELSOHN 1964).

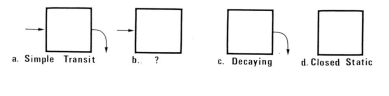

a. Simple Transit   b..   ?   c. Decaying   d. Closed Static

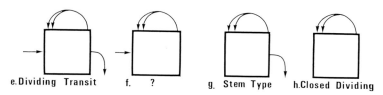

e. Dividing Transit   f.   ?   g. Stem Type   h. Closed Dividing

Fig. 7.1.   Diagrammatic representation of possible cell populations. The arrow entering indicates cells entering the population, and the arrow leaving indicates cells leaving. Double headed arrow leaving and entering indicates cells leaving on division and daughter cells entering (GILBERT and LAJTHA 1965).

7.3 *Experimental classification of cell population types*

LEBLOND et al. (1959) attempted a simple classification of the tissues of the rat on the basis of two parameters: the extent to which cells of a tissue incorporate H^3Tdr and the rate at which labelled cells are lost from the tissues. The procedure in this series of experiments was as follows. Rats were injected with H^3Tdr when they were either 3 days or 6 months old and then killed within a few hours of injection and the fraction of labelled cells in a number of tissues determined by autoradiography. In addition, a number of animals were injected with H^3Tdr when they were 3 days old and killed when they were 6 months old, and the fraction of cells that were still labelled at this time was determined for the same tissues as before. The determination of the fraction of cells labelled immediately after injection of H^3Tdr is a test of cell formation, whereas the determination of the fraction of cells which are still labelled 6 months after injection is a test of cell retention. Tissues were then characterised on the basis of whether they contained cells that were labelled in either, both, or neither of the cell formation and cell retention tests. The following three major categories of cell populations could be distinguished from the results of these tests.

(1) *Stable or non growing cell populations* (fig. 7.1c and d). In these no cells were labelled in the 6 month old adult after the cell formation test but cells were labelled in the retention test. These populations include striated, smooth and cardiac muscle and the middle sized neurons of the cerebrum. The tissues that were unlabelled in both the formation and the retention tests are those in which the cells of the tissue have completed proliferation within 3 days after birth and these include the largest neurons of the cerebrum and the Purkinje cells.

(2) *Expanding cell populations* (fig. 7.1h and perhaps g). In these populations a small percentage of cells were labelled in both the formation and the retention tests, so that there was both formation and retention of cells throughout most of the adult life of the animal. These included cells of the proximal convoluted tubules of the kidney, parenchymal cells of the liver, acinar and islet cells of the pancreas, epithelial cells of the thyroid, and cortical and medullary cells of the adrenal.

(3) *Renewing cell populations* (fig. 7.1e and g). In these populations there were numerous labelled cells in the formation tests at 3 days and 6 months,

but none in the retention test. In this case labelled cells may either have been completely lost from the population in the 6 months between labelling and death, or the label may have been diluted through successive divisions until it had become undetectable. These populations include the Malpighian cells of the epithelium in the lower surface of the tongue and the ventral skin, the cortical cells of the thymus, the epithelial cells of the ventral skin, connective tissue of the derma, bone marrow cells and the lymphocytes in the lymphatic organs.

These classifications are similar to those which can be derived on the basis of mitotic activity in tissues of animals of various ages and the mitotic index was one of the few parameters that could be used in this type of study prior to the introduction of H³Tdr. Because of the longer duration of the S phase in comparison to the duration of mitosis the labelling index in a tissue is about an order of magnitude larger than the mitotic index in the same tissue. The labelling index can consequently be determined more easily and more accurately than the mitotic index.

Many tissues could not be assigned easily to one of the three categories in the experiments of LEBLOND et al. (1959). Connective tissue was particularly difficult to assign and this tissue appeared to behave in a different manner in different parts of the body. The categories form a useful, though simplified, way of considering the tissues of the body in terms of the kinetics of their cell populations. However, the categories cannot be rigorously applied to the case of populations which are supplied from stem cell populations or where there is significant migration of cells from one population to another. These cases include the rapidly proliferating systems of the bone marrow and intestinal epithelium and these will be discussed in the following sections of this chapter.

7.4 Cell renewal systems

In the embryo and young animal most tissues consist of expanding cell populations in which the rate of cell gain exceeds that of cell loss. In the adult animal most of these tissues maintain a steady size either because of a negligible rate of cell division or because the rate of cell gain equals the rate of cell loss. These latter populations are known as cell renewal systems (see e.g. PATT and QUASTLER 1963; BOND et al. 1965) and their experimental classification has been briefly described in the preceding section.

The common feature of most cell renewal systems is that the mature functional cells only have a limited lifetime (e.g. circulating blood cells, spermatozoa, intestinal villi cells) and they must be continuously replaced by proliferation and maturation of other cells in the renewal system. The cell renewal system can then be considered in terms of several, more or less distinct, compartments or populations in which the cells have different specific characteristics of proliferation, maturation, and function. The steady state of most renewal systems is one in which the size of these compartments is constant. The steady state may be extended to include systems subject to regular cyclic changes such as diurnal variation or the menstrual cycle of the vaginal epithelium. The compartments may represent different locations in the tissue, in which case migration from one compartment to another during cell renewal would involve physical movement of the cells. Alternatively, the compartments may be intermingled and distinguished by the characteristic morphology of the cells, in which case migration between compartments involves a change in cell morphology without a change in cell location. An example of the former is found in the intestinal epithelium or the skin epithelium. Proliferation occurs in one region of the tissue and the maturing and functional cells migrate up the intestinal villi or to the skin surface. In the bone marrow, on the other hand, the various proliferative and maturation compartments are intermingled and only the mature blood cells are in a separate location. The distinctions between the compartments of a cell renewal system are rarely sharp, and there is probably a gradual loss of proliferative ability as cells progress through the various compartments from the stem cells to the final non proliferative functional cells. However, the distinction between compartments is an extremely useful one in the study of cell populations and is valid for most purposes.

The simplest type of cell renewal system would be one with two compartments, one containing proliferating cells and the other containing differentiated functional cells. In general, it is also possible to distinguish a third, intermediate, compartment of maturing cells. The simple three-compartment renewal system is illustrated in fig. 7.2. The maturation compartment may be further subdivided into a number of separate compartments in which there are different stages of maturation and in which there may also be cell division. In addition a significant fraction of the cells in the proliferating compartments may not be actually proliferating,

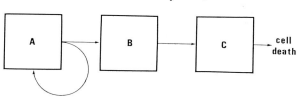

Fig. 7.2. Simple three-compartment cell renewal system. A is a self-maintaining stem cell compartment; B is a maturation compartment which does not contain dividing cells; C a mature functional compartment.

even though the cells in these compartments may be morphologically homogeneous. This type of renewal system is illustrated in fig. 7.3. It should be noted that each of the compartments of the cell renewal systems correspond to one of the population types discussed in the preceding section (fig. 7.1). Before embarking on a quantitative analysis of such renewal systems as those of figs. 7.2 and 7.3, a number of general questions need to be discussed with reference to the definitions and biological properties involved.

Although the non-proliferative, G_0, phase was first defined with reference to the stem-cell compartment (LAJTHA et al. 1962) there is no a priori reason why each proliferative compartment should not contain some cells in a G_0 phase, and this has been illustrated in fig. 7.3. The cells in the G_0 phase constitute a reserve of viable cells which can be induced to enter the

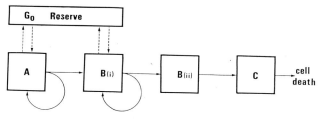

Fig. 7.3. Four-compartment cell renewal system. A is a self-maintaining stem cell compartment; B(i) a maturation compartment which contains dividing cells; B(ii) a maturation compartment which does not contain dividing cells; C a mature functional compartment. The G_0 reserve consists of cells that are indistinguishable morphologically from the cells of either compartments A or B(i) but are not involved in proliferation and cell division. Compartments A and B(i) are difficult to distinguish in practice and G_0 has been drawn as common to both. If A and B(i) are clearly distinguishable there may be a separate G_0 reserve for each.

cell cycle in the event of injury or abnormal cell loss in the renewal system. These G_0 cells may not all be permanently quiescent until required for regeneration; cells may enter and leave the cell cycle continuously and remain in G_0 for an extended but limited period of time. The G_0 cells may consequently be regarded as a fraction of the population in which one of the phases of the cell cycle (G_1 or G_2) is much longer than the rest of the population. Once injury has occurred to a system these G_0 cells respond by commencing rapid proliferation and two types of G_0 cells have been detected on the basis of their initial response. One type corresponds to cells that enter G_0 after mitosis and the initial response of these is the onset of DNA synthesis; the other corresponds to cells which enter G_0 after DNA synthesis and the initial response of these is the onset of mitosis without prior DNA synthesis. In the mouse ear epithelium (GELFANT 1962, 1963) and the gastrointestinal epithelium of the chicken (CAMERON and CLEFF- MAN 1964) both types of G_0 cells have been identified in the same tissue, although the G_0 corresponding to G_1 appears to be predominant in both cases. In the mouse ear epithelium the ability of cells to rest in a G_0 phase either after mitosis or after DNA synthesis appears to be genetically deter- mined, and if the cells rest in one phase in one cycle they rest in that phase in the succeeding cycles (GELFANT 1963).

Proliferative compartments of a cell renewal system will contain cells in all phases of the cell cycle (G_1, S, G_2 and mitosis) and possibly some cells in G_0. The maturation and functional compartments that do not contain dividing cells usually contain cells that have a DNA content that is equal to that of G_1 cells (BASERGA 1965). Direct evidence for this in the rat intestine has been obtained in the experiments of KEMBER et al. (1962) in which they measured the relative DNA contents of individual cells in both the crypts and villi of the intestine by means of Feulgen staining and microspectro- photometry. In the proliferative compartments of the crypts the DNA contents were distributed throughout the G_1, S and G_2 values whereas in the functional compartments of the villi less than 0.5% of the cells had DNA contents which differed from the G_1 value. A few exceptions to this generalisation have been identified and in a number of cell systems the mature or functional cells have DNA contents which correspond to G_2. These include the enamel producing cells of rabbit teeth (STARKEY 1963), rabbit osteocytes (OWEN and MACPHERSON 1963), human myocardial cells (SANDRITTER and SCOMAZZONI 1964), and some of the polyploid cells in the liver of many animal species (BUCHER 1963). In the case of liver cells, which synthesise DNA through several cycles without intervening mitoses during the development of polyploidy, it is difficult to decide where G_2 ends and G_1 begins and this terminology for the phases of the cell cycle cannot be easily employed.

The morphology and tissue location of stem cells and the youngest cells in the proliferation and maturation compartment may be very similar and in consequence the identification of stem cells may be difficult in practice (see e.g. PATT and QUASTLER 1963; CUDKOWITZ et al. 1964). The stem cells may, in addition, only divide at a comparatively slow rate with most of the cell production occuring in the proliferation and maturation compartments. The latter are then equivalent to amplification stages and the size and kinetics of the cell renewal system will depend mainly on the rate of cell division in these compartments (BOND et al. 1965). The stem-cell compartment, itself, would then be equivalent to a reserve population which divides very slowly, or negligibly, until there is some depletion of the maturation or functional compartments (LAJTHA et al. 1962; PATT and QUASTLER 1963).

The steady progress of cells from the proliferation to the functional compartment while the size of each compartment remains at a constant size implies that, on a statistical basis, for every cell that divides in the stem cell compartment one cell remains in that compartment and the other enters the maturation compartment. This controlled asymmetry in the progeny from cell division in the stem compartment is a vital aspect of the organisation of cell renewal systems but the way that it is attained is unknown at present. There must also be some controls which operate through feedback from the mature compartments to the immature ones which ensure the balance of cell birth and maturation and maintain the steady state in the cell renewal system. These controls are also able to alter the rates of cell proliferation and maturation to compensate for damage or perturbations such as those caused by wounding, starvation, disease, and irradiation. Little is known about these control mechanisms in any detail, but considerable knowledge has been obtained concerning the population kinetics of normal and perturbed systems through the use of H^{3}Tdr labelling and some of the quantitative aspects are discussed in the next section.

7.5 Definitions of kinetic parameters in cell renewal systems

The study of quantitative aspects of population kinetics is associated to a great extent with the work of Quastler. A useful introduction to this subject can be obtained by consulting a number of his publications from 1959 onwards (QUASTLER 1959a,b, 1960, 1963; QUASTLER et al. 1959; QUASTLER and SHERMAN 1959; SHERMAN and QUASTLER 1961; DORNFEST et al. 1962a,b; LIPKIN and QUASTLER 1962; LAMERTON et al. 1963; PATT and QUASTLER 1963; WIMBER and QUASTLER 1963; MOROWITZ et al. 1964). The concepts and analysis in this section draw extensively on the work of Quastler and as far as possible his notation is followed.

If compartment sizes are large and fluctuations of cell number due to the migration of individual cells between compartments are neglected, then the cell renewal systems of figs. 7.2. and 7.3 can be considered in terms of a steady flux of cells through compartments of constant size. The quantitative features of the renewal systems can then be described by three types of parameters for each compartment, associated with size, time and cell flux (QUASTLER 1959b):

> *Size, n_i.* Relative or absolute number of cells in the ith compartment, or some alternative measure of compartment size such as cell mass or volume.
>
> *Time, t_i.* Mean time of sojourn of cells in the ith compartment or the time elapsing between a cell acquiring and subsequently losing the characteristics of the compartment in question. Cell division may or may not occur in the compartment.
>
> *Flux, k_{in}, k_{out}, k_{ij}.* The relative or absolute number of cells entering or leaving a compartment, or migrating from the ith to the jth compartment respectively. Entry may be by birth through cell division or by migration, and exit by cell death or migration to other compartments.

For experimental purposes a number of other parameters are commonly employed in addition to the three listed above. In particular, a number of different time parameters may be defined which are easier to interpret in terms of the cell cycle durations, cell fluxes etc., than the time t_i defined above. These parameters include the following:

> *Birth rate, k_b or k_{ii}.* The absolute or relative rate of cell production by division alone. This is equal to MI/t_m or LI/t_s in the steady-state system (BERTALANFFY 1964; LALA et al. 1964). If all of the cells in the compartment are involved in the cell cycle (i.e. no G_0) then the birth rate is also equal to the reciprocal of the cell cycle time, $1/T$, and these relationships are identical to those introduced in ch. 4 § 4, eqs. (4.1) and (4.2). If a significant fraction of the cells in the compartment are not dividing

then the birth rate cannot be equated with $1/T$, but the other expressions are valid irrespective of the G_0 fraction.

Transit time. The time that elapses between a cell entering from a previous compartment and the cell or its progeny leaving in order to enter a subsequent compartment. If there is cell division in the compartment the transit time will equal the product of the cell cycle time with the average number of divisions that occur within the compartment plus any time spent in a non-dividing state in the compartment.

Turnover time. The time required for the replacement of a number of cells equal to the size of the compartment (LEBLOND and WALKER 1956). For the case of a non-dividing compartment the turnover and transit times are identical. In the case of a stem compartment the turnover time equals the reciprocal of the birth rate, i.e., the cell cycle time when all cells are proliferating.

Growth fraction, G.F. The fraction of a particular population or cell renewal system that consists of cells progressing round the cell cycle. This fraction can be determined experimentally as the ratio

'observed LI/theoretical LI'. (7.1)

The theoretical LI is the value that would be obtained if all cells were in the cell cycle and can be calculated from the durations of the phases of the cell cycle (see also ch. 7 § 13). The fraction of the population that is not involved in the cell cycle may be G_0, maturing, or functional cells, or any combination of these, and the meaning of the G.F. depends in detail on the system or population under study.

All of the above definitions may be used with reference to the whole renewal system or to compartments with a heterogeneous composition, in addition to the homogeneous compartments that have been illustrated in figs. 7.2 and 7.3. For compartments of heterogeneous composition the terms cannot be directly related to parameters associated with individual cells and compartments and represent gross average sizes, rates and times (QUASTLER 1960, 1963).

A steady state implies that the size of each compartment and the cell fluxes are constant with time and under these conditions the following relationships hold. (It is assumed that cell death within the renewal system is insignificant, or occurs at the end of the system and is included as one of the flux parameters.)

$$k_{in} = \Sigma_j k_{ji} = k_{out} = \Sigma_j k_{ij} \qquad (7.2)$$

$$t_i = n_i/\Sigma_j k_{ij}. \qquad (7.3)$$

In this notation (QUASTLER 1959b) $\Sigma_j k_{ji}$ signifies the sum of all the inputs from other compartments into the ith compartment, and $\Sigma_j k_{ij}$ the sum of all the outputs, summation being carried out over all values of j. Equations (4.1) and (4.2), previously quoted for the relationships between the duration of mitosis and the mitotic index, and the duration of the S phase and the labelling index, respectively, are examples of the application of the general relationship stated above in eq. (7.3). In the case of cell renewal systems eq. (7.2) can be expressed in the following ways for the various types of compartment (PATT 1963):

stem cell,	birth rate = efflux
dividing and maturing,	influx + birth rate = efflux
maturing, functional,	influx = efflux
any compartment,	efflux = cumulative birth rate from all earlier compartments.

From the last of these equations it follows that the mean turnover time in the dividing compartments can be determined independently from the efflux of cells from the renewal system or from the birth rates, if these two parameters are determined separately. The determination of turnover times from the efflux of cells will be discussed in detail in ch. 7 §§ 9, 10.

An extremely large number of parameters need to be determined for renewal systems which contain a number of interconnected compartments and the general case of a system containing R compartments, all of which are interconnected with one another has been described by QUASTLER (1960) and QUASTLER and SHERMAN (1959). This type of system is not very common in practice, and the systems of figs. 7.2 and 7.3 are the most common types. In these systems there is a unidirectional flow of cells from the stem cell compartment, through maturation compartments to the functional compartment. If there are R compartments connected in this manner, and the total size of the system is normalised to 1, there will be $(R-1)$ size parameters, R time parameters, and $(R+1)$ transition parameters, if birth only occurs in a single stem cell compartment and death only occurs from the final functional compartment. If the possibility of cell birth and cell death from each compartment is included, as may occur in a number of compartments in myelopoiesis (MALONEY et al. 1962) and erythropoiesis (STOHLMAN 1959) for example, there will be $(3R-1)$ transition parameters. There will then be a total of $(5R-2)$ parameters, taking into account birth and death in each compartment. Equations (7.2) and (7.3) lead to $2R$ equations so that it will be necessary to determine $(3R-2)$ independent parameters to fully characterise the simple renewal system discussed here. The more general case discussed by

QUASTLER (1960) and QUASTLER and SHERMAN (1959b) in which each compartment may be connected to every other requires the determination of a much greater number of independent parameters, (R^2+R). Because of the large number of parameters involved it has not yet been possible to analyse any renewal system fully at this time, but a number of the important parameters such as birth rates, transit and turnover times have been determined in tissues such as the intestinal epithelium and bone marrow (see ch. 7 §§ 11, 12). Many tumours are relatively simple systems which approximate to closed proliferating populations but only a few of these have been even partially characterised (see MENDELSOHN 1964; LALA and PATT 1966).

7.6 Population kinetics in a model renewal system

The significance of the various parameters in a cell renewal system and their partial determination by means of H³Tdr labelling can be illustrated

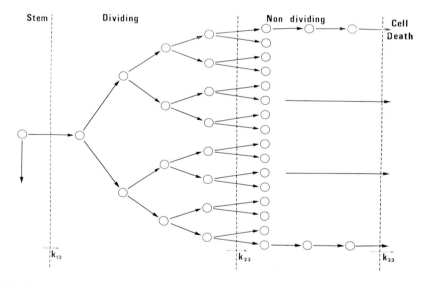

Fig. 7.4. Model cell renewal system containing stem, dividing and non-dividing compartments. Cells pass through four divisions in the dividing compartment before entering the non-dividing compartment. Relative sizes of the stem, dividing and non-dividing compartments are 1:15:48.

Population kinetics in animal tissues

with reference to the model system of some animal tissue shown in fig. 7.4. In this renewal system there is a small stem cell compartment, a maturation and proliferation compartment which contains dividing cells and a third compartment which contains non-dividing cells of both maturation and functional compartments. Cells pass through four divisions in the proliferative compartment before entering the non-dividing compartment. On the assumption that the cell cycle duration is the same throughout the renewal system and cells progress at a steady uniform rate through the successive compartments, the values of the various parameters of the compartments have been summarised in table 7.1. It is clear that

TABLE 7.1

Compartment parameters for the model cell renewal system of fig. 7.4.

Compartment parameter	Stem	Dividing	Non-dividing
Size*	1	15	48
Cell cycle time (hr)*	T	T	–
Number of divisions, d*	–	4	–
Birth rate (cells/hr)	$1/T$	$15/T$	–
Input, k_{in}, (cells /hr)	0	$1/T$	$16/T$
Output, k_{out}, (cells/hr)	$1/T$	$16/T$	$16/T$
Transit time (hr)	–	$4T$	$3T$
Turnover time (each comp.)	T	$15T/16$	$3T$
Turnover time (dividing comps. combined)		T	

* These values are defined for the compartments of the system illustrated in fig. 7.4. The other values are derived from these in accordance with the flow of cells through the compartments as illustrated. The number of divisions in the second compartment is related to the input and output by $d = 3.322 \log_{10} k_{in}/k_{out}$, eq. (7.4), ch. 7 § 7.

the relationship between the transit time, turnover time and cell cycle time is not the same in each compartment. In the stem cell compartment the turnover time and cell cycle time are the same but the transit time is indeterminate. In the dividing compartment the turnover time and cell cycle time are almost the same, because most of the cell output comes from cell division within the compartment. If the rate of cell influx from the stem cell compartment was not negligible in comparison to the birth rate within the dividing compartment, then the turnover time would be significantly less than the cell cycle time. If the stem and dividing compartments cannot be distinguished experimentally, then in the combined dividing compartment, that has no input, the cell cycle time and turnover time are identical. In the non-dividing compartment the transit and turnover times are the same and determined by the compartment size and the cell flux.

The qualitative difference in the relationship between these various time parameters in different types of compartments must be borne in mind in experimental work and it is important to distinguish them carefully for any particular system that is under investigation.

7.7 Transit time and the number of divisions in a dividing compartment

Once the values for the flux of cells from one compartment to the next have been determined these values can be used to estimate the average number of divisions that each cell must pass through during transit through a dividing compartment. If each cell which enters the dividing compartment passes through d divisions within the compartment, then it will produce 2^d progeny which leave the compartment (see fig. 7.4). Consequently the following relationship will hold between the influx and efflux of cells and the number of divisions within the compartment.

$$k_{out} = k_{in} \, 2^d$$

or $\quad d = 3.322 \log_{10} k_{out}/k_{in}.$ \hfill (7.4)

In the derivation of this formula it is assumed that there is no cell death within the compartment. If cell death does occur the number of divisions during transit will not be given by this simple relationship but will depend also on the manner of death, i.e., whether cells die only at the end of the compartment or at random through the compartment. In such cases the number of divisions during transit will be more difficult to estimate. The concept of an average number of cell divisions during transit through a compartment cannot strictly be applied to a stem cell compartment, but only to subsequent compartments in a renewal system. This is because a stem cell compartment is self renewing and has no input, so there is no transit through the compartment but only a rate of turnover. Although this formula has been derived for the case of an integral number of divisions, it will be assumed to hold for compartments in which the average number of divisions is non integral. In the latter case any particular cell will pass through an integral number of divisions in transit but this integer will not be the same for every cell that passes through the compartment.

7.8 *Transit times through non-dividing compartments*

It is usually assumed that cells enter the first non-dividing compartment in a renewal system after the final mitosis in the dividing compartment. This assumption is made because the majority of non-dividing, maturing or functional cells are diploid and correspond to cells in G_1 (BASERGA 1965, see ch. 7 § 4). The interval between labelling with H^3Tdr and the appearance of labelled cells in a given morphological stage in the non-dividing compartments is then the minimum duration of $G_2 + t_m$ plus the total transit time up to the stage in question. The transit time through any particular non-dividing compartment is, similarly, the interval between the entry of labelled cells into the compartment in question and the entry of labelled cells into the successive compartment. Transit times have been measured in this way in the small intestine and the bone marrow and some of the results are discussed in ch. 7 § 11 and 7 § 12.

If the labelling index in the first non-dividing compartment is determined as a function of time after the injection of H^3Tdr, this index will increase from zero because of the entry of labelled cells. The labelling index will reach a plateau after a time equal to the duration of the final S phase in the dividing compartment, if the transit time through the non-dividing compartment is longer than the S phase (PATT and MALONEY 1963; LALA et al. 1966). After the labelling index has reached a plateau, the entry of cells that were labelled in earlier S phases into the non-dividing compartment may lead to a further increase in the labelling index (MALONEY et al. 1962; PATT and MALONEY 1963). Once labelled cells have begun to enter a non-dividing compartment the rate of increase of the labelling index will give an estimate of the rate of influx of cells into the compartment (k_{23}, fig. 7.4). The transit time will then be the inverse of this, $1/k_{23}$. If the influx is, for example, 5 % per hour then the transit time will be 20 hr. This estimate, however, can be biased by the straggling of cells with slow rates of maturation, and the rate of increase of the labelling index must be determined as soon after labelling as possible. The estimate of transit time will also be greatly overestimated if the transit time in the non-dividing compartments is very short or if cells are removed from this compartment randomly, rather than on a first-in-first-out basis (BOND et al. 1965).

Labelled cells will be lost from the renewal system as a whole after a time that is equal to the sum of the transit times through all of the matura-tion and functional compartments plus G_2 and t_m. This total transit time is the interval between the injection of H^3Tdr into the renewal system and the time at which the specific activity or the total activity of the system begins to fall. This interval is illustrated in figs. 7.5 and 7.6. If cells are lost from the renewal system by cell death, etc., at earlier stages of maturity than the end of the final non-dividing compartment, then the transit time determined in this way will be less than the true transit time.

7.9 Turnover times in dividing compartments

After labelled cells have completed transit through the non-dividing compartments they will begin to be lost from the renewal system and the specific activity of the system will fall with time. In approximately one cell cycle time the dividing cells in renewal system will all divide, but to maintain the renewal system in a steady state an equal number of cells must be lost from the system. The rate of cell loss will consequently equal the birth rate in the whole renewal system. If it is assumed that the mean activity of labelled cells that leave the system at any time is equal to the mean activity of the cells remaining, then the time for the specific activity to fall half of its starting value will equal the reciprocal of the mean birth rate or the median cell cycle time (STEEL 1963; QUASTLER 1963). Strictly, the halving time will only equal the median cycle time in the dividing compartments when sufficient time has elapsed for labelled and unlabelled cells to be randomly distributed amongst one another, and this randomisa-tion normally occurs within a few cycle times. The halving time of the specific activity of a renewal system is often loosely referred to as the turnover time. This reference will only be strictly true under the conditions in which cell cycle time and turnover time are identical and these conditions have already been discussed (see ch. 7 §§ 5, 6).

If there is a single cell cycle time throughout the dividing compartments, and no inter cell variation, then the specific activity will halve after each time interval that is equal to the cycle time. The specific activity at a time t, after the loss of label has begun, will be represented by the following equation (STEEL 1963).

$$A = A_0 \exp -0.693 \, t/T, \tag{7.5}$$

where A_0 represents the specific activity after the injection of H^3Tdr and before any labelled cells have been lost from the renewal system.

If the system contains compartments with different cell cycle times then the specific activity will be the sum of several exponential terms (fig. 7.5) and is represented by,

$$A = \Sigma A_1 \exp -0.693 \, t/T_1, \tag{7.6}$$

where A_1 represents the specific activity of the ith compartment and will be determined by the compartment size, rate of H^3Tdr incorporation, and availability of H^3Tdr to the compartment in question.

From this it can be seen that the slope of the specific activity curve alters with time and is eventually dominated by the slowest component. This analysis can be extended to renewal systems in which there is a variation in the cell cycle times within the dividing compartment. The specific activity is then expressed in an integral form,

$$A = A_0 \int F(T) \exp -0.693 \, t/T \cdot dT, \tag{7.7}$$

where $F(T)$ represents the distribution function for the cell cycle times and the range of integration is over the whole range of cycle times.

An alternative definition of halving time to the one adopted above has been used by STEEL (1963). This alternative definition equates the halving time to the time at which the slope of the specific activity curve is equal to the average rate of loss of H^3 activity over the whole time range. This time will be equal to the harmonic mean of the cell cycle times. This definition is less useful than the definition adopted above, since it depends on the measurement of the slope of a curve fitted to the experimental data and this can rarely be measured very accurately. The former definition of halving time as the time at which the specific activity falls to half the starting value will be used throughout the following discussions. Similar curves to the specific activity curves described above may be obtained by determining the mean grain counts per cell in the whole system. These will decline as a function of time in a similar manner to the specific activity curves and the same information about transit and turnover times can be obtained from both.

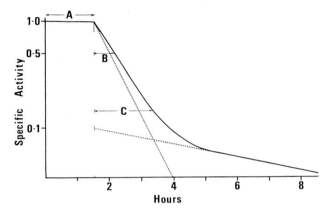

Fig. 7.5. Specific activity of a cell renewal system as a function of the time after a single injection of H^3Tdr. A is the time that elapses before labelled cells pass through the non-dividing compartments and begin to be lost from the system. The declining curve has been drawn for the case of a renewal system with two equal dividing compartments in which the cell cycle times are approximately 0.5 and 5 days. B is the time for the specific activity to fall to one half of the starting value, the halving time. C is the time for the rate of loss of activity, i.e. the slope of the specific activity curve, to reach the mean of the initial and final rates of loss and is equal to the harmonic cycle time.

7.10 Turnover and transit times in animal tissues

A number of workers have studied the variation in tissue specific activity after a single injection of H^3Tdr in the manner described in the previous section (fig. 7.5) and some of the results obtained by STEEL and LAMERTON (1965) are shown in fig. 7.6. These results are given for the jejunum, colon, stomach and bone marrow and show the characteristic plateau and declining exponential portions, although the plateau is small and difficult to

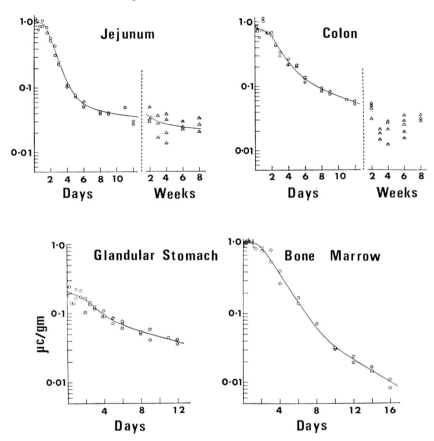

Fig. 7.6. The turnover of H³ in four tissues labelled with H³Tdr in the normal rat. Results are expressed as microcuries of H³ per gram of wet tissue following a standard dose of 0.5 Ci/g body weight (reproduced from STEEL and LAMERTON 1965).

measure accurately in the stomach. The values obtained for the plateau and exponential portions in a number of tissues are given in table 7.2 for a number of different experimental groups.

In some of these tissues, particularly the lung and thymus, the specific activity falls to a low level and then remains constant or subsequently falls at a very slow rate. The label remaining at these longer times is due either to cells with extremely long cell cycle times or the presence of additional

TABLE 7.2

Plateau length and turnover times for the specific activity of H³Tdr and C¹⁴Tdr labelled rat tissues.

Strain and age at start of experiment	Organ	Pre-cursor	Plateau (days)	Initial halving time (days)	Remarks	Ref.
F₁ Marshall and August hybrids. 6–8 weeks, 100–200 g male.	Small intest.	H³Tdr	1.4	0.8	Second component with halving time of 7.5 days	1
	Colon	H³Tdr	1.0	1.8	halving time increased to 2.7 days after appr. 1 wk.	1
	Glandular stomach	H³Tdr	<1.0	3.8–5.0		1
	Spleen	H³Tdr	<1.0	2	Halving time increased to 8 days	1
	Thymus	H³Tdr	2.5	3	Levels after 20 days	1
	Testis	H³Tdr	25	8–10		1
	Lung	H³Tdr	3	3	Levels after 6 days	1
August	Bone marrow	H³Tdr	1.6	1.5		1
Sprague-Dawley 3–4 months 200 g female	Bone marrow	H³Tdr C¹⁴Tdr	– –	2 2		2
	Bone marrow	I¹³¹Udr	–	1.2–1.3		2
Sprague-Dawley 45 days 180 g male (a)	Small intest.	C¹⁴Tdr	1.8	1.0	Second component with halving time 4 days	3
	Spleen	C¹⁴Tdr	0	1.2	Second component with halving time 4 days	3
	Thymus	C¹⁴Tdr	0	5		
	Bone marrow	C¹⁴Tdr	0	1.8		
	Small intest.	H³Tdr	–	1.7 ᵇ	Second component 30 ᵇ days	4

TABLE 7.2 (cont.)

Strain and age at start of experiment	Organ	Pre-cursor	Plateau (days)	Initial halving time (days)	Remarks	Ref.
174 g male (a)	Spleen	H³Tdr	–	4 [b]	Second component 40 [b] days	4
	Thymus	H³Tdr	–	2.5 [b]	Second component 70 [b] days	4
	Testis	H³Tdr	–	60 [b]		4
	Liver	H³Tdr	–	20 [b]		4
	Muscle	H³Tdr	–	25 [b]		4
	Kidney	H³Tdr	–	55 [b]		4

(a) Specific activity data all corrected for growth, corr. sp. act. = actual sp. act./(body wt. at death).

(b) Times for specific activity to fall to $1/e$ of starting value.

References:

1) STEEL and LAMERTON (1965)
2) FEINENDEGEN et al. (1966)
3) NYGAARD and POTTER (1960)
4) GERBER et al. (1960)

renewal systems with long turnover times in these tissues. LIPKIN and QUASTLER (1962) have reported the retention of a small fraction of labelled cells in the regions of the colon and stomach in mice and rats for up to 1 week and in the frog up to 3 weeks, and the relatively high grain counts over these cells indicated that they had passed through few cell divisions over this period of time. The decline in the specific activity of a number of the tissues can be described in terms of more then one exponential component; in the case of the jejunum, for example, there is a fast component with a halving time of 0.8 days and a slow component with a halving time of 7.5 days (STEEL and LAMERTON 1965). The former is due to the rapid proliferation of the cells on the intestinal villi and the latter to the slower proliferation of cells in the intestinal wall and these two cell types are from cell renewal systems that are only remotely connected with one another. In a number of the tissues listed in table 7.2 there may be more than one renewal system and the turnover times are difficult to relate directly to the cell cycle times. In the jejunum the faster turnover time of

0.8 days which is due to the cells of the intestinal crypts and villi may be compared to the cell cycle time in these cells which ranges between 0.4 and 0.6 days, depending on the location of the cells in the crypts (CAIRNIE et al. 1965a). The turnover time determined experimentally may be different from the cell cycle time because the specific activity of the tissue may be affected by the salvage of labelled breakdown products from dead cells and by the growth of the tissue during the course of the experiment.

The effect of the incorporation of labelled breakdown products on the turnover time is clearly evident in the data of FEINENDEGEN et al. (1966) for the rat bone marrow in table 7.2. When the animal was labelled with $I^{131}Udr$ the turnover time was 1.2–1.3 days, but this tracer is incorporated much less readily into DNA than H^3- or $C^{14}Tdr$ and is salvaged to a negligible extent. In contrast, the turnover time obtained with both H^3- or $C^{14}Tdr$ was significantly longer, 2 days, and this must be due to the salvage of H^3-labelled breakdown products from the blood stream during the course of the experiment. The extent to which salvage occurs in the body has been discussed earlier (ch. 2 § 8) and the effect that this has on turnover times may need to be evaluated separately for each tissue.

The effect of tissue growth on the turnover time has not been mentioned earlier because renewal systems were defined in terms of a steady state in which growth had ceased. Many of the tissues listed in table 7.2 are still increasing in size during the course of the experiments and this would itself cause a decline in the tissue specific activity. To obtain a more accurate estimate of the turnover time the specific activities need to be corrected for the growth of the particular tissue in question, and in the young animal the most rapidly growing tissues are the testis, lung and bone marrow. In some of the results in table 7.2 the specific activities were corrected, by the experimenters, for the growth of the whole animal, but this will overestimate the turnover time in the more slowly growing tissues and undercorrect for the rapidly growing tisues. In addition to differences due the different strains of animals used in the experiments listed in table 7.2, the effects of tissue growth in animals of different age ranges may also contribute to the differences in the results obtained.

7.11 Cell renewal in the small intestine

The small intestine is an organ in which the rate of cell turnover is one of the highest in the body (BERTALANFFY and LAU 1962) and the cell cycle time in the intestine for most mammals is between 10 and 14 hr (see table 4.3, ch. 4 § 9). The small intestine is customarily considered in terms of three regions, the duodenum, jejunum, and ileum, but the distinction between these regions is not sharply defined. The surface of the intestinal mucosa projects into the illumen as numerous villi and at the base of these villi there are glands known as the crypts of Leberkühn (see, e.g. BLOOM and FAWCETT 1962). Over 90% of the cells that line the villi are columnar epithelial cells and the remainder mainly goblet cells. The crypts contain mainly undifferentiated cells and mitoses are only found in this region of the small intestine. The crypts also contain a small proportion of of goblet, argentaffine and Paneth cells and it is usual to regard the latter two as independent from the main renewal system of the small intestine.

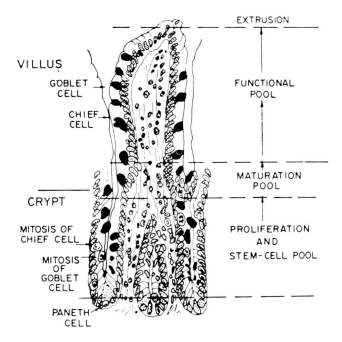

Fig. 7.7. Diagram showing the structure, cell types, and relationship of the crypt and villus in the small intestine. Regions of cell formation, migration and loss are shown. (reproduced from BOND et al. 1965).

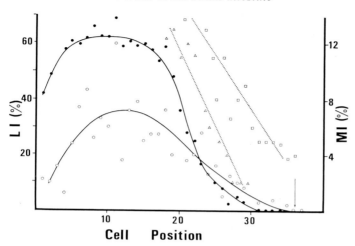

Fig. 7.8. Distributions in cell positions, counted from the base of the crypt, of mitotic (o) and of labelled cells, ● 1 hr, △ 4 hr, and □ 8 hr after giving H³Tdr, 0.5 μCi/g 10 Ci/mmole (redrawn from CAIRNIE et al. 1965a). The arrow marks the mean height of the crypt.

The basic renewal system then consists of the dividing cells of the crypt which give rise to the columnar and goblet cells of the villi and this is illustrated in fig. 7.7. The basic scheme of cell renewal in the intestine was recognised very early. BIZZOZERO (1892), for example, deduced that the restriction of mitoses to the crypts implied that cells must migrate from the crypts to the villi and differentiate to columnar and goblet cells. The first autoradiographic study of this migration was made by LEBLOND et al. (1948) in which they used P³² to label the proliferative cells of the crypts. Subsequent studies by a number of workers with H³Tdr as a precursor have enabled the rates of cell proliferation and migration to be determined in considerable detail and some of these studies will be described here.

The proliferative cells of the crypt can be labelled with H³Tdr and the distribution of labelled cells is similar to the distribution of mitoses if the intestine is fixed within an hour of the injection of label. The labelling and mitotic indices as a function of the position of cells along the length of the crypt are shown in fig. 7.8. These results are taken from the experiments of CAIRNIE et al. (1965a) in which they calculated the indices from the number of labelled and mitotic cells at each position along the crypt in a large number of sections of separate crypts. In the particular strain of rats used for these experiments the mean length of the crypts was approximately 36 cell positions and mitoses were never observed in the upper 6 cell positions. On the basis of these figures, proliferation, maturation and functional compartments can be defined with a reasonable degree of precision. In the studies of CAIRNIE et al. (1965a) the lower 30 cell positions of the crypts constituted the stem and proliferation compartments, the upper 6 positions the non-dividing maturation compartment, and the villi the functional compartment. Cell birth occurs in the base of the crypts and cell death at the tips of the villi from which cells are shed into the lumen. The duration of the phases of the cell cycle in the various regions of the proliferation compartment has been determined by CAIRNIE et al. (1965a) by means of the pulse chase method (ch. 4 § 5) and these are listed in table 4.3, ch. 4 § 9. Over most of the proliferation compartment the cell cycle is approximately 10.5 hr long (G_1 2 hr, S 6.5 hr, G_2 1 hr, M 1 hr) but there is a trend to a longer cell cycle at the bottom of the crypt. There is no region which can be strictly defined as the stem cell compartment but the cells in the first few positions at the bottom of the crypt with long cell cycle times may be comparable to stem cells. All of the proliferative cells in the crypt appear to be involved in the continuous process of cell production and within a few days of an injection of H^3Tdr the labelled cells move out from the crypts and along the villi. The concept of asymmetric cell division that was introduced with reference to the self maintaining stem cell compartment (ch. 7 § 4) consequently does not apply to the cells at the base of the crypt.

If all of the cells in the proliferative compartment of the crypts are involved in the cell cycle then the labelling index in this region should be given simply by t_s/T. This ratio equals 62%, which agrees very closely with the labelling index in the lower half of the crypt shown in fig. 7.8. Consequently, there are probably no cells in a long G_0 phase in the proliferative compartment of the crypt. If a growth fraction is calculated for the whole crypt this will merely represent the fraction of the crypt population which is in the proliferative compartment. The growth fraction defined in this way can be calculated in two ways, either from the ratio of the observed crypt labelling index to the theoretical labelling index for a growth fraction of one (eq. (7.1)), or alternatively from the fraction of the crypt that is occupied by the proliferative compartment. CAIRNIE et al.

(1965a) estimated that mean number of labelled cells per crypt was 12.7 which corresponds to a labelling index of 35.6% for the whole crypt, and the theoretical labelling index is t_s/T or 62%. The growth fraction is then equal to 0.57. The fraction of the crypt occupied exclusively by the proliferative compartment is the region over which labelled cells and mitoses are observed. This region may be considered to end approximately at the position where the labelling index or mitotic index fall one half of their maximum values, i.e. approximately at position 21 from the bottom of the crypt. If there are equal numbers of cells in the crypt at each cell position then the growth fraction will be equal to 21/36 or 0.58. The agreement between these two different estimates of the growth fraction is clearly very good. The non dividing maturation region of the crypt consequently occupies a little less than the upper half of the crypt length. A similar estimate of the growth fraction in the crypts of CAF_1 mice has been made by FRY et al. (1963) and the value they obtained was 0.55. These values for the growth fractions consequently suggest that the distribution of cells between the dividing and the non-dividing compartments of the crypts is approximately the same in both rats and mice.

The mitotic index and labelling index data for rat crypts that have been reproduced in fig. 7.8 can be used to estimate the average number of divisions that cells pass through during transit through the dividing compartment. To estimate this it is necessary to exclude the stem-cell region for reasons stated previously (ch. 7 § 7) and to an approximation the first 6 cell positions will be regarded as the stem compartment. The birth rate in this stem compartment is proportional to the area under either the mitotic index or the labelling index curve from position 1 to position 6, and this will equal the influx of cells into the dividing compartment. The efflux of cells from the dividing compartment will similarly be proportional to the area under the whole of the mitotic index or labelling index curve from positions 1 to 30. For simplicity it is assumed that the durations of the phases of the cell cycle are approximately the same throughout the crypt, although this was not strictly true. The number of divisions made during transit through the dividing compartment from position 6 onwards can then be determined from either the mitotic index or the labelling index data by means of eq. (7.4), as follows:

$$\text{MI data, No. of divisions} = 3.332 \log_{10} 325/55 = 2.6$$
$$\text{LI data, No. of divisions} = 3.322 \log_{10} 408/116 = 1.8$$

(The areas beneath the MI and LI curves have been estimated graphically and are expressed in arbitrary units.)

The number of divisions may be taken as the mean of these two estimates, 2.2. Since one cell cycle is approximately 10.5 hr long cells will spend an average of 2.2 × 10.5 hr, or 23.1 hr in transit from position 6 to position 30. Consequently the mean velocity of transit through the dividing compartment will be approximately 1.04 cell positions/hr. The velocity of cells at the top of the dividing compartment will be given by the total proliferation rate in the dividing compartment. CAIRNIE et al. (1965a) estimate this to be 1.45 cell positions /hr.

The migration of cells from the crypts to the villi can be studied by fixing intestines at intervals after a single injection of H^3Tdr and observing the distribution of labelled cells in the crypts and villi. The results shown in fig. 7.8, for example, show the distribution of labelled cells in the upper region of the crypt at 30 min, 4 hr and 8 hr after an injection of H^3Tdr. The velocity of labelled cells in this region of the crypt can be estimated from the rate of movement of the labelled cells up the crypt, and CAIRNIE et al. (1959a) obtained a value of 1.27 cell positions /hr. This agrees extremely well with the previous independent estimates for the velocity of cell migration. Two time parameters which are relatively easy to estimate from the migration of labelled cells are the time taken for labelled cells to reach the villi and the time taken for labelled cells to progress through the whole length of the villi. These times have been summarised in table 7.3 for each of a number of strains of rats and mice and it is clear that there is a certain amount of variation not only between different strains but also in the same strain at different ages.

The time that elapses between the injection of H^3Tdr and the appearance of label on 50 % of the villi is equal to the median of the minimum times taken for cells to progress through the maturation compartment from the final S phase in the dividing compartments. In the experiments of CAIRNIE et al. (1965a) this time was 12.5 hr. The minimum transit time through the maturation compartment in these experiments is consequently 10.5 hr. In similar experiments with C57 mice QUASTLER and SHERMAN (1959) estimated a lower limit of 4 hours for the transit time through the maturation compartment, based on the time at which labelled cells first appeared at the base of the villi. The transit times listed in table 7.3 were all estimated in the manner just described, and the durations of the phases

TABLE 7.3

Transit times through the proliferative, maturation, and functional compartments of the intestinal epithelium (D, duodenum; J, jejunum; I, ileum).

Animal and age		Transit time proliferative compt.* (hr)	Time for 50% of villi to be labelled (hr)	Transit time maturation compt. (hr)	Villus transit time (hr)	Total transit time from labelling (hr)
CAF₁ mice, 93 days	D	22	5.5	4.5	30.0	41
FRY et al. (1963)	J	22	7.4	6.4	29.2	44
	I	22	10.2	9.2	13.8–16.8	34–37
372 days	D	22	6.5	5.5	35	48
	J	22	9.4	8.4	33.2	52
	I	22	11.7	10.7	19.7	43
940 days	D	26	10.9	9.9	31.2	53
	J	26	11.5	10.5	30	53
	I	26	12.4	11.4	19.2	34
C57 mice, QUASTLER and SHERMAN (1959)	I	42	9.5	4	17.5	36.5
August rats, 56 days CAIRNIE et al. (1965a)	J	23	12.5	10.5	–	–

* Assuming 2.2 divisions during transit. This value is calculated in the text for August rats only but has been taken as the same for each of the examples cited in the table.

of the cell cycle that had been determined for each strain or species were used in the estimations.

The time taken for labelled cells to traverse the length of the villi is simply equal to the transit time through the functional compartment itself, and these are listed in table 7.3. If cells progressed steadily over the villus surface and were only lost through cell death at the tip of the villus there would be little loss of label until a significant number of labelled cells had reached the tip of the villi. In a series of experiments, FRY et al. (1963) compared the time for cells to reach the tips of the villi with the rate of loss of H³ activity from the intestine as a whole. They found that 60 to 70% of the original H³ activity was lost before significant numbers of cells had reached the tips of the villi. It was concluded that in the strain of mice, CAF_1, used for the experiments cells must be lost from both the sides of the villi and the tips. This may not be true for every strain or species.

A region of the intestinal renewal system that deserves attention is the region in which cells are in transition from a dividing state to a non-dividing state at the top of the crypts. Instead of a progressive lengthening of the cell cycle, which is often the prelude to a transition to a non-dividing state (see ch. 7 § 13) the cell cycle in this region is actually shorter than at any lower position (CAIRNIE et al. 1965a). Detailed analysis of the nature of the transition of a non-dividing state has been made by CAIRNIE et al. (1965b). This analysis involves a modification of the concept of asymmetric cell division introduced earlier with reference to the stem cell (ch. 7 § 4). In the early part of the proliferative compartment most cells will divide to produce two daughter cells which will both divide one cell cycle later. At some region near the end of the proliferative compartment most cells that will divide will produce two daughter cells which do not divide further but merely progress through the maturation compartment and eventually reach the functional compartment of the villi. The position at which non dividing daughter cells are first produced will be one cell cycle before the last position in the crypt at which mitoses are observed. The model of CAIRNIE et al. (1965b) allows for a gradual change-over from positions at which only dividing daughter cells are produced to ones where only non-dividing cells are produced. In this model there is an intermediate region where it is possible for cells to produce one dividing and one non-dividing daughter cell. Over this region there will be an increasing probability that as cells progress higher up the crypt they will produce non-dividing daughter cells. This transition will gradually reduce the number of cells that enter the cell cycle after division so that as cells progress higher up the crypt there will be, on the average, fewer cells in the G_1 phase, then fewer in S and eventually fewer in the whole cycle and finally none in the cell cycle at all. This will result in a fall in the labelling index and the mitotic index as cells progress up the crypt, with the former falling first. This is seen in the experimental observations in fig. 7.8. Although the analysis of CAIRNIE et al. (1956b) describes the phenomenology of the transition from the dividing to the non-dividing compartments very well, the molecular mechanisms involved in the transitions are not known. The mechanism may, for example, involve gradients of some essential compounds in the crypt or a particular concentration or structural arrangement of nuclear or cytoplasmic products, but no details are known at present.

7.12 Cell renewal in the bone marrow

In contrast to the previous example, the intestinal epithelium, no spatial boundaries can be attributed to the various compartments of the cell renewal systems in the bone marrow. The main distinguishing feature of each compartment is the cell morphology and only the final functional cells, mature leucocytes, erythrocytes, and platelets are found in a separate location from the cells of the other compartments. Even these cells are also found alongside the less mature cells within the bone marrow and a change in cell morphology is consequently the main indication of the progressive maturation of cells through the various compartments of the renewal system. The bone marrow contains a number of distinct renewal systems, each of which is concerned with the production of one of the cell types found in the peripheral blood. These systems may have a common origin in a single type of stem cell, but the nature of the stem cell and its kinetics are still a matter of some conjecture (LAJTHA et al. 1962; GURNEY et al. 1962). Although small marrow lymphocytes have been tentatively identified as marrow stem cells the evidence is not yet conclusive (CUD-KOWITZ et al. 1964). The marrow renewal systems include those of erythropoiesis, myelopoiesis, thrombopoiesis and the morphological changes involved in these systems were well described before the introduction of quantitative studies with radioactive tracers (see, e.g. WINTROPE 1961; BLOOM and FAWCETT 1962; FORTEZA BOVER 1964). These systems are summarised in table 7.4. The quantitative features of these systems have been reviewed briefly by BOND et al. (1965) and the time parameters for erythropoiesis, myelopoiesis, and thrombopoiesis are reproduced from their review in fig. 7.9. These time parameters are based on a variety of different experimental methods in addition to the methods described earlier for use with H^3Tdr labelling, and not all the methods are

TABLE 7.4

Cell renewal systems of the bone marrow excluding the lymphoid system (PATT and
QUASTLER 1963; BLOOM and FAWCETT 1962).

Stem cell compartment	Dividing and maturing compartment	Maturation compartment	Functional compartment
	Erythropoiesis Pronormoblast – basophilic normo- blast – polychromatic normoblast	–Reticulocyte	–Erythrocyte
Small marrow lymphocyte	*Myelopoiesis* Myeloblast – promye- locyte – myelocyte–	Metamyelocyte – band–	Polymor- phonuclear granulocyte
	Trombopoiesis Megakaryocyte	Platelet	Platelet

of equal precision. The time scale in fig. 7.9 is measured from the entry
of cells into the first recognisible category after the stem cell. Although
indirect information is available for stem cell kinetics (LAJTHA et al. 1962,
1964) lifetime is not a term that can be satisfactorily applied to stem cells
since by definition, they last for ever. The declining curves to the right of
the maturation compartments indicate approximately the times spent
by the mature cells in the blood stream and also the nature of their even-
tual death and removal. The leucocytes and platelets are removed at
random, by a process that is independent of the age of the cells. The
erythrocytes have a more definite lifespan and are removed as a consequence of aging and death. Rather than making an attempt to review all
of the work on H³Tdr labelling in bone marrow in this section, a limited
series of experiments have been selected in order to present a fairly complete picture of one cell renewal system in a single species. A detailed
analysis has been made of granulopoiesis by MALONEY et al. (1962, 1963),
and PATT and MALONEY (1963, 1964) and of erythropoiesis by LALA et al.
(1965, 1966), in the canine bone marrow, and the latter will be discussed in
the rest of this section.

The duration of the phases of the cell cycle in each of the dividing
erythroid precursors have been determined by the pulse chase method

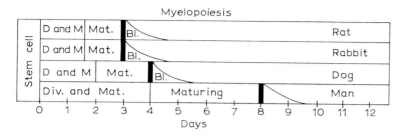

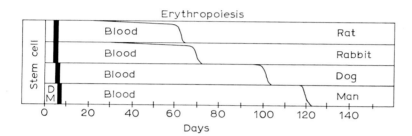

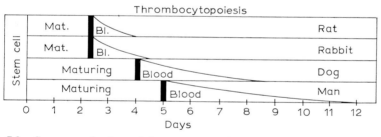

Fig. 7.9. Summary of estimated time parameters for haemopoiesis in the rat, rabbit, dog, and man, and the lifetimes of mature cells in the peripheral blood. D and M, dividing and maturing cells; MAT, non-dividing maturing cells; Bl cells in the peripheral blood (reproduced from BOND et al. 1965).

(ch. 4 § 5) and these values are G_1 2 hr, S 6 hr, G_2 1 hr, M 1 hr (LALA et al. 1966). The duration of the S phase was also determined by a C^{14}- and H^3Tdr double labelling method (see ch.4 § 6) and this has given the same value as the pulse chase method (LALA et al. 1965). The maturation of the erythroid precursors and their migration from dividing to non-dividing

compartments has also been studied by the methods described earlier
(ch. 7 §§ 7, 8). A number of dogs were given a single injection of H³Tdr
and bone marrow samples obtained at a number of subsequent intervals.
The appearance of labelled cells in the early non-dividing maturation
compartments as a function of the time after labelling is summarised in
fig. 7.10. Late polychromatic and orthochromatic normoblasts with

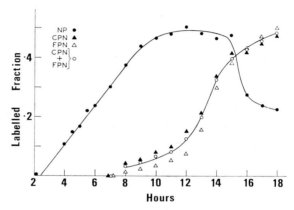

Fig. 7.10.   Labelling pattern in the non-proliferating red cells as a function of the time
after a single injection of H³Tdr; results show the mean for three dogs. ●, late polychromatic normoblasts and orthochromatic normoblasts with distinct nuclear chromatin grouped in the first non-dividing compartment (NP). Intact red cells with pyknotic
nuclei (GPN ▲), and free pyknotic red cell nuclei (FPN △) are grouped in the second non-
dividing compartment (reproduced from LALA et al. 1966).

intact nuclei were defined as the first non-dividing compartment. Intact
red cells with pyknotic nuclei and free pyknotic nuclei were defined as the
second maturation compartment. In fig. 7.10 the rate of entry of labelled
cells into the first maturation compartment is constant over a period of
approximately 6 hr, during which time the cells that were labelled in the
last S phase enter the compartment. The rate of entry is given by the
slope of this line and a value of 8 % per hour was estimated. The average
transit time through the first maturation compartment is consequently
12.5 hr, if cells progress uniformly through this compartment. A second
rise in the fraction of labelled cells in the first maturation compartment
would be expected at about 13 hr after labelling, due to the entry of cells

that incorporated H³Tdr during the S phase of an earlier cell cycle. This was not observed because at about 14 hr and later, significant numbers of labelled cells passed from the first to the second maturation compartment. Between about 11 and 14 hr there was a temporary balance in the rates of entry and efflux of labelled cells in the first maturation compartment which resulted in a constant labelled fraction over this interval. The fraction of labelled pyknotic nuclei, with or without intact cytoplasm, i.e. the second maturation compartment, did not increase at a constant rate, as can be seen in fig. 7.10. This was interpreted by LALA et al. (1966) in terms of a random transition into the second maturation compartment. This transition involves the loss of the erythroid nucleus and independent evidence has been obtained by ADAMS (1964) which shows that the transition may occur over a wide range of haemaglobin contents. This would support the kinetic evidence obtained by LALA et al. (1966) as shown in fig. 7.10.

Some of the numerical data obtained from H³Tdr labelling experiments for the erythropoietic renewal system have been reproduced in table 7.5. The data are sufficient for a complete analysis to be made of the birth rates, cell flux and number of cell divisions during transit. The results of the analysis of these parameters have been included in the table and indicate, for example, that cells pass through 2.2 divisions on average during transit through the basophilic normoblast compartment, and 1.5 divisions during transit through the polychromatic normoblast compartment. From these results the possibility of any cell death anywhere up to the transition to the first non-dividing compartment was also investigated. The rate of efflux of cells from the final proliferative compartment, i.e. from the polychromatic normoblasts, is given in the table as 36.6 cells/hr. This is based on the cumulative proliferation rates in all the dividing compartments and agrees well with the rate of entry of cells into the first non-dividing compartment, of 37.2 cells/hr, which is based independently on the observed rate of entry of labelled cells. Consequently, there appears to be no significant cell loss up to this stage of development.

A comparison between the observed number and a theoretical number of labelled cells that would be found in the non-dividing compartment at about one cell cycle time after the injection of H³Tdr, provided additional evidence for the absence of cell loss at this stage. All cells that are in S in the polychromatic normoblast compartment will be labelled after an

TABLE 7.5

Cell fluxes during erythroid development (LALA et al. 1966).

Parameter	Dividing compartment			Non-dividing compartment	
	Proeryth-roblast	Baso-philic	Early polychro-matic normo-blast	Late polychro-matic and orthochro-matic normoblast	Erythro-cytes with pyknotic nuclei
Relative number (N)	25	106	359	465	71
0.5 labelling index (N_s/N)	0.65	0.56	0.39	0	0
Number in S (N_s)	16.3	59.4	140	0	0
Birth rate (N_s/t_s) per hr	2.8	10.1	23.7	0	0
Influx (k_{in}) per hr	$+$[1]	2.8	12.9	37.3 [2]	–
Efflux ($k_{out} = k_{in} + N_s/t_s$)	2.8	12.9	36.6	–	–
Mean no. of divisions [3]	–	2.2	1.4	–	–
Transit time (no. of divs. $\times\ T$) hr	–	22	14	12.5 [2]	–

[1]   Indicates an unknown stem cell efflux into the proerythroblast pool; this is probably very small compared to the succeeding fluxes.
[2]   Determined from a turnover rate of 8% per hr.
[3]   Determined from eq. (7.4).

injection of H^3Tdr; after a time equal to $S + G_2 + t_m$ those cells that were in the final S phase of this compartment will have moved into the non-dividing compartment. If cells pass through an average of d divisions in the polychromatic normoblast compartment, then the number of cells in the S phase of the last cell cycle will be given by $(t_s/T) \cdot [2^{d-1}/(2^d - 1)] \cdot N_p$, where N_p is the number of cells in the proliferative compartment. This expression can be simply derived by reference to the illustration of a dividing compartment in fig. 7.4. After one division of the labelled cohort in the last generation the number of labelled cells accumulated in the non-dividing compartment will consequently be equal to $(t_s/T) \cdot [2^d/(2^d - 1)] \cdot N_p$. Consequently, for each labelled cell in the proliferative compartment immediately after an injection of H^3Tdr, there will be $2^d/(2^d - 1)$ labelled cells in the non-dividing compartment one cell cycle later. From the data in table 7.5, one labelled polychromatic normoblast will consequently give rise to 1.55 labelled non-dividing cells after one cell cycle time. This value has been used to calculate the theoretical number of labelled cells expected in the non-dividing compartment which is included in table 7.6.

TABLE 7.6

Experimental and theoretical recovery of labelled cell in the first non-dividing compartment (LALA et al. 1966).

	Last dividing compartment early polychromatic normoblast	First non-dividing compartment
Relative population number	359	465
Per cent labelled	28.5% (at 0.5 hr)	33.8% (at 7.5 hr)
Number labelled (experimental)	102 (at 0.5 hr)	157 (at 7.5 hr)
Number labelled (theoretical, see text)	–	$102 \times 1.55 = 158$

The agreement between this number and the actual number of cells observed is consistent with no cell loss up to the transition into the non-dividing compartment. A comparison of the total erythrocyte production in the bone marrow and the turnover in the peripheral blood suggests that there may be a small amount of cell death at some stage between the enucleation of the erythroid cells and the emergence of the mature erythrocytes in the circulation (LALA et al. 1966). The problem of cell death has been considered in detail here because cell death within the renewal system, before the final functional cell has been reached, might have important implications on the control of cell development. A similar analysis to the one considered in this section was made by PATT and MALONEY (1963, 1964) for granulocytes in the canine marrow. They concluded that about half of the granulocytes born in the marrow were lost by some other means than maturation to the non-dividing compartments. The rate of granulocyte production in the dog may consequently be controlled, in part, by means of some control of the amount of cell death during granulopoiesis. In the case of the small intestine discussed in ch. 7 § 11 there was also evidence of some cell death at more than one site in the renewal system. It is consequently clear that the extent to which overproduction and cell death occurs in various compartments has to be established carefully for each renewal system and cannot always be assumed to be negligible.

7.13 Variations in the growth fraction in tumours and normal tissues

The growth fraction has been defined and discussed in previous sections (eq. (7.1), ch. 7 § 5) but in most of the subsequent discussion (e.g. ch. 7 § 11) the term was applied to cell renewal systems which were in a steady state. The growth fraction in these cases was constant and characteristic of the distribution of cells between dividing and non-dividing compartments. Variations in the growth fraction may occur during the development of a tissue or during its regeneration after some types of damage. In general, an embryonic tissue with a rapidly expanding population would be expected to have a higher growth fraction than the same tissue in the adult animal. The decline in the growth fraction during maturation of a tissue has been studied in detail in the liver of young rats by POST and HOFFMAN (1964, 1965b). Most of the increase in size during the growing period in this tissue is due to proliferation of the diploid cells in which the length of the cell cycle increases steadily as the tissue approaches the adult size (see table 4.3, ch. 4 § 9). In 1-day-old rats the cell cycle time for the hepatocytes was found to be 13.8 hr, at 3 weeks the cell cycle was 21.5 hr, and at 8 weeks the cell cycle was 47.5 hr. The growth fraction was also determined at these ages, from ratio of experimental to theoretical labelling indices, (eq. (7.1)) and at 1 day the growth fraction was 0.32, at 3 weeks it was 0.10, and at 8 weeks it was 0.05. Most of the non-dividing cells in the adult liver probably correspond to mature functional cells, but these have not lost their capacity for cell division completely. Partial hepatectomy will cause many of these cells to enter the cell cycle and they then pass through at least one cell cycle during regeneration (BUCHER 1963).

An analysis of the cell cycle times and the growth fractions has also been made by LALA and PATT (1966) in the mouse ascites tumour. The variations in the cell cycle and the growth fraction in this tumour is strikingly similar to that found in the rat liver by POST and HOFFMAN (1964,

1965b). This tumour grows exponentially for the first 3 to 4 days after inoculation of 10^6 cells into the host animal and the growth rate then slows down until a plateau is reached at about the 10th day. The cell cycle time increases steadily during the growth of the tumour from 8 hr at day 1, to 17 hr at day 4 and 22 hr at day 7 (see table 4.3, ch. 4 § 9). Over this time period the growth fraction was determined from eq. (7.1) and was equal to 0.82 on day 1, 0.67 on day 4, and 0.53 on day 7.

MENDELSOHN (1960a, 1962a) has studied the cell cycle and the growth fraction in the solid mammary tumour of the C3H mouse but he adopted a slightly different method for determining the growth fraction to that used by POST and HOFFMAN (1964, 1965b) and LALA and PATT (1966). Each of these three separate groups measured the growth fraction as the ratio of the experimental to the theoretical labelling indices, eq. (7.1), but whereas both Post and Hoffman and Lala and Patt calculated the theoretical labelling indices from the predetermined phases of the cell cycle, Mendelsohn determined the theoretical labelling index experimentally. The experimental determination was achieved by labelling C3H mammary tumours by a single injection of H^3Tdr and waiting for several days before killing the animal and preparing autoradiographs. The period of several days was sufficiently long for the cells that were in S at the time of labelling to be uniformly distributed around the cell cycle. The fraction of labelled mitoses at this time is then equal to the theoretical labelling index, since those cells in mitosis constitute a sample of the cells which make up the growth fraction. The growth fraction is consequently given by the following relationship.

$$\text{G.F. at time of } H^3Tdr \text{ injection} = \frac{\text{Fraction of labelled cells at death}}{\text{Fraction of labelled mitoses at death}}$$

This method for the determination of the growth fraction could, in principle, be used to give a value for the growth fraction from a single autoradiograph, but this advantage is deceptive because there are numerous sources of error (Mendelsohn). If the growth fraction is time-dependent the ratio of labelled cells to labelled mitoses will not be equal to the growth fraction. It will then be necessary to determine the value of this ratio at various intervals and extrapolate back to the time of injection to determine the true growth fraction. This method will also be inaccurate if there is any migration between the growing and the non-growing parts of the population, or if there is any cell loss by death or migration to other tissues, or if there are more compartments than simply the growing and non-growing ones. By means of this method the growth fraction was found to be constant over at least 7 days of growth in an established C3H mammary tumour and equal to 0.4 after correcting for the growth that occurred between labelling and death (MENDELSOHN (1960a, 1964).

An alternative method that can be used to estimate the growth fraction is to label the tissue in question by repeated injections of H^3Tdr over a period at least equal to $G_2 + t_m + G_1$, for the cells in the cycle, and determine the maximum fraction of the population that is labelled. In principle the growth fraction should equal the maximum labelling index, since after repeated injections all of the proliferating cells will be labelled and the non-proliferating cells will be unlabelled. This method will overestimate the growth fraction if there is any migration from the dividing to the non-dividing compartment, and will not distinguish between non-dividing cells and cells with very long cycle times. This method has been discussed in detail by MENDELSOHN (1964) and has been used by him in the study of the C3H mammary tumour, and the method has also been used by BASERGA et al. (1960) in a study of metastases of the Ehrlich ascites tumour, and by LADINSKY and PECKHAM (1965) in the rat vaginal epithelium. The growth fraction determined in this way by Mendelsohn was similar to the value that he had obtained by the methods described in the previous paragraphs for the mammary tumour. In the latter two tissues growth fractions of approximately 1.0 were obtained. A good agreement was obtained between the growth fraction determined by this method and by that represented by eq. (7.1), in the experiments of LALA and PATT (1966) with the 7-day ascites tumour.

The study of growth fractions in tumours is one worth considerably more attention than it has received at present. The work of MENDELSOHN 1960a,b, 1962a,b, 1963, 1964) and LALA and PATT (1966) are examples of the detailed studies of cell cycle durations and growth fraction that are required if we are to understand the growth kinetics of tumours fully. Such an understanding will be invaluable in planning therapeutic treatment. The role of the non-proliferating fraction of the tumour population may be especially important in this respect because many therapeutic agents are mainly effective against proliferating cells. The presence of

significant numbers of non-proliferating or very slowly growing cells in a
tumour may constitute a residual fraction which are unaffected by therapeutic agents and the source of later recurrence of the tumour.

7.14 DNA turnover and repair

Throughout the preceding chapters, including the present one, it has
been assumed, though not always stated explicitly, that DNA is an extremely stable molecule. Unlike most other cell components, DNA does not
turnover in the sense of being broken down within the cell and replaced
by new molecules (HERSHEY 1954; HUGHES 1959). Consequently, once
DNA has been labelled with H^3Tdr or some other precursor, the only way
in which label could be lost is by cell death followed by degradation of the
labelled DNA. Turnover as described in earlier sections of this chapter
(ch. 7 §§ 5, 9–12) only refers to the turnover of whole cells and never to
the turnover of DNA molecules within the cell. The unique stability of
DNA molecules consequently gives a molecular basis for the stability of
genetic information in a cell through successive cycles of growth and
cell division and protracted periods of differentiation. This concept of
DNA stability has been affirmed with dogmatic intensity by many workers
and the opposition to proposals of DNA turnover has been clearly stated
by HUGHES (1959): 'In view of the strong and corroborating evidence for
the lack of turnover of DNA, I think the burden of proof is on the dis-
coverer each time a new system exhibiting exchange is reported. He must
first show that the label is in fact in DNA, and having proved this he must
show that the labelling is not introduced as a result of synthesis i.e. that
the DNA content of the cell in question remains constant during the labelling period.'

Although some experiments have been reported which attempt to
demonstrate the turnover of DNA within the cell, very few have been
unambiguous or have satisfied the criteria suggested by Hughes, quoted
above. The point that is in question here is not whether DNA is lost from
cells under some conditions but whether DNA is replaced during normal
cell metabolism. The loss of DNA from certain chromosomal regions of
insects and plants is well established and the relevant experiments have
been reviewed by LIMA-DE-FARIA (1961) and ROELS (1966). In mammals,

the whole nucleus is lost during keratinisation (PELC 1958a) and during erythropoiesis (BLOOM and FAWCETT 1962). Some of the DNA of adrenal medulla nuclei may be lost in rats exposed to cold temperatures and then restored when the animals are returned to normal temperatures (VIOLA-MAGNI 1964–1966). COHN and VAN DUIJN (1966), however, have been unable to confirm these observations of Viola-Magni. The replacement of DNA without any concomitant change in the total DNA of the cell, in the way that RNA and protein replacement occurs, has not been clearly demonstrated except of the special case of bacteria irradiated with ultraviolet light (SETLOW and CARRIER 1964; SETLOW et al. 1966; BOYCE and HOWARD-FLANDERS 1964). In the latter case, ultraviolet irradiation causes the dimerisation of a fraction of the adjacent pyrimidines in each polynucleotide chain. During the recovery of cells from irradiation these dimers are removed enzymatically as oligonucleotides and a fresh polynucleotide chain synthesised as a replacement (see, e.g. BOYCE 1966; BOYCE and HOWARD-FLANDERS 1964; HANAWALT 1965; HOWARD-FLANDERS and BOYCE 1964; HOWARD-FLANDERS et al. 1964; SETLOW 1964; 1966; SETLOW and CARRIER 1964; SETLOW et al. 1966; STRAUSS et al. 1966; WITKIN 1966). Since this type of turnover involves the enzymatic removal of a damaged portion of only one polynucleotide chain in any particular region of the DNA molecule, the genetic information is retained on the complementary polynucleotide chain and not lost during turnover.

A series of experiments have been described by PELC (1958b, 1962, 1963a,b, 1964), PELC and GAHAN (1959), and PELC and LACOUR (1959) in which they conclude that the fraction of cells that are labelled in a number of tissues after an injection of H^3Tdr is greater than would be expected on the basis of the fraction of cells in these tissues that actually divide. From this they conclude that the incorporation of H^3Tdr occurs both as a result of DNA synthesis, in preparation for mitosis, and DNA turnover. Three main lines of evidence have been invoked in these experiments in support of this conclusion. First, the ratio of LI/MI after a single injection of H^3Tdr appeared to be greater than would be expected from the relative durations of DNA synthesis and mitosis in some tissues; second, long exposure times in autoradiographs reveal a class of lightly labelled cells with grain counts about 2% of the grain counts over S phase cells; third, the number of labelled daughter cells observed several days after labelling is less than would be expected on the basis of the observed labelling index.

The interpretation of these results by Pelc and his coworkers in terms of DNA turnover has been received sceptically by many scientists because much of the evidence has been based on a comparison between the observed value of the ratio LI/MI and the expected value of this ratio. The expected value of this ratio was predicted by Pelc on the basis of observations in a number of tissues that were considered to be clearly defined as dividing or non-dividing. This reasoning is consequently circular, because there is no reason for the ratio of LI/MI to be a normative value in some chosen tissues in preference to others. This ratio is equivalent to t_s/t_m and from table 4.3, ch. 4 § 9, the value of the ratio for normal mammalian tissues in which the cell cycle has been determined lies in the range from 2 to 23. Most of the values in the table are for rapidly growing tissues with a short t_s and if there are tissues in which t_s is longer than those listed in table 4.3, the value of t_s/t_m may be higher than 23 for these slowly growing tissues. In the experiments of PELC and GAHAN (1959) a value of 80 was obtained for this ratio in the mouse seminal vesicle and in experiments of MESSIER and LEBLOND (1960) a value of 6.7 was obtained for the same tissue. These values are consistent with the range of values that are predicted on the basis of known durations of the cell cycle, and experiments by GALL and JOHNSON (1960) in the seminal vesicle clearly demonstrated that the incorporation of H³Tdr was associated with an increase in the DNA content of the cells and their progress around the cell cycle. The preceding sections of this chapter have been concerned with detailed studies of cell kinetics and it should be clear from these that simple comparisons of the ratio of labelling indices and mitotic indices in a variety of tissues after a single injection of H³Tdr is insufficient to fully determine the quantitative details of the kinetics. These comparisons of Pelc are consequently insufficient to demonstrate unequivocally that the labelling index is higher than required for cell proliferation alone. In addition, the failure to identify accurately all cells in mitosis would lead to an underestimate of the mitotic index, for merely technical reasons, and this may result in an apparently high labelling index. The importance of such a technical artefact has been shown by LALA et al. (1964) for the case of the rapidly growing cells of the bone marrow.

The observation of lightly labelled cells after long autoradiographic exposure times, in addition to heavily labelled cells in the S phase (PELC 1963a,b), is not subject to the same objections as those stated above for the arguments that Pelc based on labelling and mitotic indices. Lightly labelled cells with grain counts about 2% of the S phase cells were observed in autoradiographs of a number of mouse tissues including the seminal vesicle, cardiac and smooth muscle, brain, liver, interstitial tissue of the testes and tracheal epithelium, and mast cells. There are consequently two types of turnover that have been claimed by Pelc; in the first type H³Tdr is incorporated at the same rate as during normal DNA synthesis, and this has been discussed in the previous paragraphs; in the second type H³Tdr incorporation occurs at a very low rate. While the former must be regarded as still unproven, the latter may very well represent a small amount of DNA turnover that is associated with the repair of damaged molecules, analogous to the repair processes described above for bacteria. A certain fraction of lightly labelled cells in a population would be expected in the absence of repair because cells may enter or leave the S phase during the availability of H³Tdr and there may be intervals within S when the rate of DNA replication is very low (see ch. 5 §§ 5–8). In these cases, however, the distribution of lightly labelled cells and heavily labelled cells would form a continuous distribution, but in the experiments of Pelc the distribution of lightly labelled cells was clearly separated from that of the heavily labelled cells. Consequently, these observations may be regarded as evidence for repair of DNA during the adult life of the animal although more evidence is required before this interpretation can be regarded as proven.

Some observations have been reported of the incorporation of H³Tdr into mammalian cells during G_1, G_2 and mitosis after irradiation with ultraviolet light (RASMUSSEN and PAINTER 1964, 1966; CLEAVER 1967a,b) and this may also be interpreted in terms of repair of damaged DNA molecules analogous to the repair that occurs in bacteria. This radiation enhanced labelling is illustrated in fig. 7.11 for human amnion cells. The enhanced labelling appears to be due to DNA replication that is not semiconservative, possibly on account of the incorporation of H³Tdr into single polynucleotide chains during repair and the labelling also increases with dose whereas the incorporation of H³Tdr into S phase cells decreases with dose (RASMUSSEN and PAINTER 1966). There are several puzzling things about this radiation enhanced labelling. Not all species or all tissues of every species respond to ultraviolet irradiation in this manner, and mouse tissues, for example, do not show the enhanced labelling (RASMUSSEN and

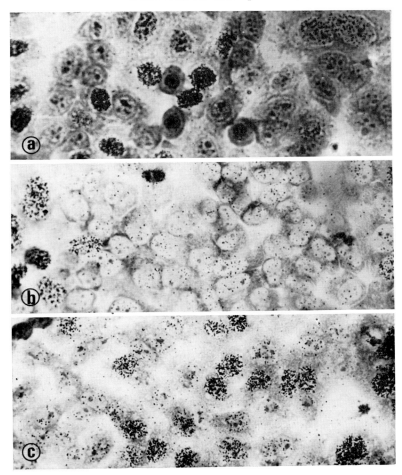

Fig. 7.11. Autoradiographs of human amnion cells labelled for 4 hours with H³Tdr, 1.7 μCi/ml 6 Ci/mmole, immediately after irradiation with ultraviolet light. (a) control, no irradiation. (b) 400 ergs/mm² UV. (c) 400 ergs/mm² UV, 10⁻³ M caffeine added 20 hr before irradiation and maintained throughout the experiment (CLEAVER, unpublished experiments).

PAINTER 1966; CLEAVER 1967). The enhanced labelling can be produced in the cells that do not normally show it if they are grown for at least one generation time in BUdr before irradiation. This effect of BUdr is different to that observed in bacteria because in the latter the presence of BUdr interferes with the repair replication and the incorporation of H³Tdr during repair does not then occur (BOYCE 1966). Also, it has not been possible to detect any removal of the ultraviolet photoproducts from DNA in mammalian cells, which would be a prerequisite for repair replication (TROSKO et al. 1965). Further evidence which makes the interpretation of this ultraviolet induced labelling difficult to interpret in terms of repair comes from studies with the metabolic inhibitor caffeine. A repair mechanism for ultraviolet damage which is inhibited by caffeine at 10^{-3} M concentrations has been detected in mouse L strain cells by RAUTH (1966). Caffeine at this concentration, however, has no effect on the enhanced labelling that is observed G_1, G_2, and mitotic cells after ultraviolet irradiation and this is illustrated in fig. 7.11 (CLEAVER 1966). These observations of the effect of caffeine may indicate that either the enhanced labelling after irradiation has nothing to do with repair of ultraviolet damage or that there are at least two repair mechanisms, one which is caffeine sensitive and the other which is caffeine insensitive. The latter would be the repair mechanism associated with increased labelling with H³Tdr. At this stage of the investigations it is not possible to come to any definite conclusion concerning the significance of this enhanced labelling after irradiation, but it is an interesting phenomenon that is worth considerable study.

In conclusion, although DNA turnover is established for the special case of repair of bacteria after irradiation, and in the cases of the loss of DNA from certain parts of the genome in a number of species, the possibility of DNA turnover in mammalian cells is still an open question.

References

ADAMS, L. R., 1964, Ph.D. thesis, University of California at Berkeley
BASERGA, R., 1965, Cancer Res. *25*, 581
BASERGA, R., W. E. KISIELSKI, and K. HALVORSEN, 1960, Cancer Res. *20*, 910
BERTALANFFY, F. D., and C. LAU, 1962, Intern. Rev. Cytol. *13*, 359
BERTALANFFY, F. D., 1964, Lab. Invest. *13*, 871
BIZZOZERO, G., 1892, Arch. f. Mikr. Anal. *40*, 325
BLOOM, W., and D. W. FAWCETT, 1962, A textbook of histology, 8th ed., Saunders and Co., Philadelphia, London
BOND, V. P., T. M. FLIEDNER, and J. D. ARCHAMBEAU, 1965, Mammalian radiation lethality, Academic Press New York and London

Boyce, R. P., 1966, Nature *209*, 688

Boyce, R. P., and P. Howard-Flanders, 1964, Proc. Natl. Acad. Sci. *51*, 293

Bucher, N. L. R., 1963, Intern. J. Cytol. *15*, 245

Cairnie, A. B., L. F. Lamerton, and G. G. Steel, 1965a, Exp. Cell Res. *39*, 528

Cairnie, A. B., L. F. Lamerton, and G. G. Steel, 1965b, Exp. Cell Res. *39*, 539

Cameron, I. L., and G. Cleffman, 1964, J. Cell Biol. *21*, 169

Cleaver, J. E., 1966, unpublished observations

Cleaver, J. E., 1967a, Radiation Res. *30*, 795

Cleaver, J. E., 1967b, Rad. Res. Soc. Mtg. Puerto Rico (abstract)

Cohn, N. S., and P. van Duijn, 1966, J. Cell Biol. *31*, 22A

Cronkite, E. P., V. P. Bond, T. M. Fliedner, and J. R. Rubini, 1959a, Lab. Invest. *8*, 263

Cronkite, E. P., T. M. Fliedner, V. P. Bond, J. R. Rubini, G. Brecher, and H. Quastler, 1959b, Ann. N. Y. Acad. Sci. *77*, 803

Cronkite, E. P., V. P. Bond, T. M. Fliedner, and S. A. Killman, 1960, in Haemopoiesis, G. W. W. Wolstenholme and M. O. Conner, eds., Churchill, London, p. 70

Cudkowitz, G., A. C. Upton, L. H. Smith, D. G. Gosslee, and W. L. Hughes, 1964, Ann. N. Y. Acad. Sci. *114*, 571

Feinendegen, L. E., V. P. Bond, and W. L. Hughes, 1966, Proc. Soc. Exp. Biol. Med. *122*, 448

Dornfest, B. S., J. Lobue, E. S. Handler, A. S. Gordon, and H. Quastler, 1962a, Acta Haematol. *28*, 42

Dornfest, B. S., J. Lobue, E. S. Handler, A. S. Gordon, and H. Quastler, 1962b, J. Lab. Clin. Med. *60*, 777

Forteza Bover, G., 1964, Atlas of Blood Cytology, Grune and Stratton, New York and London

Fry, R. J. M., S. Lesher, W. E. Kisielski, and G. Sacher, 1963, in Cell Proliferation, L. F. Lamerton and R. J. M. Fry, eds., Blackwell, Oxford, p. 213

Gall, J. G., and W. W. Johnson, 1960, J. Biophys. Biochem. Cytol. 7, 657

Gelfant, S., 1962, Exp. Cell Res. *26*, 395

Gelfant, S., 1963, Exp. Cell Res. *32*, 521

Gerber, G., G. Gerber, and K. I. Altman, 1960, J. Biol. Chem. *235*, 1433

Gilbert, C. W., and L. G. Lajtha, 1965, in Cellular Radiation Biology, Williams & Wilkins, Baltimore, p. 474

Gurney, C. W., L. G. Lajtha, and R. Oliver, 1962, Brit. J. Haematol. *8*, 461

Hanawalt, P. C., 1965, Biochem. Biophys. Res. Commun. *19*, 462

Hershey, A. D., 1954, J. Gen. Physiol. *35*, 145

Howard-Flanders, P., E. Simson, and L. Theriot, 1964, Mutation Res. *1*, 219

Howard-Flanders, P., and R. P. Boyce, Genetics 50, 256

Hughes, W. L., 1959, in Kinetics of cellular proliferation, F. Stohlman, Jr., ed., Grune and Stratton, New York, p. 83

Kember, N. F., H. Quastler, and D. R. Wimber, 1962, Brit. J. Radiol. *35*, 290

Klein, G., and L. Revesz, 1953, J. Natl. Cancer Inst. *14*, 229

LADINSKY, J. L., and B. M. PECKHAM, 1965, Exp. Cell Res. *40*, 447

LAJTHA, L. G., R. OLIVER, and C. W. GURNEY, 1962, Brit. J. Haematol. *8*, 442

LAJTHA, L. G., C. W. GILBERT, D. D. PORTEOUS, and R. ALEXANIAN, 1964, Ann. N. Y. Acad. Sci. *113*, 742

LALA, P. K., and H. M. PATT, 1966, Proc. Natl. Acad. Sci. (in press)

LALA, P. K., M. A. MALONEY, and H. M. PATT, 1964, Acta Haematol. *31*, 1

LALA, P. K., M. A. MALONEY, and H. M. PATT, 1965, Exp. Cell Res. *38*, 626

LALA, P. K., H. M. PATT, and M. A. MALONEY, 1966, Acta Haematol. *35*, 311

LAMERTON, L. F., B. I. LORD, and H. QUASTLER, 1963, Radioactive Isotopen in Klinik und Forschung *5*, 493

LEBLOND, C. P., and B. E. WALKER, 1956, Physiol. Rev. *36*, 255

LEBLOND, C. P., B. MESSIER, and B. KOPRIWA, 1959, Lab. Invest. *8*, 296

LEBLOND, C. P., C. E. STEVENS, and R. BOGOROCH, 1948, Science *108*, 531

LIMA-DE-FARIA, A., 1961, in Progress in biophys. and biophysical chemistry, Pergamon Press, Oxford, London, New York, Paris, p. 281

LIPKIN, M., and H. QUASTLER, 1962, J. Clin. Invest. *41*, 141

MALONEY, M. A., C. L. WEBER, and H. M. PATT, 1963, Nature *197*, 150

MALONEY, M. W., H. M. PATT, and C. L. WEBER, 1962, Nature *193*, 134

MAYNEORD, W. V., 1932, Am. J. Cancer *16*, 841

MENDELSOHN, M. L., 1960a, Science *132*, 1496

MENDELSOHN, M. L., 1960b, J. Natl. Cancer Inst. *25*, 485

MENDELSOHN, M. L., 1962a, J. Natl. Cancer Inst. *28*, 1015

MENDELSOHN, M. L., 1962b, Science *135*, 213

MENDELSOHN, M. L., 1963, in Cell proliferation, L. F. Lamerton and R. J. M. FRY, eds., Blackwell, Oxford, p. 190

MENDELSOHN, M. L., 1964, in Cellular radiation biology, Williams and Wilkins, Baltimore, p. 498

MESSIER, B., and C. P. LEBLOND, 1960, Am. J. Anat. *106*, 247

MOROWITZ, H. J., W. A. HIGINBOTHAM, S. W. MATTHYSSE, and H. QUASTLER, 1964, J. Theoret. Biol. *7*, 98

NYGAARD, O. F., and R. L. POTTER, 1960, Radiation Res. *12*, 131

OWEN, M., and S. MACPHERSON, 1963, J. Cell. Biol *19*, 33

PATT, H. M., 1963, Am. J. Roentgenol. Radium Therapy Nucl. Med. *90*, 928

PATT, H. M., and M. A. MALONEY, 1963, in Cell proliferation, L. F. Lamerton and R. J. M. Fry, eds., Blackwell, Oxford, p. 157

PATT, H. M., and M. A. MALONEY, 1964, Ann. N. Y. Acad. Sci. *113*, 515

PATT, H. M., and H. QUASTLER, 1963, Physiol. Rev. *43*, 357

PELC, S. R., 1958a, Exp. Cell Res. (suppl.) *6*, 97

PELC, S. R., 1958b, Exp. Cell Res. *14*, 301

PELC, S. R., 1962, Nature *193*, 793

PELC, S. R., 1963a, Exp. Cell Res. *29*, 194

PELC, S. R., 1963b in Cell proliferation, L. F. Lamerton and R. J. M. Fry, eds., Blackwell, Oxford, p. 94

PELC, S. R., 1964, J. Cell Biol. *22*, 21

PELC, S. R., and P. B. GAHAN, 1959, Nature *183*, 335

PELC, S. R., and L. LACOUR, 1959, Experientia *15*, 131

POST J., and J. HOFFMAN, 1964, Exp. Cell Res. *36*, 111

POST, J., and J. HOFFMAN, 1965a, Radiation Res. *26*, 422

POST, J., and J. HOFFMAN, 1965b, Exp. Cell Res. *40*, 333

POST, J., and J. HOFFMAN, 1967, Radiation Res. (in press)

QUASTLER, H., 1959a, in Kinetics of cellular proliferation, F. Stohlman, ed., Grune and Stratton, New York, p. 218

QUASTLER, H., 1959b, in Kinetics of cellular proliferation, F. Stohlman, ed., Grune and Stratton, New York, p. 431

QUASTLER, H., 1960, Ann. N. Y. Acad. Sci. *90*, 580

QUASTLER, H., 1963, in Cell proliferation, L. F. Lamerton and R. J. M. Fry, eds,. Blackwell, Oxford, p. 18

QUASTLER, H., J. P. M. BENSTEAD, L. F. LAMERTON, and S. M. SIMPSON, 1959, Brit. J. Radiol. *32*, 501

QUASTLER, H., and F. G. SHERMAN, 1959, Exp. Cell Res. *17*, 420

RASMUSSEN, R. E., and R. B. PAINTER, 1964, Nature *203*, 1360

RASMUSSEN, R. E., and R. B. PAINTER, 1966, J. Cell Biol. *29*, 11

RAUTH, A. M., 1966, Biophys. J. *6*, 116 (abstract)

ROELS, H., 1966, Intern. Rev. Cytol. *19*, 1

SANDRITTER, W., and G. SCOMAZZONI, 1964, Nature *202*, 100

SETLOW, R. B., 1964, J. Cell. Comp. Phys. *64* (suppl.), 51

SETLOW, R. B., 1966, Science *153*, 379

SETLOW, R. B., W. L. CARRIER, and R. W. WILLIAMS, 1966, Science *152*, 676

SETLOW, R. B., and W. L. CARRIER, 1964, Proc. Natl. Acad. Sci. *51*, 226

SHERMAN, F. G., H. QUASTLER, and D. E. WIMBER, 1961, Exp. Cell Res. *25*, 114

STARKEY, W. E., 1963, J. Brit. Dental Assoc. *115*, 143

STRAUSS, B., T. SEARASHI, and M. ROBBINS, 1966, Proc. Natl. Acad. Sci. *56*, 932

STEEL, G. G., 1963, in Cell proliferation, L. F. Lamerton and R. J. M. Fry, eds., Blackwell, Oxford, p. 38

STEEL, G. G., and L. F. LAMERTON, 1965, Exp. Cell Res. *37*, 117

STOHLMAN, F., 1959, in Kinetics of cellular proliferation, F. Stohlman, ed., Grune and Stratton, New York, p. 318

TROSKO, J. E., E. H. Y. CHU, and W. L. CARRIER, 1965, Radiation Res. *24*, 667

WIMBER, D. E., and H. QUASTLER, 1963, Exp. Cell Res. *30*, 8

WINTROPE, M. M., 1961, Clinical hematology, 5th ed., Lea and Febiger, Philadelphia

WITKIN, E. M., 1966, Science *152*, 1345

VIOLA-MAGNI, M. P., 1964, Nature *204*, 1094

VIOLA-MAGNI, M. P., 1965, J. Cell Biol. *25*, 515

VIOLA-MAGNI, M. P., 1966, J. Cell Biol. *28*, 9

Recommended texts on cell kinetics

Kinetics of cellular proliferation, 1959, F. Stohlman, Jr., ed., Grune and Stratton, New York

Cell proliferation, 1963, L. F. Lamerton and R. J. M. Fry, eds., Blackwell, Oxford

Leukopoiesis in health and disease, 1964, Ann. N. Y. Acad. Sci. *113*, 511-1092

Mammalian radiation lethality, a disturbance in cellular kinetics, 1965, V. P. Bond, T. M. Fliedner, and J. O. Archambeau, Academic Press, New York and London

Tritium in biology and medicine (in press), L. Feinendegen, Academic Press, New York and London

CHAPTER 8

Appendix

8.1 Relationship between the mean grain count in H^3Tdr autoradiographs and the mean rate of DNA synthesis

In many of the experiments described in the previous chapters the tacit assumption has been made that the uptake of H^3Tdr during labelling periods of 1 hr or less is a measure of the rate of DNA synthesis. An experimental test of the validity of this assumption has been provided by the experiments of DENDY and SMITH (1964). In these experiments the total DNA in irradiated and in control cells was measured several hours after irradiation so that the reduced rate of DNA synthesis in the irradiated cells resulted in a significantly smaller increase in the total DNA of these cells than in controls. The experimental procedure was as follows. Groups of 10 cells were chosen in cultures of mouse L strain cells in exponential growth and each group was given one of the following treatments:

(1) Irradiated in the nucleolus for 2 sec with an ultraviolet microbeam*
(2) Irradiated in the nuclear sap for 2 sec with an ultraviolet microbeam
(3) No irradiation.

The control and irradiated groups were followed by eye for 6 hr, at which time the cultures were incubated for 10 min in H^3Tdr at 5 μCi/ml, 2 Ci/mmole, and fixed. The cultures were stained with the Feulgen reaction and the DNA content of each cell in the groups (1), (2) and (3)

---

* The ultraviolet microbeam apparatus was constructed by DENDY (1962) after the model described by URETZ and PERRY (1957) and this delivered an incident flux of heterochromatic ultraviolet light of about 2×10^{-3} ergs/μ^2/sec in the focal plane over a circular area of diameter 3 μ.

measured by means of two wavelength microspectrophotometry (MENDEL-SOHN 1958). The DNA content of any cell which divided in the interval of the experiment was recorded as the sum of the contributions from each daughter cell. In addition the DNA content of a further 32 cells chosen at random from each culture was measured. The mean DNA content per cell in each culture for groups (1), (2) and (3) above was then corrected so as to correspond to a normalised value of 100 for the mean DNA content of the 32 randomly chosen cells. The results of these determinations were as follows:

(i) During 6 hr the mean DNA content of unirradiated cells, group (3) above, rose from a mean normalised value of 100 to a value of 122.6 ± 4.5. This corresponds to a mean generation time of 20.5 ± 4 hr for cells in exponential growth.

(ii) The mean DNA content of the nucleolar irradiated cells, group (1) above, increased from 100 to 109.9 ± 2.5 in 6 hr and the mean DNA content of those irradiated in the nuclear sap, group (2) above, increased to 113 ± 2.5. These values do not differ significantly. From these results the following ratio can be calculated.

$$\frac{\text{Total DNA synthesised in unirradiated cells in 6 hr}}{\text{Total DNA synthesised in irradiated cells in 6 hr}} = \frac{11.5 \pm 3.0}{22.6 \pm 4.5} = 0.5 \pm 0.2$$

From autoradiographs of these cultures the mean grain counts were also used to obtain an independent estimate of the ratio calculated above, based on the assumption that the mean grain counts are a measure of the rate of DNA synthesis at the time of labelling. In fig. 8.1 the mean grain counts in control and irradiated cultures have been shown at times after irradiation. The areas beneath the control and the irradiated curves between 0 and 6 hr represent the amounts of DNA synthesised during the 6 hr after irradiation and the ratio of these areas should be the same as the ratio calculated above. In this experiment, the ratio of the two areas is approximately 0.34.

In view of the considerable errors in both methods of measurement the agreement between the two estimates of the amounts of DNA synthesised in control and irradiated cultures may be considered reasonably satisfactory. Consequently, the mean grain count in an autoradiograph of a culture labelled briefly with H^3Tdr may be used as a valid estimate of the mean rate of DNA synthesis in that culture at the time of labelling.

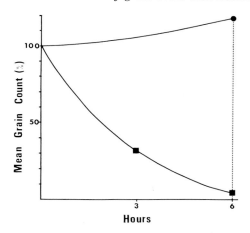

Fig. 8.1.   Mean grain counts (mean rates of DNA synthesis) during the first 6 hours after irradiation with ultraviolet light. ● control cultures, ■ irradiated cultures. The area beneath the control curve represents the amount of DNA synthesised in control cells, and the area beneath the irradiated curve represents the amount of DNA synthesised in irradiated cells (redrawn from DENDY and SMITH 1964).

8.2 *Variance and mean of grain count distribution in a heterogeneous cell population*

In this section a cell population, e.g. tissue culture cells, is considered to have been labelled briefly with H³Tdr (i.e. for less than 1 hr) and the number of grains over individual cells determined in an autoradiograph. Assuming that the number of grains is a measure of the rate of DNA synthesis in a cell at the time of labelling then the following definitions may be made.

N = total number of cells synthesising DNA

$n_1, n_2, n_3, \ldots n_p$ = total number of cells in distinct subpopulations comprising N.

$r_1, r_2, r_3, \ldots r_p$ = rate of DNA synthesis or grain count of each cell in the subpopulations n_1, n_2, n_3, respectively.

$r_m \ldots$ = mean rate of DNA synthesis per cell in the population N.

By definition $\Sigma n_p = N$ (summation is over all values of p
and $\Sigma n_p r_p = N r_m$.   from 1 upwards)

If it may be assumed that the rate of DNA synthesis in any subpopulation, n_p, is a certain fraction of the mean rate of DNA synthesis, then this fraction a_p is defined by $r_p = a_p \cdot r_m$. This implies a model of the cell life cycle in which an individual cell progresses through the cycle by spending a certain time as a member of each subpopulation and passes instantaneously from one population to the next. In exponential growth the fractions of the population n_1/N, n_2/N,... etc. and the rates r_1, r_2... are assumed to remain constant with time and are characteristic of the particular cell type. The following analysis could also be performed for an infinite number of infinitesimal subpopulations and integrations substituted for summations.

The variance of the grain count distribution is expressed by

$$s^2 = 1/(N-1) \cdot \Sigma n_p \cdot (r_m - r_p)^2$$

or $$s^2 = 1/(N-1) \cdot \Sigma n_p \cdot r_m^2 \cdot (1-a_p)^2$$

$$= r_m^2/(N-1) \cdot \Sigma n_p \cdot (1-a_p)^2.$$

Since, by definition, $N, n_1, n_2, ..., a_1, a_2...$ are constants characteristic for the particular cell population under consideration, the expression above may be simplified to the form

$$s^2 = r_m^2 \cdot (x/100)^2,$$

where $x/100 = 1/(n-1) \cdot \Sigma n_p \cdot (1-a_p)^2$ and $x\%$ is the standard deviation of the grain count distribution. This derivation has ignored the contribution of random errors etc., to the variance and it has been assumed that these will be small compared to the contributions from the different synthetic rates in the subpopulations. The validity of the derivation depends on the assumption that the rates of DNA synthesis can be expressed as a constant fraction of the mean rate of synthesis, and in other respects the calculation is identical to that by which variance itself is defined. On the basis of this assumption, the ratio of variance to mean should be a linear function of the mean

$$s^2/r_m = r_m \cdot (x/100)^2. \tag{8.1}$$

This relationship has been plotted in fig. 8.2 for autoradiographs of several cell types. It can be seen that eq. (8.1) does describe the results, approximately, for mean grain counts above 20 in the case of asynchronous populations. In the case of a synchronous cell population the grain count distributions appear to correspond more closely to Poisson distributions, in which the variance and the mean are equal. Consequently, it seems likely that most of the variation in grain counts in asynchronous populations is due to different DNA synthetic rates in different regions of the cell cycle, as suggested in ch. 5 §§ 5–8.

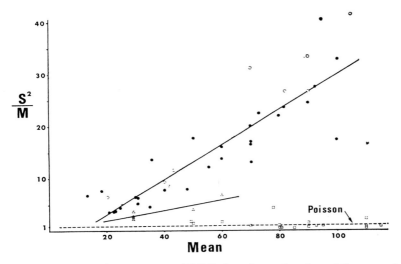

Fig. 8.2. Ratio of variance to mean (S^2/M) plotted as a function of the mean for grain count distributions in autoradiographs of tissue culture cells labelled for 1 hr, or less, and tissue sections from an animal labelled by a single injection of H³Tdr. ○ mouse L strain cells; ● human amnion FL strain cells; △ mouse intestinal crypt cells (from the data of KOBERG 1963); □ synchronous L strain cells within the same 10% of the cell cycle, selected as a synchronous subpopulation from an exponentially growing population on the basis of their DNA contents as determined by two wavelength microspectrophotometry of Feulgen-stained cultures.

8.3 *The incorporation of H³Tdr into DNA in the presence of deficient media*

Several experiments have been reported in which certain cell types appear to have a limited ability for the incorporation of H³Tdr, in vitro. After periods of only a few hours these cells were unable to incorporate H³Tdr into DNA even though the medium was not totally depleted of H³Tdr. This has been reported mainly in bone marrow cells (RUBINI et al. 1962) and in ascites cells (ZAJICEK and GROSS 1964; ZAJICEK et al. 1963; CRATHORN and SHOOTER 1960, 1963). One possible explanation of these observations is that the medium in which the cells were suspended was deficient in essential precursors for continued DNA synthesis even though there was sufficient H³Tdr. In the case of the bone marrow experiments the medium was a physiological saline and serum and in the case of the ascites experiments the medium was the ascitic fluid.

The influence of a deficient medium on the incorporation of H³Tdr into DNA is illustrated by the following experiment with tissue cultures (CLEAVER 1965a). Mouse L strain cells were supplied with H³Tdr under two different conditions; in one case the precursor was supplied as a component of the normal tissue culture medium and in the other as a component of a physiological saline which contained the same amount of glucose as the medium. The incorporation of H³Tdr under these two conditions is shown in the results of fig. 8.3. It is clear that DNA synthesis cannot be maintained in the presence of saline for more than a mere 5 to 10 min, whereas synthesis continues at a uniform rate throughout the duration of the experiment in the presence of the normal medium. Similar observations have also been made for the effect of saline on RNA synthesis (CLEAVER 1965a) and protein synthesis (ERRERA et al. 1961). The cessation of synthesis is probably due to the exhaustion of the intracellular pools of precursors for DNA, RNA and protein synthesis and these results indicate that the pools require a continuous supply of material from the tissue culture medium in order to maintain the necessary size and turnover. In the case of DNA synthesis shown in fig. 8.3, the precursor pools were exhausted within about 10 min. This figure can be used to obtain an estimate for the upper limit of the size of the pools of deoxyribonucleotides, if it is assumed that during the 10 min of DNA synthesis in the presence of saline the DNA that is synthesised all comes from these pools. The pools containing precursors of DNA thymine are obviously not exhausted, but rather those of DNA purines and DNA cytosine. These mouse L strain cells required approximately 10^7 molecules/cell/min of each nucleotide to maintain DNA synthesis (ch. 3 § 9) so the precursor pools will contain approximately 10⁸ molecules/cell of each nucleotide, and it may be tentatively assumed that this will be the size of the pool for each precursor of DNA, including the thymidine derivatives. This must be taken to represent an upper limit for the pool size since it includes all precursors, and not merely the final deoxyribonucleotides on the pathways of DNA synthesis, and should be compared with the lower values for the pool size of TMP, TDP and TTP given in table 3.3, ch. 3 § 10.

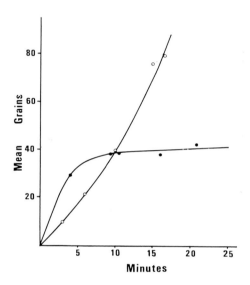

Fig. 8.3.   Mean grain count over labelled L strain cells as a function of the incubation time in H³Tdr, 5 μCi/ml 2 Ci/mmole, under two experimental conditions. ○ H³Tdr supplied as component of normal growth medium. ● H³Tdr supplied in Tyrode's balanced salt solution as a substitute for growth medium (CLEAVER 1965a).

8.4 Incorporation of thymidine into DNA after a single injection in vivo under flooding conditions

The four factor model has been described earlier (ch. 3 § 1–9) and it was briefly stated (ch. 3 § 3) that under flooding conditions in vivo the relationship between the amount of Tdr supplied in the injection and the amount incorporated into DNA was more complex than the simple relationships derived for tissue culture conditions. The following calculation for in vivo conditions is based on that of QUASTLER (1963).

Following a single injection of Tdr into an animal it may be assumed that the total pool size within individual cells rises instantaneously to $S_0 + b_4 P/b_3$ molecules/cell (the symbols used here are those defined in ch. 3 for a four-factor model without end product inhibition, S_0 is the natural pool size). The pool size then declines exponentially on account of the degradation pathway and at a time t after injection the total pool size and the amount of label in the pool may be represented by

$$S(t) = S_0 + (b_4 P/b_3) \exp{-b_3 t}$$
$$\text{and } S^*(t) = (b_4 \cdot P^*/b_3) \exp{-b_3 t}.$$

Since flooding conditions, only, are under consideration here the natural pool size may be neglected and the incorporation of label into DNA from the pool will occur at a rate equal to b_1 molecules/minute until the pool has fallen to a level near to S_0 (say $(1+k)S_0$). If the time taken for the pool to fall to $(1+k)S_0$ is represented by t_c then

$$kS_0 = (b_4 \cdot P/b_3) \cdot \exp{-b_3 t_c}$$
$$\text{and } t_c = (1/b_3)(\ln P + \ln b_4 - \ln b_3 k S_0).$$

The amount of label incorporated into DNA at times after t_c will be very small compared to the amount incorporated up to t_c, and to a first approximation may be neglected. Hence, the total amount of label incorporated into DNA after the single injection, L^*, will be represented by $b_1 z t_c$ (z represents the specific activity)

$$L^* = (b_1/b_3)z\ln P + (z/b_3)(\ln b_4 - \ln b_3 k S_0).$$

The second term in this expression will be a constant for any particular cell type. Since the natural pool size is equal to $(b_2-b_1)/b_3$ the second term is then $(z/b_3) \cdot \ln b_4/(b_2-b_1)k$. The relationship between the amount of Tdr supplied and the amount incorporated into DNA, for a given constant specific activity of the exogenous H^{3}Tdr, is then,

$$L^* = z \cdot (b_1/b_3) \cdot \ln P + \text{constant}.$$

In the experiments of STEWART et al. (1965), which were described in ch. 3

§ 3, this relationship was found to fit the experimental results when Tdr in amounts above about 10 μg/g body weight were supplied to mice in a single injection. It has been assumed in the above calculation that the pool size created by injection of Tdr is directly proportional to the amount of Tdr supplied (i.e. $S-S_0 = (b_4 \ P/b_3) \exp{-b_3 t}$) and this may not be true for extremely large amounts of Tdr. The linear relationship between L^* and ln P may consequently break down at this extreme, though the relationship was found to be valid up to 300 μg/g body weight in the experiments of Stewart et al.

8.5 *The distribution of cells around the cell cycle during exponential growth*

The distribution of cells around the cell cycle is not uniform during exponential growth since, for every cell which enters mitosis at the end of the cycle, two will complete mitosis at the beginning of the cycle. There is consequently a predominance of young cells during exponential growth. The distribution for the special case in which every cell has the same cycle duration may be calculated simply in the following manner (LENNARTZ and MAURER 1964).

For the purpose of the calculation the following definitions are made (fig. 8.4):

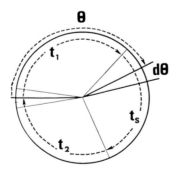

Fig. 8.4. The cell cycle showing the definitions of the time intervals used in cell cycle analysis. t_1 duration of G_1 phase plus half mitoses, t_s duration of S phase, t_2 duration of G_2 phase plus half mitosis, θ position in the cycle measured from the midpoint of the previous mitosis.

$T =$ duration of the cell cycle

$t =$ time from the start of measurement of population size

$N(0) =$ population size at time zero

$N(t) =$ population size at time t

$\theta =$ position in the cellcycle (in time) measured from the previous mitosis

In all of these calculations the duration of mitosis is assumed to be short with respect to the other phases of the cell cycle and is divided equally between the G_1 and G_2 phases, i.e. $t_1 =$ duration of G_1 plus half the duration of mitosis, $t_2 =$ duration of G_2 plus half the duration of mitosis, $t_s =$ duration of S.

If all of the cells of the population are passing through the cell cycle then the cell cycle time and the population doubling time are equal and, by definition,

$$N(t) = N(0) \cdot \exp \ln 2 \cdot t/T.$$

The number of cells, dN, in a fraction $d\theta$ of the cell cycle is the same as the increase in cell number between the time $t+T-\theta$ and $t+T-(\theta+d\theta)$, i.e.

$$
\begin{aligned}
dN &= N(t+T-\theta)-N(t+T-\theta-d\theta) \\
&= N(0)\exp{(t+T-\theta)}\ln 2/T - N(0)\exp{(t+T-\theta-d\theta)}\ln 2/T \\
&= N(t)\exp{(T-\theta)}\ln 2/T - N(t)\exp{(T-\theta-d\theta)}\ln 2/T \\
&= N(t)[1-\exp{-(\ln 2\, d\theta/T)}]\exp{(T-\theta)}\ln 2/T \\
&= N(t)\cdot(\ln 2\, d\theta/T)\cdot\exp{(T-\theta)}\ln 2/T.
\end{aligned}
$$

The fraction of cells in the population which occupy the interval $d\theta$ of the cell cycle at any one time t will be given by $dN/N(t)$. i.e. age distribution during exponential growth is

$$dN/N(t) = (\ln 2\, d\theta/T)\exp{(1-\theta/T)}\ln 2. \qquad (4.3)$$

This age distribution has been illustrated in fig. 4.4. If it is necessary to allow for variation in the durations of the cell cycle between cells in the population the calculation is more complex and will be found in detail in the work of POWELL (1956). A typical distribution based on the age distributions derived by Powell has also been illustrated in fig. 4.4.

8.6 *The relationship between the mitotic and labelling indices and the duration of the phases of the cell cycle during exponential growth*

On the basis of the age distribution which has been derived for exponential growth in the preceding section expressions can be derived for the mitotic index and the labelling index during exponential growth.

(1) *Mitotic index.* If the duration of mitosis is small compared to the cell cycle durations then the fraction of the population in mitosis will be equal to the fraction in the final interval $d\theta$ of the cell cycle, where $d\theta = t_m$, and $\theta = T$ (see also SMITH and DENDY 1962).

$$\text{i.e.} \quad \text{MI} = \ln 2 \cdot t_m / T. \tag{4.4}$$

(2) *Labelling index.* The labelling index is the fraction of the population which incorporates H^3Tdr or $C^{14}Tdr$ during a brief period and corresponds to that fraction which occupies the region of the cell cycle between $\theta = t_1$ and $\theta = t_1 + t_s$ (see also CLEAVER 1965b).

$$\text{i.e.} \quad \text{LI} = \int_{t_1 - t_s}^{t_1} dN/N(t)$$

$$= \int_{t_1 - t_s}^{t_1} (\ln 2 \cdot d\theta / T) \exp (1 - \theta / T).$$

It is more convenient to express the labelling index in terms of t_2 than t_1 because the former can be determined with greater precision, experimentally (see ch. 4 for the experimental methods).

$$\text{i.e.} \quad \text{LI} = \int_{T - t_s - t_2}^{T - t_2} (\ln 2 \cdot d\theta / T) \exp (1 - \theta / T)$$

$$= 2(- \exp - \theta \ln 2/T) \Big|_{T - t_s - t_2}^{T - t_2}$$

$$= (\exp t_s \ln 2/T - 1) \exp t_2 \ln 2/T. \tag{4.5}$$

8.7 *The labelling index as a function of time exposed to H^3Tdr and colchicine during exponential growth*

If colchicine is added to an exponentially growing culture at a concentra-

tion which blocks mitosis immediately there will be no increase in cell
number with time and the increase in labelled cells is then due to the
continued entry of cells in the S phase. The fraction of the cell population
which enters S during a time t will be equal to the fraction of the population which occupies the interval, of length t, that is immediately prior to
the beginning of S. Hence, the increase in the labelling index in a period
of time t will be given by the following integral,

$$\text{Increase in LI} = \int_{t_1-t}^{t_1} (\ln 2 \, d\theta/T) \exp (1-\theta/T).$$

This calculation is mainly employed for the method of determining the cell
cycle durations by means of the collection functions for mitoses and
labelled cells (see ch. 4 § 7, PUCK and STEFFEN 1963). Since the duration of
G_2 may be determined from the collection function for mitoses (see fig.
4.8) it is more convenient to express the integral for the increase in the
labelling index in terms of t_2 rather than t_1.

$$\text{Increase in LI} = \int_{T-t_2-t_s-t}^{T-t_2-t_s} (\ln 2 \, d\theta/T) \exp (1-\theta/T)$$

$$= \exp (t_2+t_s)\ln 2/T \cdot (\exp t \ln 2/T-1).$$

The fraction of cells which will be labelled immediately after the addition
of H³Tdr is given by eq. (4.5), and the total fraction of labelled cells after
an interval t is given by the expression,

$$\text{LI} = (\exp t_s\ln 2/T-1) \exp t_2\ln 2/T+\exp (t_2+t_s)\ln 2/T \cdot (\exp t \ln 2/T-1)$$

By rearrangement, and taking logarithms, this becomes the collection
function for labelled cells which has been illustrated in fig. 4.8.

$$\log_{10} [1+\text{LI}/\exp (t_2 \ln 2/T)] = (t_s+t) \, 0.301/T. \qquad (4.8)$$

In this derivation it has been assumed that colchicine blocks all cells in
mitosis immediately, including those cells which were in mitosis at $t = 0$.
The LI will consequently reach a constant value when all of the cells
which were in the G_1 phase at $t = 0$ have entered the S phase, and this
will occur after a time equal to the duration of G_1, i.e. at $t = t_1-t_m/2$
(by definition).

If colchicine is used at a concentration which only blocks cells which enter mitosis after it has been added, the population will increase by a small amount due to the division of those cells which were in mitosis at $t = 0$. If the population size at $t = 0$ is represented by $N(0)$ then at later times

$$N(t) = N(0) \exp t \ln 2/T \qquad \text{when } 0 \leq t \leq t_\mathrm{m}$$
$$N(t) = N(0) \exp t_\mathrm{m} \ln 2/T \qquad \text{when} \qquad t_\mathrm{m} \leq t.$$

Equation (4.8) may then be modified to allow for this increase in cell number and takes the forms

$$\log_{10}\left[1 + \mathrm{LI}/\exp(t_2 - t) \ln 2/T\right] = (t_\mathrm{s} + t)\,0.301/T \qquad \text{when } 0 \leq t \leq t_\mathrm{m}$$
$$\log_{10}\left[1 + \mathrm{LI}/\exp(t_2 - t_\mathrm{m}) \ln 2/T\right] = (t_\mathrm{s} + t)\,0.301/T \qquad \text{when} \qquad t_\mathrm{m} \leq t$$

In this case the LI will reach a constant value when all of the cells which were in G_1 and mitosis have entered the S phase. This will occur after a time equal to the duration of G_1 and mitosis, i.e. at $t = t_1 + t_\mathrm{m}/2$ (by definition). This is the case that has been illustrated in fig. 4.8. Since the duration of mitosis is short compared to the duration of the other phases of the cell cycle it is often satisfactory to use the simple form of the collection function (eq. (4.8)) and to ignore the small correction introduced, above, for the division of cells in mitosis at $t = 0$.

8.8 Fluctuations in the incorporation of H³Tdr into DNA during the S phase

In ch. 5 variations in the rate of DNA synthesis during the S phase have been described. The experimental methods used, however, did not give sharp resolution of changes that may occur over short time intervals and higher resolution can be obtained using synchronous cultures. One such series of experiments by STUBBLEFIELD (1966) will be described here. These experiments have not yet been published and are consequently confined to this appendix rather than ch. 5, since the experimenter's interpretation of them is unknown to myself and the following discussion is my own responsibility.

Synchronous cultures of Chinese hamster cells were obtained by washing the mitotic cells from monolayer cultures which had been treated with colcemide to increase the mitotic index (STUBBLEFIELD and KELVECZ 1965). During the first interphase following this treatment the cultures maintained good synchrony and DNA synthesis during the cell cycle was investigated by growing the cells continuously in H³Tdr. Individual cultures were fixed at intervals from 1 to 15 hr after the start of the experiment and three methods were used to assay the incorporation of labelled material into DNA. These methods were: autoradiography and grain counting over whole cells, scintillation counting of intact cells, and scintillation counting of DNA extracted from the cells. The first two methods give essentially the same type of results and the counts obtained in both cases are derived from the β-particles that penetrate the material of the cells and strike the emulsion or scintillation fluid. In these methods the counts are affected by the self absorption of the cells and the distribution of labelled DNA within the nucleus as has been described in ch. 1 § 9.

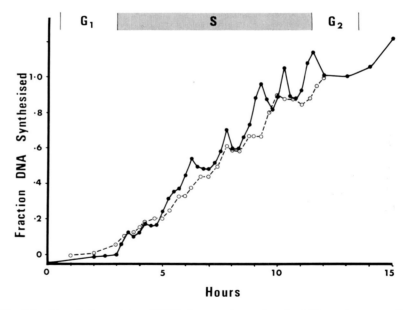

Fig. 8.5. Cumulative uptake of H³Tdr into DNA in synchronised Chinese hamster cells. ● grain counts, and CPM obtained in liquid scintillation counting, of whole cells. ○ CPM obtained from DNA extracted from the cells. (Drawn on the basis of personal communication from STUBBLEFIELD, 1966.)

The third method, scintillation counting of the extracted DNA, should give results which are less influenced by self-absorption. The results obtained are illustrated in fig. 8.5 and it is clear that in this system the total H^3 in DNA does not increase steadily as the S phase progresses but fluctuates considerably. These results were reproducible and a very high degree of synchrony is necessary in order to reveal these fluctuations. The majority of the cells in each culture must be at the same stage in the cell cycle within a time interval of less that 30 min throughout the whole duration of the experiment.

It is difficult to reach a convincing interpretation of these results at the time of writing since it appears that H^3Tdr is both incorporated and lost from some acid insoluble DNA-like component of the cell nucleus. Radioactivity in this component is registered in autoradiographs but is lost during extraction of DNA. Such turnover is at variance with the popular opinion of the stability of DNA which has been stated explicitly, for example, by HUGHES (1959). If turnover of labelled material is accepted on the basis of these results then this material must be some precursor of DNA which is intermediate between TTP and DNA, since the former is acid soluble and would not be registered in autoradiographs.

An alternative interpretation which does not require the turnover of any DNA-like component is possible on the basis of changes in the self absorption of the intact cells to H^3 β-particles (ch. 1 § 9). The range of fluctuation of the grain count shown in fig. 8.5 amounts to about 15%, at the most, of the total count at any particular time in the cycle. If DNA molecules move within the nucleus during replication, then fluctuations in the total count would result when labelled DNA moved away from, or towards, the cell surface that was in contact with the emulsion. The results obtained from extracted DNA are consistent with this interpretation, since these results simply indicate that DNA synthesis is not continuous throughout the S phase, but there are short periods during which very little synthesis occurs and the specific activity of the DNA consequently remains constant during these periods. Movement of labelled DNA during these quiescent periods may be expected to have a more noticeable effect on the grain counts than when DNA synthesis is in progress and the grain counts are increasing. This may be an explanation for the correspondence between the fluctuations in the grain counts and the plateaus in the activity in extracted DNA which can be seen in fig. 8.5.

In conclusion, this discussion of the results of STUBBLEFIELD (1966) must be regarded as mere tentative suggestions which may be extensively changed or rejected in the light of subsequent work.

References

CLEAVER, J. E., 1965a, Nature *206*, 401

CLEAVER, J. E., 1965b, Exp. Cell Res. *39*, 697

CRATHORN, A. R., and K. V. SHOOTER, 1960, Nature *187*, 614

CRATHORN, A. R., and K. V. SHOOTER, 1963, Intern. J. Radiation Biol. 7, 575

DENDY, P. P., 1962, Ph.D. thesis, University of Cambridge

DENDY, P. P., and C. L. SMITH, 1964, Proc. Roy. Soc. *B 160*, 328

ERRERA, M., A. HELL, and R. P. PERRY, 1961, Biochim. Biophys. Acta *49*, 58

HUGHES, W. L., 1959, The kinetics of cellular proliferation, F. Stohlman, Jr., ed., Grune and Stratton, New York, p. 83

KOBERG, E., 1963, in Cell proliferation, L. F. Lamerton and R. J. M. Fry, eds., Blackwell Scientific Publications, London, p. 62

LENNARTZ, K. J., and W. MAURER, 1964, Z. f. Zellfors. *63*, 478

MENDELSOHN, M. L., 1958, J. Biophys. Biochem. Cytol. *4*, 407

POWELL, E. O., 1956, J. Gen. Microbiol. 15, 492

PUCK, R. H., and J. STEFFEN, 1963, Biophys. J. *3*, 379

QUASTLER, H., 1963, in Actions Chimiques et Biologiques des Radiations, M. Haissinsky, ed., Masson et Cie, Paris, p. 147

RUBINI, J. R., A. KELLER, A. EISENTRAUT, and E. P. CRONKITE, 1962, in Tritium in the physical and biological sciences II, International Atomic Energy Agency, Vienna, p. 247

SMITH, C. L., and P. P. DENDY, 1962, Nature *193*, 555

STEWART, P. A., H. QUASTLER, M. R. SKOUGAARD, D. R. WIMBER, M. F. WOLFSBERG, L. A. PERROTTA, B. FERBEL, and M. CARLOUGH, 1965, Radiation Res. 24, 52

STUBBLEFIELD, E., 1966, Personal communication

STUBBLEFIELD, E., and R. KLEVECZ, 1965, Exp. Cell Res. *40*, 660

URETZ, R. B., and R. P. PERRY, 1957, Rev. Sci. Instr. *28*, 861

ZAJICEK, G., and G. GROSS, 1964, Exp. Cell Res. *34*, 138

ZAJICEK, G., N. BERNSTEIN, A. ROSIN, and G. GROSS, 1963, Exp. Cell Res. *31*, 390

Index

(References to Tdr and H³Tdr are omitted since these are covered by the table of contents on pages 11, 12 and 13).

DATE DUE

DEC 1 4 1995			

RENEWALS 362-8433

DEMCO 38-297